TWINS
A STUDY OF HEREDITY AND ENVIRONMENT

THE UNIVERSITY OF CHICAGO PRESS, CHICAGO

THE BAKER & TAYLOR COMPANY, NEW YORK; THE CAMBRIDGE UNIVERSITY
PRESS, LONDON; THE MARUZEN-KABUSHIKI-KAISHA, TOKYO, OSAKA,
KYOTO, FUKUOKA, SENDAI; THE COMMERCIAL PRESS, LIMITED, SHANGHAI

TWINS,

A STUDY OF HEREDITY AND ENVIRONMENT

By

HORATIO H. NEWMAN

FRANK N. FREEMAN

KARL J. HOLZINGER

THE UNIVERSITY OF CHICAGO PRESS
CHICAGO · ILLINOIS

270

PREFACE

IT IS now ten years since the three authors agreed to pool their intellectual resources in an attack upon the much-debated nature-nurture problem, using twins as the most favorable weapons for such an attack. It was thought that the three of us together—a psychologist, a statistician, and a specialist in the biology of twins—might be able to go more deeply into this problem than could one person with one particular type of training.

Originally the plan was to compare, in as many ways as we could, a group of identical twins reared together with an equivalent group of fraternal twins reared together. Subsequently, when we began to secure for study a number of pairs of identical twins reared apart, it seemed advisable to postpone an attempt to arrive at final conclusions until the number of twins reared apart became sufficiently large to have statistical value. These cases came in slowly, and it was only a little over a year ago that we decided that the time had come for publishing a general report of the whole project.

In this study there has been continuous collaboration, each of us contributing his own type of specialized knowledge to each part of the study, in addition to participating in making the general plan of the investigation. Dr. Freeman has had charge of all the psychological tests; Dr. Holzinger has been responsible for the statistical aspects of the work, including tabulation and analysis of data, and the derivation of the formula for the estimate of the relative effect of nature and nurture, and has also participated in the collection of data on twins reared together; Dr. Newman has been responsible for diagnosing the twins into identical and fraternal groups and has personally collected most of the data concerning the physical resemblances and differences.

The actual administration of intelligence and personality tests was carried out by a considerable group of assistants who had received their training under Dr. Freeman. Dr. Newman has been chiefly responsible for the discovery of the cases of identical twins reared apart and has made arrangements for having them come to us for study. He is also responsible for obtaining the life-histories of all but one of these interesting pairs. Tentative reports on the first nine pairs were written for the *Journal of Heredity* by Dr. Newman with the co-operation of Dr. Freeman. These reports, together with those of ten new cases not previously reported, have been worked over by Drs. Newman and Freeman in collaboration.

The general conclusions discussed in the final chapter represent a consensus of the views of all three authors arrived at after considerable discussion of divergent interpretations of the data. In this chapter we have attempted, first, to give a summary of the facts themselves in as objective a manner as possible, and, second, to draw up a statement of interpretation which is sufficiently guarded to be acceptable to those having a somewhat different bias toward the problem.

Grateful acknowledgments are herewith made to all those who have given of their time and energy to this investigation. Especially do we wish to thank the nineteen pairs of separated identical twins for coming to us, sometimes from great distances, and for their thoroughly co-operative spirit in submitting themselves for study. We sincerely hope that what we have written about them will be accepted as our best efforts to state the facts without in any way causing them embarrassment in case they should chance to read this book.

The copies of the paper form of the International Test and the directions for administration were furnished for use in the study of the separated twins by Drs. Carl C. Brigham and Stuart C. Dodd. The authors are greatly indebted to these gentlemen for these tests. The tests of the one hundred pairs of twins of the first part of the study and of the first few separated pairs were given by Mrs. Blythe C. Mitchell. Mrs. Mitchell also did the statistical work of the first part of the study. Part of the statistical work on the separated cases was done by Miss Frances Swineford. The remaining tests of the separated twins were administered by Drs. Ethel M. Abernethy, Charles D. Flory, Herman G. Richey, Arthur E. Traxler, Edward C. Bolmeier, and the late Mrs. Eula S. Williams. Mrs. Williams also made a special study of the Kent-Rosanoff Test, and Dr. Richey rescored all the International Test papers. The physical examination of the later separated cases was made by Dr. Gladys Kindred Dolan. The palm prints of the separated cases were made by Mr. Marshall T. Newman. Assistance in the reading and checking of the proof was given by Miss Frances Swineford, Mrs. Mary Jordan, and Mrs. Elizabeth Nordberg. The Index is largely the work of Walter Thiele in consultation with the authors.

Financial support for the investigations was obtained from appropriations from an annual research grant from the Rockefeller Biological Research Fund and from funds of the Departments of Education and Zoölogy and the Social Science Research Committee of the Division of the Social Sciences, all of the University of Chicago.

All these forms of assistance are gratefully acknowledged.

THE AUTHORS

March 1937

TABLE OF CONTENTS

LIST OF ILLUSTRATIONS

LIST OF TABLES

xiii

PART I
INTRODUCTION AND BIOLOGICAL ASPECTS

CHAPTER I

PREVIOUS STUDIES OF THE PROBLEM

THE scientific interest in twins may be said to center in two general questions. The first question has to do with the explanation of the origin of twins and of the mechanism by which they develop. Under this topic would come the investigation of the causes which produce twinning and of the physiology and development of the organism throughout its life from the fertilization of the ovum to death. A study of the distinction between identical and fraternal, or monozygotic and dizygotic, twins, is a part of this general problem. The theory which is accepted in this investigation is that there are two distinct types of twins—the monozygotic or identical twins, developed from a single egg, and the dizygotic or fraternal twins, developed from two eggs. Dizygotic twins are held to be as separate in their origin as are brothers and sisters in general. The investigation of twins throws light upon the characteristics of these two types of twins, the ways in which they are distinguished from each other, and the methods by which they may be diagnosed.

The second problem in a study of twins is the question of nature and nurture, or heredity and environment. We may study the differences between identical twins, on the one hand, and fraternal twins, on the other hand, in order to get some light on the origin of these differences. The study of twins may throw light upon the nature-nurture question in several ways. In the first place, we may inquire whether the close likeness which is usually found between pairs of twins which are classed as identical is an indication that heredity is the dominant factor in their development. The suggestion that this may be the case grows out of the circumstance that when inheritance is exactly the same, as in the case of monozygotic twins, the traits of the developed individual are often almost indistinguishable. The first investigator to interpret the likeness of twins as an evidence of the predominance of inheritance was Francis Galton. Another way in which the study of twins may throw light upon the question of heredity and environment is to compare their likeness at an early age and at a later age. A third method of study is to compare the likenesses of twins in tests which may be assumed to measure chiefly unlearned capacities with those which are assumed to be more largely influenced by training. In the fourth place, we may attack this question by comparing the likenesses or differences between identical twins with the likenesses and differences between fraternal

3

twins. Finally, we may secure more crucial evidence on this question if we can find identical twins who have been separated from early infancy and brought up under diverse environmental conditions. A comparison of their traits will reveal whether or not the identity of inheritance has kept them alike in spite of the influence of different environments. In the present study all these methods of attack on the problem are employed.

The way in which the problems have been attacked in previous investigations of the subject will be shown by a brief sketch of the chief studies which have been made. This sketch will not go into details of the various studies. These details will be commented on at those points in the discussion of the results of our own study to which they are pertinent. This sketch will review only the main features of the investigations, including the problems and the major conclusions.

HISTORICAL SKETCH OF PREVIOUS STUDIES

The first scientific attempt to study the mental abilities of twins was made by Francis Galton.[1] Galton was interested in twins because of the light that a study of them might throw upon the relationship between heredity and environment. His chief object was to determine whether or not very similar twins become unlike as a result of a difference in environment, and whether, on the other hand, twins who were unlike in early life become more similar as a result of living in the same environment. Galton believed that there were two distinct types of twins, one of which developed from a single ovum and the other from two separate ova. The evidence on which Galton based his conclusions concerning the existence of the two types consisted of reports of the characteristics of the twins which he obtained at second hand through correspondence.

By this means Galton obtained information concerning thirty-five pairs of twins who were reported to be so closely similar that it was difficult to distinguish one from the other by their appearance. He also obtained reports concerning twenty pairs who were not closely similar and who were thought by their friends and relatives to be no more alike than are brothers and sisters in general. It is probable, in the light of our later evidence, that the twins of the first group were chiefly identical twins and those of the second group chiefly fraternal twins.

Most of the facts which Galton obtained regarding the similar twins relate to their very close resemblance in physical characteristics. For example, both members of seven of the pairs suffered from the same physical ailment. Both members of one pair had the same kind of crook in the little finger of

[1] *Inquiries into Human Faculty and Its Development* (New York: Macmillan Co., 1883), pp. 216–42.

the same hand. Both members of another pair developed a toothache in the same tooth at about the same time, and each had the tooth extracted. Both individuals of another pair were afflicted with ophthalmia and had attacks at about the same time even though one was in Vienna and the other in Paris. There were two cases of similar insanity. Eleven pairs said that they had similar association of ideas. For example, one would begin a sentence and the other complete it. On the other hand, there were differences in disposition noticed in the case of nineteen pairs of very similar twins. In some cases the differences in disposition were caused by a serious illness or an accident. Galton reported that illness or accident was the only cause which appeared to be adequate to make similar twins unlike. The ordinary differences which are characteristic of current life did not perceptibly affect their likeness.

In contrast to the similar pairs, those who were unlike at the beginning did not become more alike as a result of their similar environment. Little detail was reported concerning the dissimilar twins except that some reports of their differences indicated that they were no more alike than are brothers and sisters. Galton concluded that environmental differences, such as are to be found in the same community and at the same time, produce slight change in the individual's physical and mental makeup and that physical and mental characteristics are determined chiefly by inborn nature. It is to be noticed, however, that Galton's evidence is much stronger in relation to physical traits than it is in relation to mental characteristics and abilities. It should be noticed further that the differences in environment which were brought to bear upon the similar twins did not appear until adult life.

The first study of twins which made use of tests was made by Thorndike in 1905.[2] Some of the tests which Thorndike used were measures of educational achievement, some of them measures of mental ability not affected by formal training. The first two were regarded by Thorndike as being most subject to training. They were tests in addition and multiplication. The second two were tests in misspelled words and in giving the opposites of words. These were regarded as moderately subject to education or training. The last two, crossing out a's in a printed text and in crossing out words containing a and z, or r and e, were considered least subject to training.

Thorndike chose these tests with a view to finding out whether twins were more alike in abilities subject to training than in abilities not subject to training. This, he thought, would give an indication whether the likeness

[2] Edward L. Thorndike, "Measurement of Twins," *Archives of Philosophy, Psychology, and Scientific Methods*, No. 1 (September, 1905), pp. 1–64.

of twins is due to any considerable extent to similarity in training. There is some question concerning the reasoning which lies back of this procedure. The assumption is that twins probably receive very similar amounts or kinds of training in such abilities as addition and multiplication and that this training may be widely different from the training received by other twins or other individuals. Since the training in these school subjects is received in school, and since the methods employed in the school are fairly uniform, the assumption is of doubtful validity. Thorndike found that there was no higher correlation between the attainments of twins in the so-called "trained" functions than in the so-called "untrained" functions and concluded from this that the similarity of twins was inherent rather than acquired.

The second comparison which Thorndike made was between the correlation of abilities in the case of twins nine to eleven years of age as contrasted with twins of twelve to fourteen years of age. The assumption underlying this comparison was that if the likeness of twins is due to environment it ought to increase as the twins become older and are subjected to the same environment for a longer period of time. Since he found that the correlations between abilities of older twins are slightly less than those of younger twins, he concluded that the resemblance is due to inheritance and is not influenced by environment.

A difficulty with the comparison by ages is the narrow range of the ages. The average difference between the ages of the pairs in the two age groups cannot be much more than three years. Even if a similar environment were assumed to increase the likenesses of twins, we should not expect to find much increase between the ages of ten and thirteen. Furthermore, the finding that the older twins are actually somewhat less alike than the younger ones seems to prove rather too much from the standpoint of heredity. On the other hand, it is quite conceivable that the adolescent period may bring with it a greater diversification in friendships and in occupations which may in turn make twins more dissimilar.

Thorndike made no attempt to distinguish between identical and fraternal twins, nor did he make separate correlations for twins of like sex and twins of unlike sex. He presents a curve to show the distribution of the differences between pair members. Each difference is calculated in the form of a correlation coefficient adapted from the product-moment method. The use of this correlation coefficient would not now pass muster. On the basis of this curve Thorndike infers that there are not two distinct groups of twins since there is no evidence of bimodality in the curve. If there were two distinct classes of twins, he argues, the curve of differences would show two distinct modes. Without explaining the difference biologically, however, Thorndike finds that twins of the whole group are much more similar than siblings, just as siblings are more similar than children picked at random. He concludes that this progressive increase in similarity is evidence of the effect of inborn nature. But why twins should be more alike than brothers and sisters is not explained.[3]

The next study of importance was reported nearly twenty years later by Merriman in 1924.[4] Merriman's was the first study in which modern intelligence tests were used. He employed the Stanford-Binet Scale, the Army Beta Scale, the National Intelligence Test, and also gathered and used teachers' estimates of intelligence.

Merriman followed Thorndike's procedure of finding the correlation for the younger and the older age groups. The age limits of the younger group were five to nine years and of the older group ten to sixteen years. In the case of three of the tests, the correlation was somewhat lower for the older group than for the younger. The scores on the Army Beta constituted a slight exception, but not a marked one.

This author added a new comparison by finding the correlation between twins of like sex and twins of unlike sex separately. The reason for making this separation is that identical twins are found to be always of the same sex. At least no clear exception to this rule has been reported in cases in which origin from a single egg has been established. Twins of unlike sex, then, will always be fraternal twins. Twins of like sex include some fraternal and some identical twins. In this comparison Merriman found that the correlations between the scores of twins of like sex were higher, and in most cases considerably higher, than the correlations between twins of unlike sex. He interprets this as meaning that identical twins are much more alike than fraternal twins and that the presence of these in the group of like-sex twins raises the correlation.

Merriman pursued the problem of the distinction between identical twins and fraternal twins further. He devised a different formula for expressing the pair differences in the measurements of twins, and by an application of this formula obtains a distribution. In the case of the I.Q.'s of like-sex twins and of unlike-sex twins, separately, he found a much larger percentage of like-sex twins who are very similar than of unlike-sex twins. Approximately twenty-five out of sixty-seven like-sex pairs are considered by him to be practically identical in I.Q. on this comparison.

[3] Since this early study, made thirty years ago, Professor Thorndike has accepted the distinction between identical and fraternal twins on biological grounds.

[4] Curtis Merriman, *The Intellectual Resemblance of Twins* ("Psychological Monographs," Vol. XXXIII, No. 5; Whole No. 152). Princeton, N.J.: Psychological Review Co., 1924. Pp. 58.

Merriman also found the raw differences in I.Q. between the pairs of like-sex and of unlike-sex twins and compared the distribution of these differences with that of the differences between siblings. He found that the curve of distribution for siblings resembled that for unlike-sex twins more than that for like-sex twins. This suggests that unlike-sex twins have the same relationship to each other as have siblings except that they are born at the same time. He made a similar comparison between the like-sex and the unlike-sex twins for the National Intelligence Test.

Finally, Merriman tabulated the distribution of the I.Q.'s of the entire group of twins and found the mean I.Q. and the distribution to resemble very closely the mean and the distribution for children in general.

In the next year, 1925, another important study was reported by Lauterbach.[5] Lauterbach examined 212 pairs of twins, taking them as they came without discrimination as to sex or degree of similarity. He found 149 pairs of same-sex twins and 63 pairs of opposite-sex twins. Not all of these were given all the tests, but an adequate number of scores were obtained on each test. The number and variety of tests which were used by Lauterbach were large. They included several intelligence tests; arithmetic and handwriting tests; two or three tests of special ability; measurements of height, weight, and cephalic index; and an examination of the color of the eyes and of the hair; and the whorl of the head hair; handedness; and the palm patterns.

Lauterbach made a number of the same comparisons as were made by Merriman and obtained similar results. The comparison of the correlation between younger and older twins revealed no consistent differences. He found, as did Merriman, that the correlation was higher in the case of like-sex than of unlike-sex twins. He also found that twins are more closely similar than are other siblings. His comparison of correlations in the various tests did not reveal any clear indication of a closer correlation in the case of traits which may be ascribed to training than those which are usually not so ascribed. The comment which was made in reference to Thorndike's experiment applies here.

Merriman's conclusion that the intelligence level of twins is about the same as that of children in general was also confirmed. He made an interesting comparison of the handwriting of twins and found only a few cases in which it was so closely similar that it could not be distinguished. This suggests that the similarity in growth and structure which is found to obtain between many pairs of twins may not necessarily extend to the finer organization of the nervous system.

[5] C. E. Lauterbach, "Studies in Twin Resemblance," *Genetics*, X (November, 1925), 525–68.

Lauterbach devotes a large share of his attention to the study of various traits which have been suggested as marks of distinction between identical and fraternal twins. One characteristic which has sometimes been thought to be a crucial mark of distinction is the asymmetry reversal of several traits. Among these are the reversal in the direction of the whorl of the hair,[6] the reversal in handedness, and the reversal in the pattern of the finger ridges and palm ridges. Reversal would be represented in hair whorl by a clockwise whorl on one head and a counterclockwise whorl on the other. In handedness, reversal is represented by right-handedness in one twin and left-handedness in the other. In palm patterns the matter is more intricate, but, in general, reversal would be indicated by a closer resemblance between the right hand of one twin and the left hand of the other than between the right hand of one twin and the right hand of the other, or to the presence of an identical pattern in the right palm of one twin and the left palm of the other.

Lauterbach gives a minute description of a number of cases in which reversal is found between twins of the opposite sex. He also illustrates cases of very closely similar twins in which reversal is not found to exist. Both types of cases indicate that asymmetry reversal cannot be taken as an infallible sign of the distinction between monozygotic and dizygotic twins. Lauterbach confirms the conclusion that asymmetry reversal is not particularly significant for diagnosis by showing that a group of those showing asymmetry reversal does not give notably higher correlations than groups which do not exhibit asymmetry reversal.

The chief comparisons made by Merriman and Lauterbach are repeated in Wingfield's study, reported in 1928.[7] Wingfield applied his tests to 102 pairs of twins collected at random from the public schools. The chief correlations were calculated with the scores of the Multi-mental Scale and the National Intelligence Test combined to give an average I.Q., and with the Stanford Achievement Test. To these were added an arithmetic test and a spelling test. Wingfield found the mean I.Q. of all the twins to be 97.2, approximately the same as was found by Lauterbach.

In his three main comparisons Wingfield confirmed the findings of Merriman and of Lauterbach. In two of his findings he agrees also with Thorndike. There is no significant difference in the correlation for younger and older twins. The age limits are eight and eleven years for the younger group and twelve and fifteen years for the older group. No significant differ-

[6] In our own terminology these kinds of reversal are called "mirror-imaging." See chap. iv for the full account of the types of reversal and their definition.

[7] Alex H. Wingfield, *Twins and Orphans: The Inheritance of Intelligence.* London and Toronto: J. M. Dent & Sons, Ltd., 1928. Pp. xii+127.

ence was found, furthermore, between the correlation of the intelligence quotients and that of the educational quotients. This corresponds to Thorndike's comparison between likeness on tests which are supposed to be little affected by education or much affected by education. Wingfield found like-sex pairs to resemble each other much more closely than unlike-sex pairs, the latter resembling each other about as closely as do brothers and sisters. Finally, Wingfield made a fourth comparison by selecting twins who seemed to be physically identical. No objective method and no elaborate examination were used to identify the identical twins. The author reports that those twins who were physical duplicates of each other were called "identical" while those who were not were called "fraternal" twins. The correlations between the abilities of identical twins as measured by the I.Q. were much higher than those of the fraternal twins, the two being .90 and .70, respectively.

Hirsch[8] reports a study of thirty-eight pairs of "similar" twins reared together, of fifty-eight pairs of "dissimilar" twins reared together, and of twelve pairs of "similar" twins who have lived apart for various periods of time. The "similar" twins include only those who are very much alike not only in physical characteristics and appearance but also in mental ability and attainment. Seventeen pairs who were very similar physically, and were probably identical, were rejected because they were dissimilar in school work. Conversely, thirteen pairs who were physically unlike and hence probably fraternal were excluded because they were judged to be very similar mentally, scholastically, and temperamentally. This mode of selection involves reasoning in a circle or begging the question. The problem is to determine whether identical twins are more alike in ability than are fraternal twins. If only those who are more alike are called "identical," identical twins, as thus defined, will of course be more alike. To avoid this fallacy the diagnosis must be based on other grounds than tests of ability. Again, if only the most similar of the identical twins are compared with the most dissimilar fraternal twins, the effect of the hereditary difference between the two groups is seriously exaggerated.

Hirsch makes three comparisons. The first is a comparison of the pair differences of similar and of dissimilar twins, all of whom have been brought up together. The greater resemblance of similar twins is ascribed to their identical heredity, and the ratio of the similar-pair differences to the dissimilar-pair differences is taken as a measure of the difference which may be produced by a difference in heredity. In six characteristics the ratio varies from $1:2.2$ in the case of head width to $1:6.0$ in the case of I.Q. As

[8] Nathaniel D. M. Hirsch, *Twins: Heredity and Environment*. Cambridge, Mass.: Harvard University Press, 1930. Pp. 159.

has already been said, the comparison is invalidated by the fact that the two groups are selected in such a way as to exaggerate the contrast between them.

The second comparison is between similar twins brought up together and similar twins brought up for part of their lives apart. The ratio of the pair differences of twins brought up together to pair differences of twins brought up apart is taken as a measure of the difference which may be produced by a difference in environment. This comparison would be significant if the separated pairs had been separated early enough and had remained apart long enough, if the difference in their environment had been great enough to produce a measurable contrast, and if a large enough number of cases had been examined. The calculations are based on only four cases, and, so far as can be judged from the meager description given, none was separated before about ten years of age. Two pairs had been separated three years, and two, eleven years. The latter two were then adults. No marked contrast in early life or education seems to have existed. For these reasons the comparison of these twins with similar twins brought up together cannot be taken as a measure of the influence of environment. For the same reason the effect of heredity, as brought out by the comparison of similar and dissimilar twins, cannot be compared with the effect of environment, as brought out by the comparison of twins brought up together with twins brought up apart. Hirsch's data on reversals in handedness will be used in our own discussion of this topic.

Besides these printed reports, the writers have had the privilege of examining a copy of a Doctor's dissertation by John C. Page, of Harvard University, entitled "Heredity versus Environment: A Study of Twins." This dissertation is dated 1928. The report presents a variety of comparisons among twenty-two pairs of twins who were found in the population of children included in the program of the Harvard Growth Study conducted by Professor W. F. Dearborn. Twenty-two pairs of twins were included in the report. Nine of these were judged to be probably monozygotic, and nine, dizygotic, although of the same sex. The comparisons had to be in the form of differences since the numbers were too small to justify the calculation of correlation coefficients.

As is to be expected, the identical twins were found to resemble each other more closely than the fraternal twins. An interesting comparison was made between the differences in the various traits. The traits were compared in couples or pairs by finding the correlation between the differences existing between these pairs of traits. For this purpose, the entire group of twenty-two pairs of twins was used. For example, the correlation was calculated between the differences in height and the differences in cephalic index to see whether the differences in height corresponded to the differences in cephalic index. If the pairs which showed large differences in one also showed large differences in the other, and vice versa, there would be a correlation. A fairly high correlation was found between the differences in the case of the physical traits, averaging about .50. The correlation between the differences in physical traits and mental traits, however, was low, the average being only .165. In other words, twins who are very much alike in physical traits are not necessarily very much alike in mental traits.

A few miscellaneous studies deal with special features. The recent study of handedness by Wilson and Jones[9] bears on the question of asymmetry reversal. These authors compare the incidence of left-handedness in 140 identical twins, 246 fraternal twins, and 521 single-born persons. Certain previous investigators (Weitz, Dahlberg, and Newman) have found more left-handed individuals among identical twins than among fraternal twins or single-born individuals. This has been interpreted as due to the operation of an asymmetry reversal mechanism in the process of embryological development. The fact itself has been disputed by other investigators (Siemens, Verschuer, and Lauterbach), who do not find a greater number of reversals among identicals than among fraternals but do find more in both kinds of twins than in the single-born.

Wilson and Jones agree with this latter finding. They find about 11 per cent of left-handed individuals among both types of twins as against $6\frac{1}{2}$ per cent among the single-born. They discuss four hypotheses. The possibility that the excess of left-handed in the two types of twins is due to different causes they reject as inferior on general principles to a single explanation. Lauterbach's suggestion that the excess among both identicals and fraternals is due to the asymmetry reversal mechanism, on the assumption that the excess left-handed fraternal twins are survivors of triplets or quadruplets, is rejected on the ground that this would require statistically that every fraternal pair should contain a survivor of a monozygotic pair. A third hypothesis is that twinning and left-handedness are genetically linked and that both types of twins have a common genetic basis. A fourth suggestion is that the prenatal life of twins may predispose to left-handedness more than does that of the single-born. A fifth possibility should probably be considered, namely, that the classification of the pairs into identical and fraternal was imperfect in that the less similar identicals were placed in the group of fraternals. This possibility and its consequences will be discussed in the chapter on asymmetry reversal.

Few systematic studies of twins have been made in the field of interests.

[9] Paul T. Wilson and Harold E. Jones, "Left-Handedness in Twins," *Genetics*, XVII (September, 1932), 560–71.

Carter's[10] study of the occupational interests is therefore important. He used the Strong Vocational Interest blanks with 120 pairs of twins, mostly of junior and senior high school age. He used 43 pairs of identicals, 43 pairs of like-sex fraternals, and 34 pairs of unlike-sex twins. The like-sex twins were evenly divided between males and females. The main finding was that the correlation between the interest scores was found to be .50 for identicals and .28 for fraternals. This difference Carter attributes chiefly to the closer genetic resemblance of identicals, though he admits that it may be due somewhat to environment. The lesser resemblance between twins in interests than in intelligence and educational achievement may be due partly to less reliability of the test of interest or to greater influence of environment on interests or to both. The study appears to give convincing evidence that genetic factors influence interests to an important degree but do not give the basis for an accurate estimate of the relative weight of genetic and environmental factors.

A number of studies have dealt with similarities in the handwriting of twins. In his pioneer study of similar and dissimilar twins Galton noted that handwriting seemed to constitute an exception to the rule. It was the only characteristic studied by him in which similar twins differed to a marked degree. In fact, Galton reports that the handwriting of twins who were so much alike in appearance as to be indistinguishable was not ordinarily alike at all. He did not attempt to explain this surprising fact.

Galton's comparison was based on the general appearance of handwriting and on those characteristics which give writing individuality and enable one to recognize a specimen of writing as belonging to a given person. A comparatively recent study by Kramer and Lauterbach[11] uses as the basis of comparison the quality of writing as measured by a scale and its speed. These authors found the correlation between the writing of siblings and of like-sex and opposite-sex twins. They found, in brief, a closer resemblance in the writing of like-sex twins than of opposite-sex twins or siblings. This contradicts Galton's findings.

A series of studies of the handwriting of identical twins has been made by Saudek and Seeman, and by Saudek. These studies use a modern form of graphological analysis. Since they do not compare the identical twins with fraternal twins or siblings as controls, the resemblances found must be interpreted more analytically than quantitatively. That is, resemblances and differences may be pointed out, but it is not possible to say whether the

[10] Harold D. Carter, "Twin Similarities in Occupational Interests," *Journal of Educational Psychology*, XXIII (December, 1932), 641–55.

[11] Emily Kramer and Charles E. Lauterbach, "Resemblance in the Handwriting of Twins and Siblings," *Journal of Educational Research*, XVIII (September, 1928), 149–52.

resemblances are greater than in other types or pairs, or, if so, how much greater. In general, these authors find some marked similarities and some marked differences. The similarities are more marked in some pairs than in others.

An examination of the handwriting was made in both parts of the present study. A more intensive review of the previous studies will be made in connection with the report of our own investigation of this subject.

The incidence of disease in similar and dissimilar twins was noted by Galton. A special study of the incidence of the mental malady, schizophrenia, is contributed by Rosanoff et al.[12] These authors recognize as a major difficulty in such a study the danger that cases which show a corre-

TABLE 1

NEW CASES OF SCHIZOPHRENIA IN TWINS

	SAME-SEX TWINS				OPPOSITE-SEX TWINS (DIZYGOTIC)	TOTAL
	Probably Monozygotic		Probably Dizygotic			
	Males	Females	Males	Females		
Both affected........	10	18	3	7	5	43
One affected........	9	4	8	35	{Males 21 Females 22}	99
Total..........	19	22	11	42	48	142

spondence will be discovered in a larger percentage of the total number than will cases in which there is no correspondence. They, therefore, attempted to obtain an "uninterrupted series" of cases of schizophrenia in both identical and fraternal twins. If this is not done, it is likely that a larger proportion of cases of identical twins who are both affected will be found than of fraternal twins because they are more likely to attract notice. The authors' method was to investigate all of a large unselected group of schizophrenic cases, to ascertain all who are one of a pair of twins, and then to seek out and investigate the condition of the other twin in each case wherever he may be. By this method they found and studied 142 pairs, of which 41 were probably identical, 53 of the same sex (probably fraternal), and 48 of the opposite sex (definitely fraternal). The statistical findings are shown in Table 1.

[12] Aaron J. Rosanoff, Leva M. Handy, Isabel Rosanoff Plesset, and Sandye Brush, "The Etiology of So-called Schizophrenic Psychoses," *American Journal of Psychiatry*, XCI (September, 1934), 247–86.

The percentage of monozygotic twins is a little high, being 29 per cent, and the number of opposite-sex dizygotic twins a little less than of same-sex twins. However, the proportions are fairly close to those in the un-selected population, indicating that the authors were fairly successful in securing an "uninterrupted series."

In general, the authors find many more cases in which both twins are affected among the monozygotic than among the dizygotic twins, the pro-portions being 68.3 per cent and 14.9 per cent, respectively. However, they find that the nature and course of the malady is often not identical or even closely similar in the case of identical as well as of fraternal twins. In fact, they report that close similarity or identicalness in the expression of the neurosis is the exception rather than the rule.

Instances of similar psychoses, quantitative dissimilarity (i.e., dissimilarity of age of onset, particular symptomatology, course, outcome, etc.), qualitative dis-similarity (i.e., one twin having a schizophrenic psychosis and the other some neuro-psychiatric condition belonging to a different clinical group, such as mental de-ficiency, epilepsy, etc.), and total discordance (i.e., one twin having a schizophrenic psychosis and the other not affected at all), are to be found among both monozygotic and dizygotic twins, but not with the same relative frequencies.

The following general conclusions are drawn from this study:

1. In the etiology of so-called schizophrenic psychosis hereditary factors seem to play an important part.

2. The hereditary factors, in themselves, are often inadequate; that is to say, they do not suffice to produce a schizophrenic psychosis.

3. The pathogenic effect of the hereditary factors is not highly specific. Other factors often play a part with resulting dissimilarities of manifestation or total dis-cordance of findings even in monozygotic twins.

4. Hereditary factors are not always present, therefore not essential, in the etiology of so-called schizophrenic psychoses.

The most crucial studies of twins are those which use the method of co-twin control. In these studies the two members of a twin pair (usually identical) are kept under relatively identical conditions, with the exception of a specific form of training, which constitutes the experimental variation. This makes it possible to determine how much change in behavior may be brought about by the specified training, or, conversely, how much simi-larity in development obtains in spite of the difference in training.

The pioneer studies by this method have been made under the direction of Gesell. Three elaborate experiments have been reported dealing with one pair of identical twins: One on climbing and manipulation by Gesell and Thompson,[13] one on memory and three types of motor learning by

[13] Arnold Gesell and Helen Thompson, *Learning and Growth in Identical Infant Twins* ("Genetic Psychology Monographs," VI, No. 1 [1929]), pp. 5–120.

Hilgard,[14] and one on the development of speech by Strayer.[15] A fourth study on attention by Thompson has been reported in abstract.

The particular technique followed in these three studies is the same. It consists in giving one twin, designated T, a given type of training as soon as the infant appears to have advanced far enough in his development to profit by it, meanwhile withholding this special training from the other twin, then subsequently giving the same training to the second twin, designated C. The comparison, then, is between the effect of early training and deferred training.

The plan of these studies does not make it possible to trace the later consequences of a contrast between the possession of a specific type of training and deprivation of that training. It bears chiefly on the question whether training is more effective at a later stage of maturation than at an earlier stage, and whether, consequently, maturation is an important factor in learning. It throws comparatively little light on the opposite question, whether learning is an important factor in development.

The three studies are similar in their plan and in their conclusions. In the study by Gesell and Thompson, Twin T was given intensive training in climbing and in manipulation of cubes for six weeks, beginning at the forty-second week, when both twins were "at the threshold of climbing and combining ability." Four days after the close of T's training C was given two weeks of training. Several weeks after the end of C's training T climbed with greater facility and showed more confidence. However, a much shorter period of practice was needed to bring approximately the same facility at a later than at an earlier period. The same result was found in the case of manipulation of cubes. However, a well-marked difference in attitude appeared, in that C showed more "dependency, caution or fearsomeness."

Hilgard trained the same twins according to the following schedule: initial test, eight weeks training of first twin, retest, eight weeks training of second twin, second, third, and fourth retests. The activities studied were digit memory, object memory, ring-toss, paper-cutting, and walking boards of various widths. The twins were approximately equal on the initial and final tests. The time at which practice was given, therefore, produced no difference in the ultimate skill. Early practice produced earlier proficiency,

[14] Josephine R. Hilgard, *The Effect of Early and Delayed Practice on Memory and Motor Performances Studied by the Method of Co-twin Control* (*ibid.*, XIV, No. 6 [1933]), pp. 493–567.

[15] L. C. Strayer, *Language and Growth: The Relative Efficacy of Early and Deferred Vocabulary Training Studied by the Method of Co-twin Control* (*ibid.*, VIII, No. 3 [1930]), pp. 209–319.

but the rate of progress during early practice was somewhat slower than that during later practice. On some of the activities there was some loss after the cessation of special practice but not in all. Maturation is clearly a factor, as the author concludes, but it is evident that practice is also a factor, though the experiment was not organized to bring it into sharp relief.

Strayer gave the same pair of twins language training, one for five weeks beginning at eighty-four weeks of age, the other for four weeks at eighty-nine weeks of age. The infant who had deferred training made more rapid progress in the acquisition of vocabulary and in making extended application of words. However, the twin who was trained earlier continued to grow in vocabulary, at the end of his special training, at a slower pace, and in the application of words at a rapid pace. At the end of the whole period the twin with earlier training was still ahead, though his training had ceased.

A rather startling series of experiments in training the twins known as Johnny and Jimmy were made by McGraw.[16] These twins turned out to be not identical (a fact which robs the experiment of a large part of its significance), but they are rather similar, and the special training was given the less precocious twin. The author is at this writing engaged in similar experiments with twin girls.

The main part of the experiment continued until the twins were twenty-two months old. During this time Johnny was given special training in a variety of kinds of activities, ranging from stimulation of the reflex grasp to finding hidden objects. At the close of training in each activity the twins were compared. In a supplementary experiment Jimmy was given training in some of the more complex activities, and the twins were compared in their ability to solve certain new problems.

The activities dealt with are classified as phylogenetic activities, such as reflexes, locomotion, reaching and reaction to irritation of the skin, ontogenetic activities, such as climbing up and down inclines, climbing or jumping off stools, roller-skating, and arranging boxes so as to reach suspended objects, and associated activities, such as finding hidden objects.

In nearly all the phylogenetic activities Jimmy advanced as rapidly as Johnny. Special training appeared to produce little if any acceleration. In the ontogenetic activities, on the other hand, Johnny developed skill or ability far in advance of Jimmy or of any of the other of the sixty-eight infants studied. Some of his performances were remarkable. An equally important effect in attitude was produced. "More striking even [than success] were the differences in persistence and his [Johnny's] manner of pausing

---

[16] Myrtle B. McGraw, *Growth: A Study of Johnny and Jimmy.* New York: D. Appleton-Century Co., Inc., 1935. Pp. xxi+319.

at intervals to look the situation over before acting! On occasion he worked for thirty to forty minutes continuously."

Eleven months after the end of Johnny's training Jimmy was trained in the ontogenetic activities. In some of the activities he did not equal Johnny's performance when nearly a year younger.

At the close of the experiment, both having been trained, but Johnny a year earlier, the twins were approximately equal in securing objects with sticks; manipulating ropes, pulleys, and strings to secure objects; in size discrimination; and intelligence tests. A clear difference in attitude and manner persisted, however, Johnny being more deliberative and persistent.

As part of an extensive series of studies of twins at the Medico-biological Institute at Moscow, Mirenva[17] experimented with four pairs of identical twins, four to four and one-half years old. Three activities of varying degrees of complexity were taught the less-skilled member of each pair for four and one-half months. They were jumping, throwing a ball at a target, and rolling a ball along a board at a mark. The untrained twin was not given later training. In all activities the trained twin made the greater progress, but the difference was progressively larger. In jumping, the average gains were, respectively, 16.2 and 12 centimeters; in throwing at a target, 1.5 and 0.4; and in rolling at a mark (in terms of reduction of deviation), 27.2 and 1.7 centimeters. As in McGraw's study, the trained twins differed from the untrained in attitude, as shown in attention, control, discipline, and effort. Contrary to the other studies, the trained twins were found to have gained much also in general motor dexterity and ten points in I.Q. (Stanford-Binet), whereas the untrained twins gained only slightly in motor dexterity and not at all in I.Q.

RECENT EUROPEAN STUDIES OF TWINS

While, as we have seen, American studies of twins have had as their chief objective the study of the nature and nurture factors influencing mental characters, a parallel series of studies has gone forward in Europe— a series devoted largely to anthropological and pathological considerations. Because of the fact that the American studies are so closely linked with our own investigations, whereas European studies are not, we feel justified in discussing the former rather extensively and in presenting only a summary of the latter.

Shortly after the discovery of monozygotic twinning in the armadillos (by Newman and Patterson) and the determination of the very high but incomplete correlation within sets of armadillo quadruplets, research on

---

[17] A. N. Mirenva, "Psychomotor Education and the General Development of Preschool Children: Experiments with Twin Controls," *Pedagogical Seminary and Journal of Genetic Psychology*, XLVI (March, 1935), 433–54.

human twins took a new impetus in Europe. In 1914 Poll made the first systematic study of the degrees of resemblance and difference present within identical twin pairs, using fingerprints as material. In 1922 Jablonski, using similar methods, determined the degree of resemblance in refractive index of the eyes in identical twins. Siemens in 1924 published a book entitled *Zwillingspathologie*, in which he proposed a new method of studying pathology and human heredity in general. This method is, in brief, as follows: Assuming that it is possible to diagnose with accuracy identical and fraternal twins, it is then reasonable to say that pathological and other characters which are always or nearly always, when they occur at all, present in both members of identical twin pairs, but rarely or never appear in both members of fraternal twin pairs, are hereditary.

Following the announcement of Siemens of his new method of attacking the problems of human genetics, scores of investigators in Europe have used this method in the study of a very large number of human characters. Most active and influential of modern students of human genetics using this twin method is O. von Verschuer, who heads a large group of students of twinning at the Kaiser-Wilhelm Institut für Anthropologie, menschliche Erblehre und Eugenik (director, Professor Eugen Fischer). This group of investigators has used the twin method for the study of anthropological, clinical, serological, and psychological problems and has contributed extensively to our knowledge of these subjects and, incidentally, to our general knowledge of twins.

One of the best and most comprehensive independent studies of twins is that of Dahlberg (1926), a Swedish investigator, whose book, *Twin Births from a Hereditary Point of View*, gives a comprehensive review of twin literature up to 1926. Dahlberg also criticizes previous theories of the causes of twinning and presents a new theory of his own, which is far from satisfactory. The Bibliography presented by Dahlberg includes 252 titles of books and papers dealing with twins or allied subjects, giving one some idea of the immense amount of work that has been done in this field.

Among other independent workers on twins may be mentioned Bonnevie (1924), Leven (1924), Ganther and Rominger (1923), and Jablonski (1922)—all of whom worked on fingerprints; Weitz (1924), Curtius (1930), Korkhaus (1930), Köhler, Lassen, Glatzel, Schiff (1930), on various clinical aspects of twins; Schmidt (1928) and Wardenburg (1930) on the eyes of twins; Wiechmann und Paal (1927) on blood groups in twins; Leicher (1928), on nose and ear conditions in twins; Meierowsky (1926) on dermatology of twins; and Diehl und von Verschuer (1930), on tuberculosis in twins. Other important contributions by the European group of students of twins are referred to in various reviews of the subject of which von Verschuer's paper, "Ergebnisse der Zwillingsforschung" (1931), is one of the most concise and recent. The existence of such reviews as those of Dahlberg and of von Verschuer makes it rather superfluous for us to go exhaustively into the whole literature or even to give specific citations. It seems sufficient for our purposes to give a brief account of the methods used by the leading investigators and to compare these methods and some of their implications with the methods used by us.

THE CONCORDANCE VERSUS DISCORDANCE METHOD

Siemens was the first to introduce this method of determining whether characters are hereditary or to what extent they are hereditary. Von Verschuer and his school have adopted the method and have used it very extensively. All sorts of normal and pathological conditions in man have been investigated by this method, and the results have afforded an ample justification of the value of the method as a quick and ready means of obtaining genetic data in man. The method is essentially as follows:

Same-sexed twins are diagnosed by the similarity method of Siemens as either one-egg twins or two-egg twins. The German writers use the abbreviated expression E.Z. and Z.Z. to designate these two types of twins— E.Z. standing for *Eineiiger Zwillinge* and Z.Z. for *Zweieiiger Zwillinge*. In this review we may be permitted to use these abbreviations, which are standard in modern German papers.

A comparison is made of the degree of similarity of any character in the two groups of twins, E.Z. and Z.Z., in the following manner:

1. In the case of alternative characters a comparison of the frequency of concordance (+ +) and discordance (+ −) is made for the two kinds of twins. High concordance in E.Z. and low concordance in Z.Z. indicate that the character is hereditary.

2. In characters that are not clearly alternative, it is customary to divide the twin pairs into three divergence groups. Divergence Group I = concordance (+ +), Divergence Group II = slight differences between partners of pairs (+ [+]), and Divergence Group III = discordance (+ −).

3. In characters that are always present in both partners of a pair but differ only quantitatively (in number or in size), the number of measurement of the smaller individual is subtracted from that of the larger individual of each pair. One can then arrange the absolute or percental differences (*Abweichungen*) in variation classes and compare their frequency, or compare the mean values of the differences in the two groups of twins, E.Z. and Z.Z. If the classes showing small differences are far more numerous in E.Z. than in Z.Z., the character is believed to have a genetic basis but to be influenced by environmental differences.

4. The method used by German workers in determining the relative shares of genetic and environmental factors in producing observed differences in fraternal twins is as follows: The total differences found in identical twins are regarded as being wholly environmental in origin, while part of the difference in fraternal twins is due to environment and part to heredity. Assuming that environmental differences are the same for both identical and fraternal twins, it is then necessary merely to subtract the mean differences of identical twins from those of fraternal twins to get the amount of difference in the latter due to genetic factors alone. The percentage that this is of the total difference represents the share of genetic differences, and this subtracted from 100 per cent gives the percental share for environmental factors. This is a very simple procedure, and it is regrettable that we find it unacceptable for reasons given below.

5. In all the foregoing kinds of characters one can also determine and represent the degree of similarity by calculating the coefficient of correlation. It is assumed that a high percentage of concordance or a high correlation in E.Z. and a relatively low concordance or correlation in Z.Z., for a given character, signifies that the character is hereditary. Failure of complete concordance in E.Z. is attributed either to unknown prenatal or postnatal environmental differences, or to minor inaccuracies or accidents in development. No other factors are considered as having an influence in the expression of characters.

Siemens goes so far as to exclude from the list of hereditary characters those that have a unilateral expression in the individual, the assumption being that if a character is really hereditary it should express itself not merely bilaterally in the individual but should be regularly present in both members of E.Z. pairs and not in one partner alone or on one side only. The failure of a character to appear in one member of an E.Z. pair means to him that the character is not inherited. This view and its implications have been rather generally adopted by German students of twins and has greatly influenced their conclusions as to the relative potency of hereditary and environmental differences in modifying the expression of characters.

In a subsequent chapter we take the position that, just as characters of all sorts express themselves differently on the two sides of the body, without assuming that the two halves are either genetically different or are subjected to different environmental influences, so may characters of the same sort express themselves differently in the two partners of identical twin pairs.

The differences in the expression of such characters in both cases are believed by us to be due to an asymmetry mechanism, a factor neither genetic nor environmental, but an independent third factor, which should not be ignored. Since there is abundant evidence that monozygotic twins are frequently derived through the bilateral fission of prospective right and left sides of an embryo, we would expect just as much difference in character expression in the two partners of some E.Z. pairs as occurs on the two sides of single individuals.

Denying as they do the reality of the asymmetry mechanism in identical-twin production, these writers then proceed to simplify the problem by considering all real differences in one-egg twins as environmental in origin. This procedure renders an estimation of the relative values of hereditary and environmental factors rather simple. We have no desire to complicate the problem through the introduction of a third factor, but the facts force us to do so. Our treatment of twin data differs from that of the German school rather sharply in this respect, namely, that we recognize this third factor and attempt to calculate its effects before proceeding to calculate those due to the two major factors—hereditary differences and environmental differences. Further comments on the contributions of German writers on twins will be made in the body of the book.

The most recent investigations of the nature-nurture problem using twins as material for study are those that have come out of Soviet Russia. A volume of 281 pages has recently come to hand reporting the results of a very extensive study of twins in the Maxim Gorky Medico-biological Research Institute of Moscow (director, S. G. Levit).[18] Over 800 pairs of twins have been studied by a large group of medical men, geneticists, statisticians, and psychologists. Many pairs of identical twins of pre-school age are cared for in a dormitory connected with the Institute. Controlled laboratory experiments have been carried on with these twins as material. One of each pair is used as a control, and the other is experimented upon in various ways. It would be too long a story to give an adequate review of the twelve investigations reported in Russian with English summaries. Suffice it to say that this extensive program of twin research promises to surpass in results all previous work on twins. This newest work, together with the extensive German research along similar lines, has served to raise the field of twin research out of the obscurity it occupied a decade ago to one of the leading places in biological research.

Any adequate review of the immense amount of literature on twin research published in Europe during the last decade or so would occupy far more space than could be afforded in a volume such as this. We must be pardoned for any apparent overemphasis upon American as compared with European work since the former work is much more definitely along the same lines as our own studies than is the latter.

[18] *Proceedings of the Maxim Gorky Medico-biological Institute*, Vol. III (1934), pp. 1–131.

CHAPTER II

A CRITIQUE OF METHODS AND THE PROBLEM
AND METHOD OF THE PRESENT STUDY

FOR ages there has been a heated controversy as to the relative importance of heredity and environment in determining the characteristics, mental and physical, of individual human beings. Extravagant statements have been made by partisans attributing either to heredity or to environment a major determining role. Such statements are wholly unscientific.

In order to make any progress in the solution of this problem, we should review carefully the conditions of a scientific method of attack and should examine the various types of studies in the light of these conditions.

In the first place, it should be clearly understood that no character ever develops without a hereditary basis and without an appropriate environment. Every character is an expression of an interplay of hereditary factors and environmental factors. What we really want to know is the extent to which existing differences in environment, chiefly those in the postnatal environment, modify the expression of particular characters. Each character must be studied as a separate unit, for environmental differences may well modify some characters far more than others. Hence, any statements as to relative potency of heredity and environment in general are meaningless.

Some characters, such as eye color, hair color, fingerprints, etc., appear to be so little modified by existing differences in postnatal environment that they might be considered as purely hereditary. Yet, even such characters as these must have an appropriate environment during development in order to express themselves at all. Other characters, such as test intelligence, body weight, muscularity, etc., are known to be markedly influenced by differences in postnatal environment. It is such characters as these that offer a favorable opening for attack upon the nature-nurture problem. If proper methods are used and adequate material obtained, it should be possible to determine for each separate trait[1] to what extent individual differences are due to hereditary and to what extent to environmental differences.

We may first consider the ideal setup for the investigation of this prob-

---

[1] The word "trait" is used here in a loose sense and does not designate unit characters in the strict sense of the term.

lem and then review the various main types of investigation which have been made in order to see how nearly they approach the ideal.

Whenever an investigator has full control of the material he wishes to study, he adopts the experimental method. The essence of this method is expressed in the principle of the single variable. When it is desired to study the effect of a given factor, that factor is changed in known ways and the concomitant changes in the rest of the situation are noted. The factor which is thus changed is called the "single variable." This is exemplified in physics by the experimental determination of the effect of specified changes in temperature on the length of a metal bar.

In biological investigation the situation is not so simple. A steel bar may otherwise remain the same while its length varies in consequence of a change in temperature. But an animal or plant is subject to the influence of innumerable forces which cannot be held constant. To meet this condition a control group is commonly used. For example, to study the effect of the variation in a given item of food on the growth of rats one group is given greater and another lesser amounts, meanwhile keeping all the other conditions which might affect growth as nearly as possible the same. These include other items of food, sunshine, air, exercise, and genetic constitution. In brief, since the changes in a given individual cannot be attributed solely to the factor which is studied, the changes due to this factor are inferred by a comparison of the changes in the individuals subject to this factor with the changes in other individuals not subject to this factor but alike in other respects.

Applied to the problem of heredity and environment, this means that the ideal experimental procedure would be to apply to specified groups of persons particular environmental influences and then compare their development with that of other groups identical in heredity and in the environmental influences other than those being studied; or, conversely, to carry on experimental breeding holding the environment the same.

Neither of the two variants of this method in pure form has been applied extensively to human beings, and there are obviously serious difficulties in applying it. In the meantime, it is possible to find groups of persons among whom differences exist, not produced experimentally, but occurring fortuitously, which approximate to some degree the conditions of an experiment and, therefore, give opportunity for comparison. Some of the situations in which comparisons have been made are so far from the ideal setup as hardly to warrant comparisons at all. Others more nearly approach the desired conditions.

In general, we may say that the purpose of experimental modification is to secure groups of individuals who are similar in one of the sets of factors, either the hereditary or the environmental, and different in the other. The question regarding the fortuitous groupings is how sharp this contrast is and how clearly it may be defined.

One of the earliest comparisons is the genealogical, made by Galton, Woods, Dugdale, Goddard, and others. Members of a family group resemble one another genetically by varying degrees of closeness and all more closely than persons picked at random. If they also resemble one another by somewhat corresponding degrees in some trait, such as mental ability, it is often concluded that this resemblance is due to the genetic similarity. But there may also be a similarity in environmental conditions, and this may account for some of the resemblance in the trait. In other words, the two sets of variables may be associated and may vary together. This is a complicating circumstance which makes it difficult to draw clean-cut conclusions by the genealogical method.

Many other group comparisons have been made, particularly with regard to general ability as measured by intelligence tests. These include groups inhabiting the various states, groups in various occupations and their children, urban and rural populations, immigrant groups, and persons having different amounts of schooling. In all these cases there are differences in environment associated with possible or hypothetical differences in heredity. The comparisons are so complicated that little that is conclusive can be inferred from them.

Comparisons have been made between orphanage children and others. An orphanage is an institution in which a hereditarily diverse group of children live in ostensibly the same environment. If it is found that such a group is distinctly less variable than is a random sample of children reared in different environments, this reduction of variability might seem to be attributable to the common environment. If, on the other hand, the orphanage children should be no more similar than children in general, one might conclude that similarity of environment had no effect. The experimental setup falls far short of having the elements of control. In the first place, it cannot be safely assumed that the orphanage environment is the same for individuals with different hereditary makeup. Some tolerate the orphanage conditions; others do not. In the second place, the assumption that an orphanage population is the full equivalent, genetically, of a random assortment of the child population is probably unjustified, for it seems more than likely that, being drawn from a lower stratum of intellectual endowment, these children have a lower range of variation in native ability than would be found in an adequate sample of the general population. Since the first defect in control tends to ignore differences in environment and the second tends to lessen the normal variability in heredity, it may well be that the two defects tend to cancel each other, but whether they do so completely or only partially cannot be determined. On the whole, it seems obvious that this method involves too many loose ends to give us any satisfactory solution of the problem.

Foster-children furnish an opportunity for certain comparisons. Where tests have been made before and after adoption any change which appears may be ascribed to the influences associated with the adoptive home. The change is calculated by comparing the foster-children with children in general as a control group. This is a reasonably safe comparison to make. Another comparison is between the degree of resemblance of foster-siblings, in different homes with that of siblings living together in their own homes. These siblings living together are again a control group. A third comparison is between foster-children as a group and the average of children in general, assuming that the heredity of foster-children represents an adverse selection. Finally, the ability of foster-children may be correlated with the grade of the foster-homes or of the foster-parents, assuming that there has not been selective placement or that it is limited in degree.

Two remaining comparisons to be noted are between twins. They are both made in the present study. The first comparison is between identical twins and fraternal twins who are brought up together and are therefore subjected to the influences of rather similar environment. The difference in the degree of resemblance of these two types under relatively similar environment gives opportunity for an estimate of the effect of heredity as represented by the difference in degree of genetic similarity between them. Beyond this rather obvious comparison it is possible, by making certain assumptions concerning the genetic and environmental causes of differences in the two types of twins, to estimate the relative share of the two sets of factors in producing the differences between fraternal twins within a common home environment. The statistical analysis by which this estimate is made is set forth in detail in chapter vi.

This comparison is, of course, affected by the limitation in the range of both the genetic and the environmental factors. The genetic difference is that existing between the relationship of fraternal twins and of identical twins. The latter, of course, are genetically the same. Fraternal twins are, on the average, genetically the same to the extent of 50 per cent. If random pairs were picked, the genetic variation would be twice as much. But the environmental variation to which fraternal twins are subjected is also very limited, being only that which occurs within the same home or among those in the same home. The limitation in the range of environmental variation resulting from this fact is probably greater than is the limitation on the range of the genetic factor.

Other comparisons are made possible by the use of a number of pairs of identical twins who have been separated in infancy. In this case the genetic factor is the same for twin pairs, and the environmental factor is in some instances subject to wide variation. By comparing these separated twins with the group of unseparated identical twins, measures of mean twin differences may be set up which express the effect of difference in postnatal environment for the two groups.

In some instances the difference in environment of the separated twins does not appear to be much greater than that for the unseparated group, but in other cases this difference is considerable. In the difference between the separated and unseparated groups we find a measure that expresses the excess in environment difference of separated as compared with unseparated identical twins. The effect of this excess in postnatal environment may then be studied in its relation to certain twin characters.

Another method of attack that may be employed in the case of separated twins is based upon the rating of environmental differences according to type. From the case histories of the separated twins quantitative estimates may be made of the difference in educational, social, and physical environment of the twin pairs. On the basis of these estimates we may then study the differential effect of such environmental variation upon various twin traits. The technique for expressing this effect is that of correlation between estimated environmental difference according to type and twin difference in observed trait. The foregoing method indicates the extent to which various traits are modifiable by the environmental influences as estimated. As suggested above, it is found that some traits, such as height, are little modified by any sort of estimated postnatal environment, whereas others, such as intelligence, appear to be influenced very markedly by variation in educational and social background.

For the separated cases we may thus obtain measures of the effect of the difference in postnatal environment of the two classes of identical twins. We may also study the degree to which various traits are modified by wide variation in environment. All the foregoing comparisons would, of course, have been much more striking had the environments of all separated twins been very different. Our conclusions are, of course, all relative to the particular sample of separated twins studied.

THE METHOD OF THE PRESENT STUDY

As has been said, the present study is in two parts. The first part is a comparison of the resemblances and differences of fifty pairs of identical and fifty pairs of fraternal twins reared together. The second part is an analysis of the likenesses and differences of nineteen pairs of identical twins reared apart. The first part of the study was begun in 1926. At that time no investigation had included a careful statistical comparison of the resemblances or differences of identical and fraternal twin pairs, basing the classification into the types on biological evidence. One of the authors, on the ground of his extensive studies in the biology of twinning, took the major responsibility for the assumption that twins may be divided into two classes, monozygotic (one-egg) and dizygotic (two-egg), and for the development of a method of classifying twins into the two classes.

The general plan of the first part of the study was to secure an adequate sample of identical and fraternal twins; to give them a variety of physical, mental, and educational tests; and to make such comparisons and correlations between the scores on these tests as might be suggested. An adequate sample was judged to be fifty pairs of each kind, and this number was secured. A further precaution was taken to select only twins of the same sex. The reason for this is that identical twins belong of necessity to the same sex. If, then, fraternal twins of the opposite sexes had been included, they would have introduced a possible complication due to sex differences. Age limits of about eight and eighteen years were set up. The lower limit was set because younger children could not have taken all the tests. The upper limit was set because it was believed that test scores would be more comparable if only persons in school were included.

Twin pairs were found chiefly by inquiry in schools in Chicago or its suburbs. They were taken as they came, without any selection whatever except that based on sex and age. After examination they were classified as identical or fraternal according to a procedure to be described in a moment. The collection of cases was continued without discrimination until the full quota of fifty-two pairs of fraternal twins had been secured. As is well known, the number of identical twins and of same-sex fraternal twins in the population is about equal. To make up the quota of identical twins, three or four additional pairs had to be found. This is the only point at which selection was exercised.

Most of the twins came to the educational laboratory of the University of Chicago and were examined by the three collaborators and their assistant, Mrs. Blythe C. Mitchell. In a few cases, because of the distance, it was necessary to go to the school which the twins attended and examine them there.

Confirmation of the belief that two and only two kinds of human twins exist, namely, monozygotic (identical) and dizygotic (fraternal), is found in the statistics presented in brief in chapter iii, together with a discussion of the question whether or not it is possible adequately to diagnose the two types of twins. In chapter iv there appears an analysis of the possible and probable causes of the observed differences in identical twins presumably reared under identical, or nearly identical, environmental conditions, as they must be when reared together in the same family.

The examination given to both types of twins in the original group of 100 pairs included the following items:

PHYSICAL OBSERVATIONS AND MEASUREMENTS

Height, standing and sitting
Weight
Head length and width
Cephalic index
Hair color and texture
Hair whorl (location and direction of twist)
Eye color and pigment pattern on the iris
Skin texture and coloration
Handedness
    Subject's statement
    Mother's statement
Palm prints and fingerprints
Ears, general contour and peculiarities
Other facial features
Birthmarks, moles, etc.

TESTS

Stanford Revision of the Binet-Simon Test of Intelligence
Otis Self-administering Test of Mental Ability
Stanford Achievement Test
Downey Will-Temperament Test
    Parts dealing with speed of decision, co-ordination of impulses, motor inhibition
        and finality of judgment
Woodworth-Mathews Questionnaire
Tapping tests for the objective determination of handedness

INFORMATION GATHERED BY INTERVIEW WITH PARENTS OR OTHERS

Age
Physical history
    Birth
    Diseases
    General health
    Defects
    Handedness
School history
    School and grade
    Previous progress
    Character of work

School history—*Continued*
    Interest
    Ambitions
    Disposition
General
    Interests
    Recreation
    Reading (voluntary)
    Talents
    Siblings

The data gathered by these observations, measurements, and tests have been subjected to several types of analysis.

In the first place, the physical differences between the members of each pair of twins have been examined in detail and compared with each other and the diagnosis. The consistency between the diagnosis and the magnitude or presence of the physical differences is brought out. The distribution of the chief physical and mental differences of the two types of twins is then presented and compared.

The statistical analysis of the differences of the two types of twins is pursued further by setting forth and comparing the correlations between members of the respective twin pairs. The comparison of the correlations does not in itself give a measure of the relative weight of the various factors in producing the differences. Such a measure, or a series of measures, is found by the derivation of formulas and their application to the differences and correlations. The calculations made by these formulas yield estimates, within the limits of the assumptions laid down, of the relative influence of the genetic and environmental factors in producing the differences found in these twins. These estimates, of course, apply only to such genetic and environmental differences as occur in the case of such twins as we have studied.

Since a number of previous studies made a point of comparing the differences at different ages, we have made this comparison in our own study, though we regard the significance of the findings as difficult to interpret.

The comparisons derived from parents' reports and from handwriting are briefly summarized, though conclusions from these data must be expressed with greater reservation than those based on more exact measurements and tests.

The facts and conclusions of the study are interpreted in the light of general biological theory and of previous studies in the biology of twinning. An attempt is made throughout to combine the three points of view of biology, psychology, and statistics in the interpretation of the results of the study as well as in its planning.

The general plan of the second part of the investigation was to secure as many pairs as possible of identical twins who had been separated in infancy and reared apart up to maturity or until the time of the examination. After sufficient examination of the evidence to make reasonably sure that a pair of separated twins were identical, arrangements were made to bring them to Chicago for personal examination and testing. They were then given a detailed physical examination and were scrutinized to make sure they were identical. This examination followed the same general routine as that of the original 100 pairs of twins. A detailed account of the method of gathering the cases, and a discussion of the proofs of monozygocity of the separated cases, are given in chapter viii.

The separated pairs were, in addition, given a battery of mental and educational tests similar in nature to the tests given to the 100 pairs but somewhat more extensive. Following is a list of these tests:

Stanford Revision of the Binet-Simon Test of Intelligence
Otis Self-administering Test of Mental Ability
Thurstone Psychological Examination (American Council Test)
International Test, devised by Stuart C. Dodd
Stanford Achievement Test
Woodworth-Mathews Personal Data Sheet
Kent-Rosanoff Free Association Test
Pressey Test of the Emotions
Downey Will-Temperament Test, Individual Form (Complete)

The entire examination occupied two days.

The data from the examination of the separated cases are subjected to the same kinds of statistical analysis as in the case of the 100 pairs brought up together. In addition, two forms of treatment particularly appropriate to these cases are used. First, each pair is written up as a case study, in which the effort is made to trace particular relations between the differences in environment and the differences in the characteristics of the members of a pair. Second, the relation between estimated differences in the environment and measured differences in the members of a pair is analyzed statistically by the method of correlation. The procedures in detail are set forth in chapter xii.

A word should perhaps be said concerning the possible selection of cases in the two parts of the study. It seems unlikely that any bias occurred in the gathering of the fifty pairs of identical and fifty pairs of fraternal twins in the first part. Twins were taken just as they came, the only condition being that they be of the same sex. After they were secured, they were classified into identical and fraternal by means of the methods of physical examination which have been described. It turned out that the proportion of the types thus secured agreed very well with that calculated from large twin populations within the limits of the sampling error. When we come to the separated cases, a somewhat different situation exists. It seems possible that our group is more heavily weighted with extremely similar pairs than with identical twins of less striking similarity. Some of our pairs discovered each other because one was mistaken for the other by an entire stranger. This might not have occurred if they had been among the less similar identicals. In any case, if there is any selection at all, it is in this direction, and our separated pairs are at least as similar, and possibly more similar, in most of their physical characters than are identical twins in general.

CHAPTER III

THE TWO KINDS OF TWINS (IDENTICAL AND FRATERNAL) AND THE METHODS OF DIAGNOSING THEM

EVIDENCES THAT TWO AND ONLY TWO KINDS OF HUMAN TWINS EXIST

THIS is hardly the appropriate place to marshal all the evidences now available that bear on the existence of two types of twins in man. Twenty years ago there was some doubt on this score, but biologists are now in complete agreement that twins are either monozygotic or dizygotic in origin. For the general reader, however, it may be well to give a brief summary of the kinds of evidence that have been sufficient to convince biologists. In the main, the following lines of evidence tend to prove the existence of monozygotic (identical) twins: (a) the demonstrated fact of one-egg twinning in other mammals, notably two species of armadillos, in which the actual process of division of a single egg into four or more embryos has been repeatedly observed; (b) the discovery of several cases of early monozygotic twins in sheep and swine; (c) the discovery by Streeter of an early one-egg human twin embryo, a somewhat abnormal case but demonstrating that one-egg twinning does occur in man; (d) the existence, according to Arey, of cases of monozygotic tubal twins in man; (e) statistical studies of sex ratios in twins that can be rationalized only by assuming that at least one-fourth of all twins are monozygotic; (f) the fact that the two members of many a twin pair are practically identical, so nearly so that it is inconceivable that they could arise from two distinct zygotes with different assortments of genes from the two parents; (g) the fact that over a third of the more similar pairs of twins exhibit rather extensive mirror-imaging of asymmetrical characters, such as handedness, hair whorl, dental irregularities, palm patterns, and fingerprints—a situation unexplainable except on the basis that such twins are derived one from a right and one from a left half of a single embryo; and (h) the existence of conjoined (Siamese) twins, which are frequently attached to a common umbilical cord, which frequently exhibit *situs inversus viscerum* (reversed asymmetry of heart, stomach, liver, etc.) in one component of the pair, and which show the same sorts of differences between the components as do some of the least similar separate twins diagnosed as monozygotic.

METHODS OF DIAGNOSIS OF MONOZYGOCITY

Two methods of diagnosing twins with respect to their zygotic origin have been used: the fetal-membrane method and the similarity method.

FETAL-MEMBRANE METHOD OF DIAGNOSIS

Until recently it has been assumed by obstetricians that all monozygotic twins are monochorionic (both being surrounded by a single chorionic membrane) and that all dizygotic twins are dichorionic (each twin of a pair being surrounded by its own chorion). It has long been recognized, however, that, when two chorions are pressed closely together, they tend to fuse and sometimes to appear superficially monochorionic. Careful histological study of the regions of fusion, however, reveal to the experienced observer the true state of affairs. But the usual obstetrical reports are not based on such careful studies, and many dichorial fused cases are reported as monochorial.

Even assuming that histological examination is competent to separate the true monochorial from the fused dichorial cases, membrane diagnosis still fails to differentiate the two kinds of twins as to modes of origin. During the last few years a very disconcerting fact has come to light, namely, that many twins, diagnosed on the basis of their fetal membranes as undoubtedly dichorial, turn out later to be among the most strikingly identical of twin pairs. This must mean, then, that some monozygotic twins are monochorial and others dichorial. The observations upon which this somewhat unexpected statement is based are furnished mainly by two German workers, Curtius[1] and Lassen.[2] Curtius (1928) made a very careful diagnosis of the afterbirths of 31 pairs of twins that had survived at least some years after the membrane diagnosis was made. Of these, 12 were opposite-sexed and 19 were same-sexed pairs. Later the twins were diagnosed as identicals and fraternals by Siemen's similarity method. All 12 opposite-sexed pairs (fraternals) were found to be dichorial, and all 12 same-sexed but unlike twins (fraternals) were found to be dichorial. Of the 7 physically identical twin pairs, however, 3 were definitely monochorial, 3 definitely dichorial, and 1 uncertain because of poor condition of the afterbirth. Three years later Lassen (1931) reported on 56 pairs of twins whose afterbirths had been diagnosed by the methods of Kiffner and Curtius. Of these, 21 were opposite-sexed pairs and were all dichorial; 21 were unlike, same-sexed twins and also dichorial; and of the 14 same-sexed and "identical" pairs, 9 were monochorial and 5 dichorial. Of these 5 dichorial pairs, 2 had a single placenta and 3 had two separate placentae.

It should be emphasized that in both of these studies the similarity diagnosis agreed perfectly with the membrane diagnosis in all sixty-six cases diagnosed as fraternals, indicating the validity of both methods of diagnosis—the membrane method and the similarity method. It is only in the case of

[1] F. Curtius, *Zeitschrift für Konstitutionslehre*, Vol. XIII (1928).

[2] M.-T. Lassen, *Archiv für Gynäkologie*, Vol. CXLVII (1931).

twins diagnosed by the similarity test as identicals that there is no correlation with either type of chorionic condition. There is, therefore, apparently no escape from the conclusion that one-egg twins not infrequently have separate chorions and even separate placentae. To the embryologist this can mean but one thing: that twinning may sometimes occur at a very early period, probably prior to the trophoblast and inner-cell mass stage, possibly during early cleavage.

Practically speaking, then, the membrane method of diagnosis, even in those cases where such diagnoses are reliable and available, is of little value in determining the zygotic origin of twins. The only remaining method of diagnosis available is the so-called "similarity method."

SIMILARITY METHOD OF DIAGNOSIS

The fundamental postulate underlying the similarity method of diagnosis is that one-egg twins must have identical heredity and that two-egg twins differ in hereditary makeup in the same way as do siblings. Pairs of the former must necessarily be of the same sex, but pairs of the latter have equal chances of being same-sexed and opposite-sexed. One-egg twins, unless there are disturbing factors during development, should be identical; two-egg twins have no more reason for being identical than have siblings, except that, being of the same age, they would at any given time be somewhat more similar than the two sibs born a year or more apart.

This being the case, why should there be any difficulty in distinguishing the two kinds of twins at a glance? The answer to this question is not simple. In the first place, it is known that several factors operate during development to modify the expression of the hereditary characters of one-egg twins to such an extent that they are often as different in some modifiable characters as are two-egg twins. In the second place, the two members of a dizygotic pair may by chance inherit almost the same combinations of hereditary characters from the two parents, especially if the two parents are closely similar in their genetic constitution. The latter situation is probably exceedingly rare, but the former is almost universal. Hence the chances of making a false diagnosis of dizygotic twins, that is, diagnosing dizygotic twins as monozygotic, are negligible, especially for a person at all experienced in twin diagnosis. Whatever mistakes are likely to be made are those of diagnosing some of the least similar monozygotic twins as dizygotic. With the technique now in use, however, even this mistake is quite unlikely to be made.

Our criteria for diagnosing twins are based largely upon the well-tried and approved method of H. W. Siemens and von Verschuer—two of the most distinguished of European students of twins. Several new criteria, those on palm and finger friction-ridge patterns, were added and found to be especially valuable. The method used is designed to identify the monozygotic pairs.

The following were our criteria for diagnosing monozygotic twins. Twins are classed as monozygotic only if they meet these requirements:

1. They must be so strikingly similar in general appearance that they are likely to be mistaken the one for the other.
2. They must be essentially identical in hair color, hair texture, and hair form.
3. They must have essentially the same eye color and pigment pattern on the iris.
4. They must have the same skin color (complexion), unless one is modified by tanning, and the same amount and distribution of body down, especially on face, neck, and hands.
5. They must have essentially the same facial features, nose, lips, chin, ears.
6. They must have essentially the same types of teeth, the same irregularities in dentition. (Casts of the dentitions of most of the pairs were made by a dentist and subsequently used to check earlier diagnoses.)
7. They must have hands and fingers of the same type and proportions.
8. The general microscopic character of the friction ridges of fingers and palms must be essentially the same.
9. There must be stronger cross resemblance than internal resemblance in most of the details of finger and palm patterns. (One hand of one twin must be more like one hand of the other twin than like own other hand. This fails in only a few of the least-similar twins for the same reason that it fails in Siamese twins —a situation discussed a little later.)
10. The presence of reversed asymmetry (mirror-imaging) in handedness, hair whorl, dentition, palm patterns, etc., is confirmatory evidence of monozygocity, but its absence does not deny monozygocity. Neither does the occasional presence of left-handedness or counterclockwise hair whorl in one of a pair of decidedly unlike twins indicate that they are monozygotic.

CHAPTER IV

CAUSES OF DIFFERENCES IN IDENTICAL TWINS
REARED TOGETHER

ONE of the most striking facts that came to light in our studies of identical twins reared together is that the two members of a pair are never truly identical but differ more or less with respect to all their characters and that they differ sometimes to a disconcerting degree. It is assumed, of course, that the members of a pair of identical twins are genetically identical. Why, then, should they differ at all if they are reared together under what would seem to be as nearly identical environmental conditions as are realized under ordinary conditions of life?

It is sometimes assumed that differences which appear between identical twins reared together are due wholly to small, intangible differences in the postnatal environments of the two individuals. This assumption overlooks the possibility that at least some, if not most, of the differences are the result of causes which are associated with the monozygotic twinning process and are peculiar to that process. The authors of this book believe that such causes must be reckoned with. They recognize that the relative potency of the two sets of factors is at present debatable and inaccessible to objective investigation by any technique thus far employed. The authors themselves differ somewhat in the emphasis they place upon the prenatal and post-natal factors. They therefore content themselves with a description of the factors without attempting to evaluate them in any precise fashion.

The chief prenatal causes of differences between identical twins may be classified as (a) the fusion of fetal blood vessels between twins and the consequent inequalities of the blood supply and (b) the asymmetry mechanism.

INEQUALITIES IN FETAL BLOOD SUPPLY

While it is conceivable that there may be in the case of a pair of identical twins inequalities in the blood supply furnished by the mother to different parts of the common placenta, such inequalities would be difficult to demonstrate, for the placenta is a sort of spongy mass permeated by lymph channels that are interconnected in such a way as to distribute maternal nutritive materials evenly to all functional parts of the placenta. The real differences in fetal nutrition come about in the following way. When the two members of a twin pair begin to invade the common placenta with their blood vessels, they tend to divide the placental area somewhat equally.

But when, as is usually the case, the two vascular invasions proceed from opposite sides of the placental disk, they meet toward the center of the area and compete for this area. The blood vessels, capillaries, veins, and arteries of the two individuals push into the same area and come closely in contact with one another. There occur as the result of contact more or less extensive fusions, or anastomoses of capillary with capillary, artery with artery, and vein with vein of opposite individuals. In the majority of cases only capillary anastomoses occur, and little or no damage is done; but in many cases, where fairly extensive arterial and venous anastomoses occur, there are serious consequences. Whenever there are anastomoses of this sort, much of the welfare of the twins depends on whether such anastomoses are symmetrical or asymmetrical. A symmetrical situation involves a fair and even exchange of blood between the twins, and all is well with both; but, if there is an imbalance between the amount of blood leaving the circulation of one twin and that coming back from the other twin, a serious situation arises, the degree of seriousness being proportional to the extent of the vascular imbalance. Both twins may be seriously injured, but usually the twin that progressively loses blood is more damaged than the one that gains blood. Often the heart of the twin that loses blood dies of inanition, and circulation of both twins goes on for a time through the labor of the heart of the surviving twin, whose heart enlarges to meet the extra work required of it. Such extreme cases as these do not especially concern us in our attempt to get at the causes of differences in twins that have been born and have grown up, but there can be little doubt that twins with minor imbalance in the placental anastomoses do survive and show minor degrees of the same types of effect described for extreme cases.

It is commonly believed that one member of each pair of identical twins is lacking in vitality as compared with the other. Many even believe that one member of each pair is sterile. While such views as these are incorrect, there seems to be some basis for the general impression, for in many cases one member of a pair of twins actually is physically inferior to the other in many ways from the time of birth on. It seems probable that such early differences in vigor and vitality are the result of minor inequality in the fetal blood supply of the twins, resulting from an imbalance in the placental blood exchange.

That this imbalance in blood exchange does produce marked differences in surviving twins is evidenced by the fact brought out by the extensive observations of Schatz, who found that, at about the middle period of pregnancy, size differences in monozygotic twins average much greater than in dizygotic twins. This is the opposite of what might be expected on a genetic basis. Identical twins that survive this period tend to be more nearly equal in size, but even at birth their size differences equal on the average those of dizygotic twins, many of the former showing more marked differences than the average of the latter. As has been said, such size differences frequently persist for life, and it seems probable that differences produced by this prenatal factor extend beyond mere size and involve also differences in vigor and general health. How much of the observed size and weight differences in adult identical twins trace back to the factor under discussion we have no means of knowing, but it seems obvious that the effects of this factor are too important to be ignored. In concluding discussion of this factor it should be emphasized that it is peculiar to monozygotic twins, for there are no known cases of dizygotic twins in man in which placental anastomoses of fetal blood vessels occur.

THE ASYMMETRY MECHANISM AS A DIFFERENCE-PRODUCING FACTOR

In general, it seems safe to conclude that the asymmetry mechanism affects in identical twins primarily those kinds of characters that have an asymmetrical expression in single individuals. It may possibly affect certain kinds of quantitative differences that are not expressed asymmetrically, such as stature, body weight, head length and breadth, intelligence quotient, etc. Fortunately, it is possible to determine whether differences in these characters are correlated with asymmetry reversal in other characters. Twenty of our fifty pairs of identical twins reared together were selected as those that showed the most evidences of asymmetry reversal and mirror-imaging, and their average differences in height, weight, head length, head width, total friction ridges in ten fingers, mental age, educational age, and motor (tapping) tests were compared with those of the remaining thirty pairs that showed slight asymmetry reversal or none. In none of these characters was there a significant difference between the two groups. Contrary to theoretical expectation, the average differences in the group showing slight or no asymmetry reversal were a little greater than in those showing considerable asymmetry reversal, but the slight differences between the two groups were too small to have any statistical significance. We may conclude then, with respect to most of the kinds of characters with which we are dealing in this study, that we might safely ignore the asymmetry mechanism as a source of differences.

Such a conclusion seems to run counter to some of our findings in Siamese twins, where rather large differences in stature, weight, and head shape and size are the rule. A possible explanation of this apparent discrepancy suggests itself, namely, that in conjoined twins there is the possibility of one component affecting the other physiologically because of their bodily union, while in separate twins such interindividual influences would be impossible.

We shall now review the evidence on the question whether the asymmetry reversal mechanism induces such differences in identical twins as complete or partial reversals in handedness, hair whorl, dentition, palmar patterns, ear form, featural asymmetries, etc. There is evidence also that this mechanism may occasionally produce partial reversals in the viscera, especially in the circulatory system, and that even slight reversals in the relations of the aorta and the principal arteries may involve important physiological disturbances. Such disturbances may have secondary effects on health and growth. While such effects doubtless are possible, there are no evidences that they are present in any of our twins, and therefore they may for present purposes be ignored.

ASYMMETRY REVERSAL AND MIRROR-IMAGING

One of the earliest and most striking observations made by early students of human twins was that left-handers occur with much greater frequency among twins than in the general population. It was further noticed by several investigators that in many twin pairs one individual was right-handed and the other left-handed. Similarly, it was found, with respect to many other asymmetrical characters, that one twin was frequently the mirror-image of the other. Next to mirror-imaging in handedness that in the crown whorl of the head hair received most attention. Various writers claimed that there were many pairs of twins in which one had clockwise, and the other counterclockwise, hair whorl. Mirror-imaging with respect to dental irregularities, facial asymmetries, palm patterns, fingerprints, and numerous other characters have been reported as common in twins. Since much more attention has been paid to asymmetry reversal in handedness and in hair whorl than to all other examples of asymmetry, we shall deal with these two types of mirror-imaging in some detail and shall attempt to extract from an analysis of the data whatever of significance may be derived therefrom. We shall first examine the data on handedness.

MIRROR-IMAGING IN HANDEDNESS

A controversy has arisen among students of twins as to whether left-handedness is actually present in twins to a significantly greater extent than among persons in general. This controversy centers about the question of whether there are definitely more pairs of identical twins than fraternal twins in which one is right-handed and the other left-handed. Several different investigators have reported on the handedness situation in fairly large collections of twins. Dahlberg,[1] Hirsch,[2] and Newman[3] have all re-

[1] G. Dahlberg, *Twin Births and Twins from an Hereditary Point of View* (Stockholm, 1926).

[2] N. D. M. Hirsch, *Twins, Heredity and Environment.* Cambridge: Harvard University Press, 1930. Pp. 159.

[3] H. H. Newman, "Studies of Human Twins: II. Asymmetry Reversal, or Mirror Imaging in Identical Twins," *Biological Bulletin*, LV (1928), 298–315.

ported a considerably higher percentage of pairs of identical than of fraternal twins in which left-handedness was present, but von Verschuer[4] has reported more pairs of fraternal twins than of identical twins in which one was a left-hander. Recently, Wilson and Jones,[5] on the basis of a study of 70 pairs of twins diagnosed as identical and 123 pairs diagnosed as fraternal, reported that 11.4 per cent of fraternal twins were left-handed and 10.7 per cent of identical twins were left-handed.

If we were to compile the data of all but those from the Wilson and Jones paper, which unfortunately does not give the incidence of minor degrees of left-handedness, we should have a fairer picture of the whole situation than would be obtainable from the data of any one investigator.

TABLE 2

COMBINED DATA ON MIRROR-IMAGING IN HANDEDNESS
DERIVED FROM FOUR AUTHORS

TYPE OF HANDEDNESS	IDENTICAL		FRATERNAL	
	No. of Pairs	Percentage of Pairs	No. of Pairs	Percentage of Pairs
Both right-handed.	166	68.9	229	83.6
One left-handed, other right-handed. . .	58	24.1	41	15.0
One ambidextrous, other right-handed. .	4	1.7	3	1.1
Both left-handed.	9	3.7	1	0.4
One ambidextrous, other left-handed. . .	1	0.4	. . . .	. . . .
Both ambidextrous.	3	1.2	. . . .	. . . .
Total.	241	100.0	274	100.1

Hence we present in Table 2 the combined data of Dahlberg, von Verschuer, Hirsch, and ourselves.

This table shows rather definitely that there are more identical- than fraternal-twin pairs in which left-handedness occurs. Excluding all other pairs except those in which one is definitely right- and the other left-handed, we find such mirror-imaging pairs in 24.1 per cent of identical and in only 15 per cent of fraternal pairs. This takes no account of the cases of partial asymmetry reversal, in which one twin of a pair is ambidextrous and the other either right- or left-handed.

On the face of the raw data, then, it seems certain that left-handedness is somewhat more frequent per pair in identical than in fraternal twins. A

[4] O. von Verschuer, "Der Vererbungsbiologische Zwillingsforschung," *Ergeb. Innern. Med. u. Kinderheit.*, Band XXXI (1927).

[5] P. T. Wilson and H. E. Jones, "Left-handedness in Twins," *Genetics*, XVII (September, 1932), 560–71.

more impressive difference with respect to the incidence of left-handedness in the two kinds of twins appears if we remind ourselves of the difference in zygotic origin between the latter. A pair of identical twins represents 1 zygote, while a pair of fraternal twins represents 2 zygotes. In Table 2 we see that 548 zygotes are needed to produce the 274 pairs of fraternal twins, while only 241 zygotes are required to produce 241 pairs of identical twins. Let us see how often, per zygote, complete or partial left-handedness is expressed in one or more individuals of a pair. In 75 out of 241 (31 per cent) of the zygotes forming identical twins there is some expression of left-handedness; while in only 45 out of 548 (8.2 per cent) of the zygotes forming fraternal twins is there any expression of left-handedness. Thus left-handedness is expressed nearly four times as frequently, per zygote, in identical as in fraternal twins. In the face of this evidence, it is rather difficult to avoid the conclusion that monozygotic twinning and mirror-imaging in handedness are causally related.

The real problem that confronts us is not that of accounting for the rather high incidence of left-handedness in identical twins but that of accounting for the marked excess of left-handedness in fraternal twins, as compared with the general population. In identical twins the explanation of mirror-imaging is relatively simple, namely, that one twin has been derived from a partially differentiated left, and the other twin from a partially differentiated right half of a single embryo. In fraternal twins, however, there seems to be no reason for any more left-handers than in the general population; yet the frequency of left-handedness among them is about twice as great as among people in general. This is a real mystery which has not yet been cleared up. One suggestion has been made by Lauterbach that a good many fraternal-twin pairs may be survivors of triplet or quadruplet sets, some members of which were identical twins. This implies that left-handed members of a pair of twins derived from one zygote have survived in considerable numbers and are paired off with right-handers derived from another zygote. That such a condition must sometimes occur, judging by the high prenatal mortality of multiple embryos, cannot be denied; but whether this is the explanation of the excess number of left-handers among fraternal twins, it is impossible to decide.

The fact that there is an unexplainable excess of left-handers among fraternal twins has, however, no bearing on the fact that asymmetry reversal in handedness is of frequent occurrence among identical twins—this, in spite of the fact that various authors have attempted to use this situation to discredit the idea that asymmetry reversal among identical twins actually occurs.

Various students of handedness have reported that the expression of left-handedness varies greatly in different individuals, that some left-handers do everything in a left-handed fashion, that others do some things right-handed and some left-handed, and that still others are ambidextrous. With this fact in mind, it would be interesting to know what criteria of left-handedness have been used by the authors of the various reports on the incidence of left-handedness among identical and fraternal twins. So far as we are aware, none of them has used motor tests in his diagnosis. Wilson and Jones, who found slightly larger numbers of left-handers among fraternal than among identical twins, used as their criteria of handedness the preferred hand used in writing and in throwing. Writing is notoriously a poor test of handedness, though throwing is a good one for males and a rather poor one for females.

Because of the rather loose methods commonly practiced in diagnosing handedness, we decided to attempt to improve current methods. We used two motor tests which we called "wrist tapping" and "finger tapping," respectively. These are regarded as activities that have been uninfluenced by training and are likely to reveal the native motor superiority of the one or the other hand. Each test subject was required to tap as rapidly as possible on a recording instrument for five seconds; first, with the wrist free and stiff index finger and, second, with stiff wrist and free finger. Each test was repeated three times, allowing a period of rest between tests. The sum of the scores on three trials constituted the final score. Usually the three trials gave closely corresponding scores, about five taps being the largest normal difference. Since there were rather commonly as many as five taps difference on repetition of the same test by the same person, we regarded differences of five points or less between the scores of the two hands of an individual as equality and considered such an individual ambidextrous on the test. Arbitrarily, we shall consider an individual that shows a right-handed superiority of twenty or more points as a strong right-hander (R); one that has a right-handed superiority of from six to nineteen points, inclusive, as a weak right-hander (r). On the same basis we designate strong left-handers (L) and weak left-handers (l), while individuals showing no more than five points difference between the two hands are designated ambidextrous (A).

Table 3 gives, for our fifty pairs of identical twins, and Table 4, for our fifty pairs of fraternal twins, in Column 1 the diagnosis of handedness based on questioning the subject and his parents as to hand preference, in Column 2 the number of points of right-handed ($+$) superiority or left-handed superiority ($-$), and in Column 3 the final diagnosis of handedness

TABLE 3

DIAGNOSIS OF HANDEDNESS IN IDENTICAL TWINS

Serial No.	Diagnosis According to Statements (1)	Scores in Motor Tests (2)	Final Diagnosis and Remarks (3)	Serial No.	Diagnosis According to Statements (1)	Scores in Motor Tests (2)	Final Diagnosis and Remarks (3)
35 {A	R	+35	R	72 {A	L	−29	L
B	R	+33	R	B	R	+20	R
69 {A	R	+38	R	13 {A	R	+ 6	r
B	R	+28	R	B	L	−25	L
49 {A	l	+17	l; throws ball with left	40 {A	R	+34	R
B	R	+24	R	B	R	+18	r
78 {A	L	+ 7	L; right-hand trained	94 {A	R	+20	r; left in finger tapping
B	R	+38	R	B	L	−30	L
6 {A	R	+52	R	63 {A	R	+19	r
B	R	+34	R	B	R	+33	R
91 {A	R	+15	r	60 {A	R	+22	R
B	R	+23	R	B	R	+ 5	A
99 {A	R	+15	r	79 {A	R	+35	R
B	R	+44	R	B	L	+ 2	L; right-hand trained
96 {A	R	+14	r	97 {A	R	+23	R
B	R	+26	R	B	R	+39	R
28 {A	R	+25	R	68 {A	R	+27	R
B	R	+61	R	B	R	+35	R
41 {A	L	−25	L	62 {A	R	+44	R
B	R	+29	R	B	R	+45	R
100 {A	L(?)	+28	R; mother's statement uncertain	14 {A	R	+39	R
				B	R	+52	R
B	R	+29	R	67 {A	R	*	R
18 {A	R	+12	r	B	R		R
B	R	+60	R	38 {A	R	−14	l; left in both motor tests
53 {A	R	+27	R	B	R	+23	R
B	L	−15	L	101 {A	R	+34	R
23 {A	R	+ 2	A	B	L	+16	l; right-hand trained
B	R	+12	r	55 {A	R	+43	R
25 {A	R	+41	R	B	R	+35	R
B	R	+31	R	98 {A	R	+62	R
27 {A	R	+21	R	B	R	+26	R
B	R	−12	l; left in both motor tests	7 {A	R	0	A
3 {A	R	+ 7	r	B	R	+ 2	A
B	R	+ 8	r	44 {A	L(?)	+32	R; mother's vague statement
17 {A	R	+26	R				
B	R	+27	R	B	R	+30	R

* No motor tests given.

TABLE 3—*Continued*

Serial No.	Diagnosis According to Statements (1)	Scores in Motor Tests (2)	Final Diagnosis and Remarks (3)	Serial No.	Diagnosis According to Statements (1)	Scores in Motor Tests (2)	Final Diagnosis and Remarks (3)
73 A.....	R	−7	l; much stronger with left finger	87 A.....	A(?)	+27	R ⎫ parent's un-
73 B.....	R	+9	r	87 B.....	A(?)	+19	r ⎭ certain statement
2 A.....	R	−2	A	37 A.....	R	+28	R
2 B.....	R	−5	A	37 B.....	R	− 2	A
24 A.....	R	+25	R	33 A.....	L	+11	l; right-hand trained
24 B.....	R	+25	R	33 B.....	R	+43	R
80 A.....	R	*	R	70 A.....	R	+40	R
80 B.....	R		R	70 B.....	R	− 2	A
102 A.....	R	+30	R	34 A.....	R	+ 3	A
102 B.....	R	+34	R	34 B.....	R	+ 5	A
15 A.....	R	+21	R	43 A.....	R	+37	R
15 B.....	R	+10	r	43 B.....	R	+17	r
30 A.....	R	+31	R				
30 B.....	R	+24	R				
9 A.....	R	+41	R				
9 B.....	R	+27	R; uses left to some extent				

based on the combined data, together with qualifying remarks where such seem appropriate.

A survey of these two tables will show a very general agreement between statements of subjects and parents as to handedness and the tapping-test scores. A few minor discrepancies between the two criteria occur, and in these cases it is necessary to balance the one against the other and give greater weight to the one that seems more conclusive. Where, for example, statements of parents are very positive, to the effect that the subject was originally definitely left-handed but had been trained to prefer the right hand, this overbalances a small right-hand superiority in test scores. Usually such a left-hander is regarded as a weak left-hander and is designated as *l*. Whatever of arbitrariness in such cases may have been practiced, it is important to remember that identical and fraternal twins were treated exactly alike.

Perhaps the best method of getting before the reader the facts as to our methods of diagnosing handedness is to place before him tables showing, first, the diagnosis on the basis of motor tests alone (Table 5); second, that

TABLE 4

DIAGNOSIS OF HANDEDNESS IN FRATERNAL TWINS

Serial No.	Diagnosis According to Statements (1)	Scores in Motor Tests (2)	Final Diagnosis and Remarks (3)	Serial No.	Diagnosis According to Statements (1)	Scores in Motor Tests (2)	Final Diagnosis and Remarks (3)
12 A	L	−30	L	39 A	R	+30	R
12 B	R	+29	R	39 B	R	+26	R
56 A	R	+37	R	85 A	R	+13	r
56 B	R	+30	R	85 B	R	+ 3	A; slightly left in finger test
71 A	R	+42	R	52 A	R	+57	R
71 B	R	+12	r; slightly left in finger test	52 B	R	+35	R
84 A	R	+23	R	26 A	R	+21	R
84 B	R	+ 6	r	26 B	R	+18	r
21 A	R	+21	R	65 A	R	+17	r
21 B	R	+49	R	65 B	R	+ 1	A; equal in both motor tests
31 A	R	+37	R	95 A	R	+29	R
31 B	L	−24	L	95 B	R	+24	R
59 A	R	+23	R	16 A	R	+13	r
59 B	R	+26	R	16 B	R	+21	R
86 A	R	+12	r	82 A	R	+33	R
86 B	R	+14	r; uses left hand somewhat	82 B	R	+39	R
54 A	R	+32	R	64 A	R	+18	r
54 B	R	+13	r	64 B	R	+13	r
45 A	R	+29	R	88 A	R	+27	R
45 B	R	−13	l; right-hand trained	88 B	R	+ 9	r
75 A	R	+18	r	74 A	R	+42	R
75 B	R	+27	R	74 B	R	+28	R
48 A	R	+22	R	89 A	R	+44	R
48 B	R	+ 8	r	89 B	R	+37	R
36 A	R	+ 6	r	29 A	R	+57	R
36 B	L	−21	L	29 B	R	+27	R
32 A	R	+42	R	50 A	R	+10	r
32 B	R	+27	R	50 B	R	+40	R
83 A	R	+26	R	42 A	R	+33	R
83 B	R	+ 6	r; slight left in finger test	42 B	R	+20	R
47 A	R	+23	R	46 A	R	+19	r
47 B	R	+33	R	46 B	L	− 8	l
57 A	R	+52	R	10 A	R	+49	R
57 B	R	+49	R	10 B	R	+22	R
19 A	R	+49	R	77 A	R	+40	R
19 B	R	+17	r	77 B	R	+30	R
81 A	R	+26	R	22 A	R	+ 1	A; slightly left in finger test
81 B	R	+24	R	22 B	R	+57	R

TABLE 4—*Continued*

Serial No.	Diagnosis According to Statements (1)	Scores in Motor Tests (2)	Final Diagnosis and Remarks (3)	Serial No.	Diagnosis According to Statements (1)	Scores in Motor Tests (2)	Final Diagnosis and Remarks (3)
11 {A.....	R	+ 7	r	92 {A.....	R	+35	R
{B.....	R	+10	r	{B.....	L	−16	l
4 {A.....	L	−36	L	58 {A.....	R	+26	R
{B.....	R	+35	R	{B.....	R	+45	R
93 {A.....	L	− 4	l; mother's uncertain statement	8 {A.....	R	+54	R
{B.....	R	+23	R	{B.....	R	+39	R
66 {A.....	R	+18	r	76 {A.....	R	+26	R
{B.....	R	+58	R	{B.....	R	+33	R
20 {A.....	R	+27	R	90 {A.....	R	+36	R
{B.....	R	+33	R	{B.....	R	+30	R
61 {A.....	R	+27	R	5 {A.....	R	+25	R
{B.....	R	+26	R	{B.....	R	+52	R

based on statements alone (Table 6); and, third, that based on a combination of the two types of criteria (Table 7).

Tables 5 and 6 exhibit a close similarity in the proportions of pairs both of which are right-handed and in those in which at least one twin is completely or partially left-handed. On any basis of classification there are definitely more pairs showing left-handedness among identical than among fraternal twins. According to Table 7 (which is probably safer to follow than either Tables 5 or 6), we find 20 pairs (40 per cent of the whole) of identical twin pairs that exhibit some degree of left-handedness in one or both individuals and only 11 pairs (22 per cent) among fraternal twins. On the basis of the number of zygotes involved, it appears that in identical twins asymmetry reversal in handedness expresses itself in the products of 40 per cent of the 50 zygotes while in fraternal twins it appears in only 11 per cent of the products of 100 zygotes involved. Thus asymmetry reversal in handedness appears nearly four times as frequently, on the zygote basis, in identical twins as in fraternal twins. Need we labor further this demonstration?

An even more significant fact may be gleaned from these tables, namely, that individuals with partial reversal of asymmetry in handedness (weak left-handers, *l*, and ambidexters, *A*) are far more numerous among identical than fraternal twins. Thus there are 16 identical twins (6 *l*'s and 10 *A*'s) with partial reversals and only 7 fraternals (4 *l*'s and 3 *A*'s). This we regard

TABLE 5

HANDEDNESS IN TWIN PAIRS ACCORDING TO MOTOR TESTS

TYPES OF HANDEDNESS	IDENTICALS		FRATERNALS	
	No. of Pairs	Percentage of Pairs	No. of Pairs	Percentage of Pairs
Both right-handed.................	32	64	39	78
One right-handed, other left-handed...	8	16	7	14
Right-handed in one, ambidextrous in other...........................	5	10	4	8
Both ambidextrous.................	3	6	....	....
No motor tests given...............	2	4	....	....
Total........................	50	100	50	100

TABLE 6

HANDEDNESS IN TWIN PAIRS ACCORDING TO STATEMENTS
OF TWINS AND MOTHERS

TYPES OF HANDEDNESS	IDENTICALS		FRATERNALS	
	No. of Pairs	Percentage of Pairs	No. of Pairs	Percentage of Pairs
Both right-handed.................	36	72	41	82
One right-handed, other fully left-handed......................	8	16	6	12
One right-handed, other does some things left-handed...............	5	10	3	6
Both ambidextrous................	1	2	....	....
Total........................	50	100	50	100

TABLE 7

HANDEDNESS IN TWIN PAIRS ACCORDING TO BOTH
MOTOR TESTS AND STATEMENTS

TYPES OF HANDEDNESS	IDENTICALS		FRATERNALS	
	No. of Pairs	Percentage of Pairs	No. of Pairs	Percentage of Pairs
Both right-handed.................	30	60	39	78
One right-handed, other left-handed...	13	26	8	16
One right-handed, other ambidextrous..	4	8	3	6
Both ambidextrous.................	3	6	....	....
Total........................	50	100	50	100

as strong evidence that the asymmetry reversal mechanism has operated much more strongly in identical than in fraternal twins. The 7 per cent of fraternal-twin individuals in which partial reversal is expressed may possibly be interpreted as identical-twin survivors paired with an individual derived from another zygote.

Since partial reversals of asymmetry are evident in many other characters in identical twins (such characters as hair whorl, dentition, palm and finger patterns, etc.), some discussion of the significance of partial asymmetry reversal in general seems to be demanded in this place. In our discussions as to whether asymmetry reversal may be regarded as producing differences in identical twins, it has been argued that a mere positional shift of an asymmetrical character from right to left side, or vice versa, does not constitute either a qualitative or a quantitative difference, for the two individuals are essentially the same, one being merely the mirror-image of the other. Such differences could not be included in quantitative comparisons between identical and fraternal twins. It should be obvious, however, that when partial asymmetry reversal occurs, the reversed individual is not a true mirror-image duplicate of his twin partner but is different. Thus a weak left-hander or an ambidexter is not a reversed duplicate of his right-handed partner but is a different sort of an individual. We maintain, then, that real differences are produced by partial asymmetry reversal and that such partial reversal may readily affect any sort of asymmetrical character. Such partial reversals as those in handedness, hair whorl, dentition, palm patterns, etc., may not affect the general physical or mental welfare of the individual; but, if partial reversal were to involve any vital organs such as the brain or the heart, they might readily have far-reaching effects on health and behavior. In general, we feel that partial reversals of asymmetry are more likely to have important effects on bodily organization than complete reversals. Moreover, it seems quite improbable that complete asymmetry reversal ever occurs in separated identical twins and rarely occurs even in Siamese twins. The fact is that asymmetry reversal in identical twins never is complete in all respects. An individual may be reversed in some respects and not in others. The result is an anomalous individual with various discordances in his bodily makeup—an individual neither wholly reversed nor wholly unreversed. Such an individual might readily be different in other characters than those directly concerned with reversals of asymmetrical characters.

We have dealt at some length with handedness as an example of the results of the workings of the asymmetry mechanism in producing differences in identical twins. It would consume too many pages to present an equivalent analysis of the various other examples of asymmetry reversal for which we have data. We shall therefore confine ourselves to a brief summary of the main facts regarding a selected few of these data.

HAIR-WHORL REVERSAL IN TWINS

As is well known, the crown whorl of the head hair, when viewed from above, has a clockwise twist in the great majority of persons. There are, however, many persons with counterclockwise hair whorl. In our 100 pairs of twins (200 individuals) it was possible to diagnose the direction of whorl in 192 individuals. Of these, 31 individuals (about 16 per cent) exhibited some definite departure from normal clockwise hair whorl. In our diagnosis of hair-whorl direction we noted as reversed hair whorls only those that were obviously reversed, and we doubtless overlooked some cases of slight rever-

TABLE 8

HAIR WHORLS IN TWIN PAIRS

TYPES OF WHORLS	IDENTICAL TWINS		FRATERNAL TWINS	
	No. of Pairs	Percentage of Pairs	No. of Pairs	Percentage of Pairs
Whorls clockwise in both............	27	57.4	44	89.8
Clockwise in one, counterclockwise in other......................	15	31.9	3	6.1
Counterclockwise in both...........	4	8.5	....	....
Clockwise in one, double crown in the other......................	1	2.1	1	2.0
Clockwise in one, indefinite in the other.	....	....	1	2.0
Undetermined in both...............	3	....	1	....
Total in which whorl was diagnosed	47	99.9	49	99.9

sal. That minor degrees of reversal were overlooked seems certain in view of the fact that special students of hair-whorl direction have reported that about 20 per cent of the normal population have more or less reversed hair whorls. Be that as it may, we have used the same criteria of reversal for identical and fraternal twins and have found a much higher incidence of reversed and partially reversed whorls in identical than in fraternal twins. Table 8 gives the incidence of hair-whorl directions in our twin collection. The main facts shown by this table are:

1. Of the identical-twin pairs, 42.5 per cent show some degree of reversed asymmetry; while of the fraternal-twin pairs, only 10.1 per cent show reversals, the former being over four times as many as the latter.

2. On the basis of zygotes involved, 42.5 per cent of identical-twin zygotes express the reversed hair-whorl character; while on the same basis, only 5 per cent of fraternal-twin zygotes express it.

3. The percentage of fraternal twins with reversed hair whorls is distinctly low as compared with the reported incidence of reversed whorls in the general population, but we are primarily interested in the relative frequencies of this character in the two kinds of twins.

4. That we have, by the methods of observation employed, missed a good many cases of partial reversal is evidenced by the fact that when the same methods were used in the diagnosis of 200 singly-born individuals, which were used in another investigation, we found 15 per cent with reversed hair whorls. With more meticulous methods of diagnosis one would expect the frequencies in both fraternal and identical twins to be somewhat increased, but without affecting their relative proportions.

5. There are five identical-twin individuals showing reversal in both handedness and hair whorl, while no fraternal twin shows this combination of reversals. This may be taken as evidence that these reversals are associated and both due to the twinning process.

OTHER EXAMPLES OF ASYMMETRY REVERSAL IN TWINS

In a monograph on *Palmar Dermatoglyphics in Twins,* one of us (Newman)[6] gave an extensive analysis of the palm prints of our 100 pairs of twins. It was shown that epidermal patterns frequently showed either nearly complete or slight mirror-image resemblance in many pairs of identical twins and in only a few pairs of fraternal twins. It was also shown that palm-pattern reversals of some sort were correlated with reversed handedness in 15 identical twins and in only 3 fraternal twins; and that palm-pattern reversals were correlated with reversed crown whorl in 16 identical twin pairs and only 1 fraternal twin pair. This further emphasizes the interrelation of various types of asymmetry reversal and suggests that they have a common origin.

In an extensive study of dental irregularities in our identical twins, casts of the dental arches were made for 35 pairs. It was found that in half of the left-handers there was also evidence of more or less extensive mirror-imaging of dental peculiarities. Also it was found that in half of the twins with counterclockwise hair whorl there were also cases of mirror-image resemblance in the teeth. It was hoped to complete this study, but Dr. Goldberg, our collaborator in this work, moved to South Africa, and the study has never been completed. The investigation, however, went far enough to show beyond question that asymmetries in dentition frequently exhibit mirror-imaging and that in several pairs of identical twins such conditions are correlated with reversals of asymmetry in characters unrelated to teeth.

Some time ago we made an extensive tabulation of all the items in our study that could be interpreted as exhibiting complete or partial asymmetry reversal. It was found that out of 275 separate items involving reversed

[6] H. H. Newman, *Amer. Jour. Phys. Anthrop.*, Vol. XIV (1930).

asymmetry, 180 (about 65 per cent) were found in identical twins and 95 (about 35 per cent) among fraternal twins. This might be taken to mean that about 30 per cent of all these reversals in identical twins are a product of monozygotic twinning and are therefore nongenetic. The remainder may possibly be regarded as genetic.

Without further laboring the point, it may be regarded as proven that a considerable amount of asymmetry reversal, rarely complete and frequently only slight in extent, occurs as a concomitant of monozygotic twinning. Asymmetry reversal, and especially partial asymmetry reversal, causes differences in identical twins. Such differences are neither genetic, in the ordinary sense, nor environmentally induced. In comparing the variability of identical and fraternal twins, therefore, it is not proper to consider all differences in identical twins reared together as environmentally determined. This has frequently been done, but we shall avoid this source of error by making some allowance for the differences produced by the asymmetry reversal process. In a later connection this procedure will be explained.

WHAT KINDS OF DIFFERENCES MIGHT BE INFLUENCED BY THE ASYMMETRY MECHANISM?

While it seems obvious from the preceding discussion that the asymmetry mechanism is responsible for significant differences in identical twins, it is impossible to determine whether this mechanism affects any characters other than those of an asymmetrical sort. The fact that in conjoined twins (Siamese twins) marked differences in stature, head size, facial characters, etc., are of common occurrence suggests that equivalent character differences in ordinary identical twins reared together may be due to the same sorts of causes as have operated to make conjoined twins different. There are strong evidences in the case of conjoined twins that their differences are largely due to the asymmetry mechanism. Certainly, there could not be differences in the environments of conjoined twins unless one twin is regarded as part of the environment of the other.

PART II

COMPARISON OF FIFTY PAIRS OF IDENTICAL AND
FIFTY PAIRS OF FRATERNAL TWINS

CHAPTER V

COMPARISON OF THE DIFFERENCES OF THE TWO GROUPS

STATISTICAL RÉSUMÉ OF THE DIFFERENCES WHICH CONSTITUTE THE BASIS OF THE DIAGNOSIS OF THE TWO TYPES OF TWINS

THE procedure by which the pairs of twins were classified into the two types, monozygotic and dizygotic, was developed by one of the collaborators and has been described by him in a previous publication.[1] The purpose of the first section of this chapter is to present in systematic and statistical form those facts concerning the twins which formed the basis of the differentiation. The criteria for judging monozygocity as used in this study are listed in chapter iii.

The actual procedure which was followed was to make a provisional diagnosis based upon the preliminary inspection. This provisional diagnosis was then reviewed in the light of the detailed examination of the palm prints and fingerprints. In this review all the observations and physical measurements were taken into account, and the final diagnosis was then made.

A summary descriptive and numerical record of the characteristics upon which the diagnosis was based has been formulated and is presented in Table 9. This review of the data is supplementary to that previously reported by one of the authors.[2] In the first column of the table is given the serial numbers of the pairs. In the second column is indicated the class into which each pair was finally placed. The letter *I* indicates an identical pair and *F* a fraternal pair, as they were diagnosed. In the next column a composite measure of the physical differences is given. This composite was made up by finding the standard scores in each of the following traits: height, weight, length of head, width of head, and total number of finger ridges for ten fingers. Each standard score was found by dividing the absolute difference between the scores of the two twins of a pair by the standard deviation of the differences of all pairs in the trait in question. These five standard scores were then added to form a composite standard score. The smaller numbers, of course, indicate the least differences. The pairs are listed in the order of their likeness, based on this composite difference score. In the next four columns are recorded the degrees of resemblance or difference in respect to general facial features, eye color, hair color, and ears. If the resemblances in

[1] H. H. Newman, "Studies of Human Twins: I. Methods of Diagnosing Monozygotic and Dizygotic Twins," *Biological Bulletin*, LV (October, 1928), 283–97.

[2] *Ibid.*

TABLE 9

SUMMARY OF PHYSICAL TRAITS USED IN MAKING DIAGNOSIS

PAIR NUMBER	DIAGNOSIS	COMPOSITE PHYSICAL DIFFERENCE (Including Height, Weight, Head Length and Width, and Finger Ridges)	APPEARANCE OF FEATURES (= No Noticeable Difference; Slight—Slight Difference; Moderate—Moderate Difference; Great—Great Difference)	ORDER OF FACIAL RESEMBLANCE	EYE COLOR (= No Noticeable Difference; Shade—Difference in Shade Only; Different—Different Color)	HAIR COLOR	SHAPE OF EARS (=, Slight, Moderate, and Great, as in Features; =r, Rx Like Ly and Lx Like Ry; 3s−1d, 3 Alike, 4th Different)	PALM PRINTS; NUMBER OF DIFFERENCES OUT OF A POSSIBLE 28				REMARKS
								A (Rx with Ry, Lx−Ly)	B (Rx−Ly, Lx−Ry)	C (Rx−Lx, Ry−Ly)	D (C Minus the Smaller of A and B)	
96	I	.23	=	11	=	=	3s−1d	8½	8[c]	11	+3	
78	I	.31	=	21	=	=	3s−1d	8½	7½[c]	8½	+1	
24	I	.72	Slight	46	=	=	3s−1d	6½	7	7	+1	
38	I	.73		24	=	=	=	3½	10½	10½	+7	
99	I	.76	Slight	27	=	Shade	=	7	10	9	+2	
30	I	.84	=	15	Shade	Shade	3s−1d	5½	6	7½	+2	
35	I	.96	Slight	10	=	=	=	4	10	9	+5	
14	I	.99	Slight	43	=	=	3s−1d	3½	8½	8½	+5	
101	I	1.01	=	34	=	=	=	5½	9	9½	+4	
13	I	1.05	Slight	20	=	=	Slight	4½	6	7	+2½	
68	I	1.11	=	18	=	=	=	7	14	13	+5½	
91	I	1.17	Slight	32	=	=	3s−1d	7	12½	16½	+9½	
7	I	1.20	=	39	=	=	=	2½	3	2	−	All four hands extremely similar
15	I	1.28	=	44	=	=	=	3½	4	6½	+3	
73	I	1.31	=	12	=	=	=	2½	1½	1½	+1	
98	I	1.38	=	2	=	=	Slight	1	10	10	+9	
37	I	1.40	=	36	=	=	=	3	9	8	+5	
94	I	1.43		17	=	=	=	9	7½[c]	9½	+2	All four hands extremely similar

TABLE 9—*Continued*

Pair Number	Diagnosis	Composite Physical Difference (Including Height, Weight, Head Length and Width, and Finger Ridges)	Appearance of Features (=No Noticeable Difference; Slight—Slight Difference; Moderate—Moderate Difference; Great—Great Difference)	Order of Facial Resemblance	Eye Color (=No Noticeable Difference; Shade—Difference in Shade Only; Different—Different Color)	Hair Color	Shape of Ears (=, Slight, Moderate, and Great, as in Features; =r, Rx Like Ly and Lx Like Ry; 3s—1d, 3 Alike, 4th Different)	Palm Prints; Number of Differences out of a Possible 28				Remarks
								A $\frac{Rx \text{ with } Ry}{Lx-Ly}$	B $\frac{Rx-Ly}{Lx-Ry}$	C $\frac{Rx-Lx}{Ry-Ly}$	D C Minus the Smaller of A and B	
63.....	I	1.43	=	3	=	=	=r	$1\frac{1}{2}$	6	5	$+3\frac{1}{2}$	
27.....	I	1.45	=	48	=	=	Moderate	7	8	8	$+1$	
62.....	I	1.47	=	1	=	=	3s—1d	$5\frac{1}{2}$	7	7	$+1\frac{1}{2}$	
2.....	I	1.48	=	31	=	Shade	=r	1	4	4	$+3$	
102.....	F(I)	1.49	Slight	13	=	=	Slight	3	$6\frac{1}{2}$	6	$+3$	
39*†.....	I	1.57	Slight	55	Different	Shade	=r	10	9^c	$8\frac{1}{2}$	$-\frac{1}{2}$	All four hands very different
17.....	I	1.61	=	42	=	=	=r	9	$9\frac{1}{2}$	$6\frac{1}{2}$	$-2\frac{1}{2}$	Siamese twin type
33.....	I	1.61	Moderate	28	=	Shade	=	$11\frac{1}{2}$	14	$7\frac{1}{2}$	-4	(Siamese twin type
65*.....	F	1.68	Moderate	52	=	=	Great	8	12	6	-2	A two right hands
87.....	I	1.75	=	24	=	=	3s—1d	5	$7\frac{1}{2}$	$6\frac{1}{2}$	$+1\frac{1}{2}$	B two left hands
100.....	I(F)	1.79	Moderate	33	=	=	Slight	$2\frac{1}{2}$	$10\frac{1}{2}$	$11\frac{1}{2}$	$+9$	
6*†.....	I	1.84	=	40	=	Shade	=	5	9	8	$+3$	
97.....	I	1.89	=	41	=	=	=	6	$10\frac{1}{2}$	10	$+4$	
23.....	I	1.96	=	16	=	=	3s—1d	$9\frac{1}{2}$	12	$9\frac{1}{2}$	0	

* More or less doubtful upon the preliminary examination.   *† Tentative verdict reversed.

TABLE 9—*Continued*

Pair Number	Diagnosis	Composite Physical Difference (Including Height, Weight, Head Length and Width, and Finger Ridges)	Appearance of Features (=No Noticeable Difference; Slight—Slight Difference; Moderate—Moderate Difference; Great—Great Difference)	Order of Facial Resemblance	Eye Color (=No Noticeable Difference; Shade—Difference in Shade Only; Different—Different Color)	Hair Color	Shape of Ears (=, Slight, Moderate, and Great, as in Features; =r, Rx Like Ly and Lx Like Ry; $3s-1d$, 3 Alike, 4th Different)	Palm Prints; Number of Differences out of a Possible 28: A (Rx with Ry $Lx-Ly$)	B ($Rx-Ly$ $Lx-Ry$)	C ($Rx-Lx$ $Ry-Ly$)	D (C Minus the Smaller of A and B)	Remarks
3.	I	1.96	=	5	=	=	$3s-1d$	$6\frac{1}{2}$	5^c	$5\frac{1}{2}$	$+\frac{1}{2}$	
49.	I	1.97	Slight	19	=	=	=	4	$3\frac{1}{2}^c$	$4\frac{1}{2}$	$+1$	All four hands extremely similar
67.	I	2.12	=	8	=	=	=	4	$13\frac{1}{2}$	13	$+9$	
80.	I	2.18	Slight	7	=	=	=	$9\frac{1}{2}$	$6\frac{1}{2}^c$	12	$+5\frac{1}{2}$	
43.	I	2.22	Slight	23	=	=	$3s-1d$	5	$7\frac{1}{2}$	$11\frac{1}{2}$	$+6\frac{1}{2}$	
61*. . . .	F	2.25	Moderate	51	=	Shade	=	15	$13\frac{1}{2}^c$	10	$-3\frac{1}{2}$	
55.	I	2.31	Slight	9	=	=	$=r$	$1\frac{1}{2}$	$8\frac{1}{2}$	8	$+6\frac{1}{2}$	
28.	I	2.33	=	38	=	=	=	1	1	1	0	All four hands extremely similar
31.	F	2.36	Moderate	63	Shade	Different	Moderate	$15\frac{1}{2}$	16	$4\frac{1}{2}$	-11	
57*. . . .	F	2.49	Slight	54	=	Shade	Great	16	16	$8\frac{1}{2}$	$-7\frac{1}{2}$	
22*. . . .	F	2.56	Slight	56	=	=	Great	10	9^c	$10\frac{1}{2}$	$+1\frac{1}{2}$	No two hands at all alike
72.	I	2.56	=	26	=	=	=	$11\frac{1}{2}$	$10\frac{1}{2}^c$	$16\frac{1}{2}$	$+6$	
60*. . . .	I	2.57	Slight	50	=	=	=	$8\frac{1}{2}$	$12\frac{1}{2}$	12	$+3\frac{1}{2}$	
25.	I	2.72	=	14	=	=	=	1	7	$7\frac{1}{2}$	$+6\frac{1}{2}$	
53.	I	2.78	Slight	29	=	=	$3s-1d$	$9\frac{1}{2}$	9^c	9	0	
19.	F	2.81	Moderate	87	Shade	Different	Moderate	23	$22\frac{1}{2}^c$	8	$-14\frac{1}{2}$	
8*†. . .	F(I)	2.86	Moderate	73	Shade	Shade	$3s-1d$	26	23^c	3	-20	
59.	F	2.86	Great	80	Shade	Different	Slight	$12\frac{1}{2}$	12^c	3	-9	
56.	F	2.88	Great	92	Shade	Different	Moderate	$9\frac{1}{2}$	$9\frac{1}{2}$	6	$-3\frac{1}{2}$	

TABLE 9—*Continued*

PAIR NUMBER	DIAGNOSIS	COMPOSITE PHYSICAL DIFFERENCE (Including Height, Weight, Head Length and Width, and Finger Ridges)	APPEARANCE OF FEATURES (=No Noticeable Difference; Slight—Slight Difference; Moderate—Moderate Difference; Great—Great Difference)	ORDER OF FACIAL RESEMBLANCE	EYE COLOR (=No Noticeable Difference; Shade—Difference in Shade Only; Different—Different Color)	HAIR COLOR	SHAPE OF EARS (=, Slight, Moderate, and Great, as in Features; =r, Rx Like Ly and Lx Like Ry; 3s−1d, 3 Alike, 4th Different)	PALM PRINTS; NUMBER OF DIFFERENCES OUT OF A POSSIBLE 28				REMARKS
								A — Rx with Ry; $Lx-Ly$	B — $Rx-Ly$; $Lx-Ry$	C — $Rx-Lx$; $Ry-Ly$	D — C Minus the Smaller of A and B	
18*	I	2.89	Slight	47	Shade	=	Great	9	5°	9	+4	
9	I	2.92	=	6	=	=	=	2½	5½	6½	+4	
26	F	2.96	Great	57	Different	Different	Moderate	10½	11	7	−3½	
21	F	3.05	Great	85	Different	Shade	Moderate	18	15½°	12½	−3	
40	I	3.07	=	4	=	=	3s−1d	2½	17	15½	+13	
70	I	3.14	Great	35	Shade	=	Moderate	4	5½	7	+3	
76	F	3.17	Slight	94	=	=	Moderate	11½	11°	4	−7	
44	I	3.21	Slight	30	Different	Different	Slight	10	13	9	−1	
66*	F	3.43	Great	67	Different	Different	Great	9½	8½°	7½	−1	
54	F	3.46	Moderate	98	Different	Different	Moderate	14	13½°	9	−4½	
12	F	3.58	Moderate	72	Different	Different	Great	11	13½	5½	−5½	All four hands very different
50	F	3.72	Moderate	70	Shade	Different	Great	11	14	12	+1	
69	I	3.73	=	45	Shade	Shade	3s−1d	5	10½	8	+3	
83	F	3.82	Great	25	=	=	Moderate	9	9½	5	−4	
79*	I	3.84	Great	77	=	Different	3s−1d	8	5½°	10	+4½	
81	F	3.90	Great	79	=	=	Moderate	15	15	8½	−6½	
41	I	4.04	Slight	49	=	Different	3s−1d	10½	10½	5½	−5	
34	I	4.08	=	37	=	=	Slight	6	11½	10½	+4½	A marked exception. One of the least similar identicals.

TABLE 9—*Continued*

Pair Number	Diagnosis	Composite Physical Difference (Including Height, Weight, Head Length and Width, and Finger Ridges)	Appearance of Features (= No Noticeable Difference; Slight—Slight Difference; Moderate—Moderate Difference; Great—Great Difference)	Order of Facial Resemblance	Eye Color (= No Noticeable Difference; Shade—Difference in Shade Only; Different—Different Color)	Hair Color	Shape of Ears (=, Slight, Moderate, and Great, as in Features; =r, Rx Like Ly and Lx Like Ry; 3s−1d, 3 Alike, 4th Different)	Palm Prints; Number of Differences out of a Possible 28: A — Rx with Ry, Lx−Ly	B — Rx−Ly, Lx−Rx	C — Rx−Lx, Ry−Ly	D — C Minus the Smaller of A and B	Remarks
71	F	4.28	Great	58	Different	Shade	Great	9	9½	7½	− 1½	
10	F	4.36	Moderate	69	Different	Shade	Moderate	10½	18	9½	− 1	
75	F	4.37	Moderate	62	Different	Shade	Moderate	9½	8[c]	4	− 4	
52	F	4.42	Moderate	71	Shade	Shade	Great	9	10	8	− 1	
16	F	4.51	Moderate	61	=	Shade	Great	9	11½	7	− 2	
45	F	4.68	Moderate	65	Different	Different	Great	10½	10½	10	− ½	
29	F	4.71	Great	84	Shade	Different	Moderate	12½	20½	12½	0	No two hands at all alike
77	F	4.83	Great	83	Different	Shade	Great	13½	10½[c]	7½	− 3	
82	F	4.86	Great	76	Shade	Different	Moderate	8	8	5	− 3	
64	F	5.26	Great	100	Different	Different	Moderate	15	16½	11½	− 3½	
36	F	5.37	Moderate	90	Different	=	Moderate	14½	14[c]	5½	− 8½	
32	F	5.39	Great	95	Shade	Different	Great	9	9½	7	− 2	
47	F	5.79	Great	82	=	Shade	Slight	8	8	8	0	No two hands at all alike
42	F	5.82	Moderate	86	Different	Shade	Moderate	16	14[c]	9½	− 4½	
11	F	5.84	Moderate	89	=	=	Great	14½	15	10	− 4½	
4	F	5.96	Moderate	91	=	Different	Great	12	10[c]	8½	− 1½	All four hands very different
95*	F	6.22	Moderate	60	=	Shade	Great	16½	17½	10½	− 6	
5	F	6.24	Slight	67	Different	Different	Moderate	12	12	7½	− 4½	
58	F	6.25	Great	81	Shade	Different	Great	10	11	5½	− 4½	

TABLE 9—*Continued*

Pair Number	Diagnosis	Composite Physical Difference (Including Height, Weight, Head Length and Width, and Finger Ridges)	Appearance of Features (=No Noticeable Difference; Slight—Slight Difference; Moderate—Moderate Difference; Great—Great Difference)	Order of Facial Resemblance	Eye Color (=No Noticeable Difference; Shade—Difference in Shade Only; Different—Different Color)	Hair Color	Shape of Ears (=, Slight, Moderate, and Great, as in Features; =r, Rx Like Ly and Lx Like Ry; 3s—1d, 3 Alike, 4th Different)	Palm Prints; Number of Differences out of a Possible 28				Remarks
								A Rx with Ry $Lx - Ly$	B $Rx - Ly$ $Lx - Ry$	C $Rx - Lx$ $Ry - Ly$	D C Minus the Smaller of A and B	
88......	F	6.40	Great	78	Different	Different	Slight	16	17	$3\frac{1}{2}$	$-12\frac{1}{2}$	
74*.....	F	6.58	Moderate	53	Shade	Shade	Slight	11	$10\frac{1}{2}$°	$6\frac{1}{2}$	-4	
90......	F	6.59	Great	75	=	=	Great	$7\frac{1}{2}$	$12\frac{1}{2}$	$5\frac{1}{2}$	-2	
86......	F	6.86	Moderate	59	Shade	Shade	Great	$11\frac{1}{2}$°	13	4	$-7\frac{1}{2}$	
46......	F	6.88	Great	97	=	Different	Moderate	10	10	6	-4	
89......	F	7.03	Moderate	64	=	Different	Moderate	$9\frac{1}{2}$	$8\frac{1}{2}$°	$7\frac{1}{2}$	-1	
20......	F	7.23	Moderate	96	Different	Different	Great	$10\frac{1}{2}$	15	$13\frac{1}{2}$	$+3$	All four hands very different
85......	F	7.65	Great	74	Different	Different	Slight	18	$15\frac{1}{2}$°	$12\frac{1}{2}$	-3	
84......	F	8.47	Moderate	66	=	Different	Great	$9\frac{1}{2}$	19	$11\frac{1}{2}$	$+2$	All four palms very different
48......	F	8.75	Great	99	Different	Different	Slight	$7\frac{1}{2}$	$11\frac{1}{2}$	$12\frac{1}{2}$	$+5$	All four palms very different
92......	F	8.76	Great	93	Different	Different	Great	10	13	$9\frac{1}{2}$	$-\frac{1}{2}$	All four palms very different
93......	F	9.53	Moderate	88	=	Different	Moderate	7	8	6	-1	

these characteristics are so great that the features of a pair are indistinguishable, the equation sign ($=$) is used. If a difference is noticeable, the degree of this difference is represented by a descriptive term, such as "slight," "shade difference," "moderate difference," "great difference," etc.

In the last four columns is recorded the number of differences between the patterns of palms and fingers. Twenty-eight points of comparison are considered in this measure of difference. These points are classified into three groups. The first group includes the pattern of the finger tips. There are, of course, five possible comparisons of this type, one for each finger. The second type of comparison consists of the terminal points of the system of main lines on the palms. There are four possible comparisons of this type. The third type of comparison is based on the presence or absence of patterns in five palm areas. There are, then, in all, fourteen items on which one palm may be compared with another. Other comparisons might possibly be made, but these are the ones which previous investigations have shown to be significant. Since both right and left hands are considered, there are twenty-eight possible comparisons. The numbers in the first three columns represent the number of comparisons out of the twenty-eight on which the pair are not alike. The smaller numbers thus represent the greater degree of similarity.

These comparisons are as nearly objective as we have been able to make them and may be checked by persons interested in doing so on the basis of previously published records of the palm and finger patterns of the 100 pairs of twins (Newman, 1930 and 1931). The only feature used in this comparison that is not recorded in these previous studies is one that has to do with the height of finger patterns. If a whorl or a loop is very high in one finger and very low in another, the difference is given a value of $\frac{1}{2}$ point. Even without the use of this criterion, the cases will all give essentially the same plus or minus index. One of the writers (Holzinger), on the basis of a rough, preliminary formulation of the palm and finger patterns, determined the indices for all twins. Subsequently, another of the writers (Newman), on the basis of a more elaborate formulation and weighting of differences according to their size and extent, determined these indices independently. There was complete correspondence in the direction of the index (plus or minus) in 92 of the 100 pairs. The eight discrepancies occurred in pairs Nos. 65, 23, 22, 44, 83, 71, 45, and 84—2 identical pairs and 6 fraternal pairs. Pair No. 23 was indexed $+2$ by Holzinger and 0 by Newman and does not constitute a reversal of sign of the index.

The other discrepancies in the two ratings are the result of weighting differences in Newman's method and nonweighting in Holzinger's. The weighting method, which seems a little more accurate, involves distinguishing differences according to the same method adopted in weighting differences in features, eye colors, ear shapes, and other characters listed in the other columns of the table which were weighted as "great," "moderate," or "slight." Thus, in palmar main lines, which are represented numerically, a difference such as that between 7 and 11, or between 5 and 2 or 1, is considered to have four times the value of such differences as those between 5 and 6, 7 and 8, 8 and 9, etc., the former being given a value of 2 and the latter of $\frac{1}{2}$. In rating palm patterns proper, the presence of a well-defined pattern as contrasted with its entire absence is rated 1; the difference between a well-defined pattern and a vestigial one is rated $\frac{1}{2}$; and the difference between a vestigial pattern and its total absence is counted $\frac{1}{2}$. If both patterns are vestigial, though somewhat different, no points are recorded. In the finger patterns the difference between the three main pattern types—whorls, loops, and arches—counts 1 point; a radial as against an ulnar pattern, $\frac{1}{2}$ point; a twisted as against a nontwisted pattern, $\frac{1}{2}$ point; and a high as against a low pattern, $\frac{1}{2}$ point. In a few cases only does weighting greatly change the index; but in pair No. 83 the change involved a difference between $+8$ and -4; pair No. 50 from -5 to $+1$; pair No. 22 from -5 to $+1\frac{1}{2}$.

In Column A are recorded the differences between the right hand of one twin (x) and the right hand of the other twin (y) of the pair, plus the differences between the left hand of one twin (x) and the left hand of the other (y). This will be called a direct comparison. In Column B are recorded the differences between the right hand of one (x) and the left hand of the other (y), and vice versa. This is a measure of cross resemblance. If the number of differences in this Column B are less than that in Column A, it indicates that the cross resemblance is greater than the resemblance between hands of the same side. Those cases in which this cross resemblance is greater than the direct resemblance are indicated by the small letter c.

In Column C are recorded the differences between the two hands of the same individual. The numbers represent the sum of these differences for the two twins of the pair. As before, there are twenty-eight possible differences. The purpose of tabulating these differences in Column C was to get a basis for interpreting the differences between the hands of the two twins. If the hands of one member of the pair resemble those of the other member more than do the two hands of the same individual, this is regarded as peculiarly significant. It is not taken by itself as an infallible sign of monozygocity, but it is judged to be the most important single indication in those cases in which dizygocity is not clearly indicated by some definite qualitative difference, such as difference in eye color. When all four palms are much alike, the relative difference between the hands of the same individual and the hands of members of a twin pair is not very significant; but the fact that all four palms are alike is in itself an evidence for monozygocity.

In order to determine whether the hands of the two members of a twin pair are more alike than are the hands of the same individual, the smaller of the two numbers in Column A and Column B is subtracted from the number in Column C. This difference is recorded in Column D. If this difference is positive, it means that the hands of one twin resemble those of the other more closely than their own right hands resemble their lefts. In other words, a positive number indicates that the right hand of one twin of the pair is more like the right (or left) hand of the other member than it is like his own left hand.

We may now review the classification into the two types of twins in the light of the data which are presented in this table. A few general facts may be noted first. It will be remembered that the pairs are listed in the table in the order of the size of the difference in composite of physical measurements, beginning with the least difference. This is not perhaps the most significant measure of resemblance between twins, but it is the most convenient basis of preliminary arrangement and is definitely objective. The first general fact we may note is that the twenty-three pairs who are most alike in physical measurements are classed as identical, that the thirty-one who are least alike are classed as fraternal, and that there is an overlapping region in which some are classed as identical and some as fraternal. Eight pairs classed as fraternals fall among the first fifty, and nine classed as identicals fall near the top of the second fifty. These cases are deserving of careful examination and will receive attention a little later.

The correspondence between the composite physical measurements and the classification of the pairs as either identical or fraternal is noteworthy. It will be recalled that the calculation of the composite physical difference was made long after the diagnosis into fraternal or identical was made. It is therefore rather remarkable that, when the physical measurements came to be tabulated, we found that every one of the twenty-three pairs found to be most alike by these measurements had been classed as identical and that every one of the thirty-one found to be least alike had been classed as fraternal.

The fact that there is an intermediate range in the scale of physical resemblance, in which some pairs are classed as identical and some as fraternal, is no cause for concern. It will be remembered that only twin pairs of the same sex were used in the study. It is to be expected, therefore, that some fraternal pairs should be much alike as a result of a chance combination of genes. In fact, siblings of different ages sometimes resemble one another closely. On the other hand, identical twins may differ to an appreciable degree due to factors influencing the course of their development. Even conjoined twins usually differ more in size and other physical characteristics than do separate identical twins (see chap. iv). The two sides of an individual's body are not exactly alike, as was also brought out in chapter iv. The fact, therefore, that there is a middle range in the scale of differences, in which some pairs are diagnosed as identical and some as fraternal, is just what we should expect.

A second general fact to be observed is that the items "appearance of features," "eye color," "hair color," and "shape of ears" are noted as equal or as only slightly different as between members of the pairs which appear at the beginning of the list; and that they are usually noted as different in greater degree in the case of pairs toward the end of the list.

The description of the ears deserves special attention. In the case of most of the identical twins who are strikingly similar, both ears of one twin resemble closely both ears of the other twin; or three of the four ears of a pair are alike and one is different. In all but two of the fraternal pairs, Nos. 61 and 8, the ears are described as different by either a "slight," "moderate," or "great" amount. In the cases in which three are the same and one is different, it is evident that the two ears of one individual differ from each other more than one of them differs from the ears of the other individual. This fact that the two sides of the same individual may differ from each other emphasizes the possibility that identical twins, developing from the two halves of a single embryo, may exhibit differences of considerable degree.

A third fact to be noted from the table is that most of the numbers in Column D in the first part of the list are positive and that most of those in the last part are negative, indicating that the palm and finger patterns of the first group are, in general, alike and that those of the second are in general different, as judged by excess of pair likeness over likeness within individuals.[3]

A more detailed examination of the data which have been assembled in this table may be introduced by analyzing the entries concerning the pairs which were considered to be doubtful on the preliminary examination and the cases in which the tentative diagnosis made at this examination was later reversed.

Out of one-hundred pairs, thirteen were considered more or less doubtful upon the preliminary examination. These cases are marked with a star

---

[3] The palmar formulas of fraternal twins are often much more similar than are the actual configurations, for large qualitative differences are often masked by similarities in formulas. Conversely, the formulas of identical twins are frequently more different than the actual configurations, which may be extremely similar in appearance even when their formulas are different.

in the first column of the table. It will be noted that, while some doubt was expressed in these cases, the provisional judgment was reversed in only three out of the thirteen—Nos. 39, 6, and 8. The cases in which the tentative verdict was reversed are indicated by a dagger in addition to the star.

The physical measurements of pair No. 39 are closely similar, yielding a small composite difference. The features, hair color, and ears are only slightly different. The difference in eye color, however, is inconsistent with the diagnosis of monozygocity, and the index of differences in palm prints is negative. These are very young boys with a strong family resemblance. The photographs reveal much greater differences in features than we had originally reported. This is one of the earliest cases in our series. They are surely fraternal. The next doubtful pair is No. 65. The note made concerning this pair at the time of the first examination was as follows: "No. 65 probably fraternal." In the case of this pair there is a moderate difference in the general appearance of the features, a great difference between the ears of the two twins, and a large difference between the palm patterns. There is, to be sure, a large difference between the palms of the two hands of the same individual, but, even so, the index seen in the last column is −2, which is consistent with the general diagnosis that they are very similar fraternals. The general likeness of the two twins in size is indicated by a small measure of composite difference in physical traits, namely, 1.68. We should not be surprised to find an occasional fraternal pair who are so nearly alike that it is not easy to distinguish them from identical twins. Even siblings, who are born at different times, occasionally resemble each other so closely that they might be taken for identical twins. By pure chance we should expect the conjunction of hereditary determiners derived from the ovum and sperm cell to be occasionally repeated in nearly the same way. This is one case where the palm-print and fingerprint criteria constitute very helpful evidence favoring a diagnosis already nearly complete.

In the case of pair No. 6 the provisional diagnosis was changed from "fraternal" to "identical." The differences in physical measurements, in features and in eyes, hair, and ears, would not be decisive one way or the other. The difference in palm prints is, however, favorable to the diagnosis of identity, the index being +3. Nearly a year later we made a second examination of this pair, which was one of the earliest to be examined and came before we had had much experience. This second examination left no doubt that they are identical. They seemed different the first time because one had an accidentally injured eye, which changed her expression so much that we judged them fraternal. The palm patterns of all four hands are extremely similar and clinch the diagnosis.

The fourth doubtful case is No. 61—also a fraternal pair. A note upon this case is "Provisional guess is fraternal." The composite physical measurements are rather similar in the case of this pair. The features resemble each other about as closely as those of pair No. 65. There is a shade difference in hair color, but no noticeable difference in the ears. There is a rather large difference between the palm prints, and these differences are greater than those between the two hands of the same individual. The index in the last column is $-3\frac{1}{2}$, which is consistent with the provisional diagnosis.

The note concerning the next pair, No. 57, is "Probably fraternal." In this case there is a fairly close resemblance in the features, a shade difference in hair color, and a large difference in the shape of the ears. The palm prints in this case are decisive. There is a large excess of difference between the palms of the two individuals as compared with the palms of the same individuals, the index being $-7\frac{1}{2}$, and this is consistent with the original diagnosis.

Concerning the next pair, No. 22, the note is "Doubtful" in one record, while in another they were put down as "slightly similar fraternals." The data on this case are very similar to those of No. 57. There was a slight difference in features and a great difference in ears. A subsequent study of photographs of these twins reveals greater feature differences than had been at first noted. The palm-print diagnosis is unsatisfactory because all four hands are so different that it is difficult to be sure which ones are more similar. By our method of comparison the total value is $+1\frac{1}{2}$, which would favor diagnosis as "identical." Other evidences, however, especially the fact that the ears are of an entirely different type and some of the features differ sharply, necessitate a diagnosis as "fraternal." This is one of the few cases in which the palm-pattern criteria were of no value.

On pair No. 60 the note is "A slight doubt." This is the first identical case which was considered doubtful on the first examination. This doubt was due to the fact that there is a moderate difference in the physical measurements, indicated by the composite score of 2.57, and a slight difference in features. The similarity in the palm prints of the two twins as compared with the palm prints of the same individual, however, confirms the diagnosis of identity. The index is $+3\frac{1}{2}$. This case remains the most questionable of all the cases diagnosed as identicals. The difference in state of health and in the hair (one having short hair and the other having long hair) made the diagnosis difficult.

The next case, pair No. 8, is the third of the thirteen pairs regarded as doubtful on first examination, for which the classification was reversed in the later diagnosis. The note concerning this case on first examination was "Doubtful, but probably identical." The amount of difference in physical measurements would not be decisive one way or the other. The difference in features, which is described as moderate, is greater than that of any twins which were diagnosed as identical except one, pair No. 6. (This pair was diagnosed as fraternal in the provisional judgment, and the diagnosis was changed on other grounds.) There is a shade difference in hair color and eye color, and three of the ears are similar and one different. The decisive factor, however, is the difference in palm- and fingerprints. The excess of the difference between the hands of the different individuals over that of the two hands of the same individual is -20—the largest minus index found among 100 pairs of twins—amounting to no cross resemblance at all. According to this criterion, then, this pair is considered to be clearly fraternal.

The next case, No. 18, was judged to be "probably identical," and this provisional diagnosis was retained. There is a moderate difference in the physical measurements, a slight difference in features, a shade of difference in eye color, a moderate difference in ears, but a small difference in palm prints. The palm prints have an index value of $+4$ and were taken as the deciding factor.

The next case, No. 66, was recorded as "very doubtful" on first examination. This is a fraternal pair with moderate differences in physical measurements but only slight difference in features, identity in color of eyes and color and texture of hair, and slight difference in ears. The palm prints were not very decisive, although the index, -1, is consistent with the original diagnosis.

Pair No. 79 was judged to be identical but "very slightly doubtful" on first examination. The doubt was due to the difference in general physical measurements. Over against this, however, is the great similarity in features and color of eyes and color and texture of hair, similarity of ears, and the close similarity in palm prints and fingerprints. Similarity in size is therefore not so decisive as similarity in form. The index for palm prints and fingerprints was $+4\frac{1}{2}$ and therefore is in agreement with the original diagnosis.

Pair No. 95 was described in the preliminary examination as "fraternal, a little doubtful." There would have been no grounds for doubt if this pair were examined in the light of experience of this study. The index is -6, clearly indicating fraternal relation. The same thing is true of pair No. 74, which has an index of -4.

It will be noticed that all the pairs in which the composite physical difference is 1.49 or less are diagnosed as identical, whereas all those pairs in which the difference is 4.28 or more are diagnosed as fraternal. Between the limits of 1.49 and 4.28 in the composite physical measurement there is an overlapping of cases. The exact limits of this area of overlapping, as set by the composite of physical measurements, are not important, since other criteria taken together are more important than is size. The composite measure, however, constitutes the most convenient basis for this rough classification; and the middle cases, constituting as they do those which are the least sharply differentiated, are most instructive to examine in detail. Those twins in this region of overlapping who have not already been described because they were doubtful on first examination or because the diagnosis was changed will be commented on very briefly.

No.

17. (I) Practical identity in all features. Palm prints very similar in appearance in spite of an index of $-2\frac{1}{2}$. The condition, however, is like that commonly found in Siamese twins in which x has two left-handed patterns and y two right-handed patterns.

33. (I) All features similar except a slight shade of difference in hair color. Palmprint difference moderate, with an index of -4. Here again the condition is just the same as in No. 17.

87. (I) All indications consistent, with index of $+1\frac{1}{2}$.

100. (I) All indications consistent with the exception of slight difference in ears. Index $+9$.

97. (I) All indications consistent. Index $+4$.

23. (I) All indications consistent. Palm patterns are three alike and one different. Index 0.

3. (I) All indications consistent. Index $+\frac{1}{2}$.

49. (I) Slight difference in features but eyes, hair, and ears the same. All four palm and finger patterns are extraordinarily similar, giving an index of $+1$. But the very great resemblance is itself evidence of monozygocity.

67. (I) All indications consistent. Index $+9$.

80. (I) All indications consistent except slight difference in features. Index $+5\frac{1}{2}$.

43. (I) Same as No. 80. Index $+6\frac{1}{2}$.

55. (I) Same as Nos. 43 and 80. Index $+6\frac{1}{2}$.

28. (I) All indications consistent. All four hands are almost exactly alike, giving an index of 0 (see No. 49).

31. (F) Some difference in all features and a minus index for the palm prints indicates fraternal. Index -11.

72. (I) All indications consistent. Index $+6$.

25. (I) All indications consistent. Index $+6\frac{1}{2}$.

53. (I) Other similarities outweigh a slight difference in the appearance of the features. Index 0.

19. (F) Difference in all features and a minus index indicate fraternal. Index $-14\frac{1}{2}$.

59. (F) Difference in all features and a minus index indicate fraternal. Index -9.

56. (F) Same as No. 59. Index $-3\frac{1}{2}$.

9. (I) All indications consistent. Index $+4$.

26. (F) All indications consistent. Index $-3\frac{1}{2}$.

21. (F) All indications consistent. Index -3.

No.

40. (I) All indications consistent. Index $+13$.
70. (I) All indications consistent. Index $+3$.
76. (F) All indications consistent. Index -7.
44. (I) A slight difference in features and a moderate difference in the shape of the ears are outweighed by the same shade of eye color and of hair color and a close likeness in palm prints. Although the index is only -1, there are striking cross resemblances in peculiar pattern details.
54. (F) All indications consistent. Index $-4\frac{1}{2}$.
12. (F) All indications consistent. Index $-5\frac{1}{2}$.
50. (F) All indications consistent except the palm-pattern index, which is $+1$. This is due to the fact that the two right hands have both the very common formula $11 \cdot 9 \cdot 7 \cdot 5$, but when examined these two palms show wide differences in appearance.
69. (I) In spite of a moderate difference in general physical measurements, the other indications are that the twins are identical. Index $+3$.
83. (F) All indications consistent. No two palms are at all similar. Index -4.
81. (F) All indications consistent. Index $-6\frac{1}{2}$.
41. (I) Moderate difference in general physical measurements. Slight difference in features is balanced by identity in eye and hair. Index -5.
34. (I) In spite of a moderate difference in physical measurements, the other indications indicate monozygocity. Index $+4\frac{1}{2}$.

This inspection will give some notion of the criteria which were used in making the diagnosis between identical and fraternal twins and of the way in which these criteria were applied. The only cases that fail to comply readily with our eighth criterion of monozygocity are pairs Nos. 17, 33, 49, 28, and 41. Of these, the first two (Nos. 17 and 33) have the condition found regularly in Siamese twins and, therefore, cannot be considered as aberrant; while pairs Nos. 49 and 28 exhibit such close resemblance of all four palms that they can hardly be distinguished, giving indices of $+1$ and 0. Such cases are surely identical twins. The fact that an occasional pair of quite unlike fraternal twins have a plus index merely signifies great unlikeness of all four hands.

The review of the statistical data indicates that they point, in most cases, quite unambiguously in the direction of the classification finally adopted, and which was used in the tabulations of the study. The cases which might seem, from a mere examination of the data presented in the table, to suggest doubt as to their classification are so few that, even if some of them were assumed to be wrongly diagnosed, the error could have very little effect on our tabulations or on the conclusions which are drawn from them. The authors believe that the classification is perhaps more accurate than that which has been made in any previous study and that it is entirely adequate for its purpose.

In the next section we shall present a few bits of evidence which seem to confirm from the statistical point of view the general thesis that there are two and only two types of twins.

STATISTICAL EVIDENCE CONFIRMING THE EXISTENCE OF THE TWO TYPES OF TWINS

One form of statistical confirmation of the hypothesis that there are two distinct types of twins is found in the relative number of twins of the same sex and those of the opposite sex in comparison with the theoretical expectation. If the members of all twin pairs developed from separate ova, as is held to be true of fraternal twins, we should expect to find approximately the same number of twins of like sex as of opposite sex. The argument is as follows: If the sex of the two members of twin pairs is of independent origin, we should expect by pure chance an equal number of the following pairings: boy-boy, girl-girl, boy-girl, girl-boy. Half of the pairings would thus be of the same sex and half of the opposite sex. Instead of this, there are actually nearly twice as many twins of the same sex as of the opposite sex. For example, Lauterbach (p. 529)[4] reports, for a given twin population, 13,123 same-sex and 6,898 opposite-sex twins. J. B. Nichols has given twin sex ratios on a much larger scale. In a twin population of 717,907 pairs, 234,497 were ♂♂, 264,098 ♂♀, and 219,312 ♀♀. From this larger population the following tabulation is made:

a) Total number of twins 717,907
b) Opposite-sex fraternal (actual)...................... 264,098
c) Same-sex fraternal (hypothetical)................... 264,098
d) Total same sex (234,497 + 219,312)............... 453,809
e) Identical $(d - c)$................................. 189,711
f) Ratio identical to total (e/a)...................... .26
g) Ratio identical to same-sex fraternal (e/c)........... .72
h) Ratio identical to same-sex fraternal in this study (43/52) .83

The excess of same-sex over opposite-sex twins (189,711) are taken to be identical pairs. Thus the ratio of identical to total number of pairs of twins is .26 and the ratio of identical to same-sex fraternal pairs is .72. Our ratio is a little larger. Taking same-sex twins as they came until we secured 50 or more fraternal pairs, the number was 43 identicals to 52 fraternals, giving a ratio of .83.

In the analysis which follows we have tabulated and distributed the measured differences between the two twins of a pair in three traits—namely, height, weight, and intelligence quotient—in order to inquire whether the distribution of these differences gives any indication as to whether iden-

[4] C. E. Lauterbach, "Studies in Twin Resemblances," *Genetics*, X (November, 1925), 525–68.

tical twins belong in a separate class or are simply an artificially selected group of twins who are most alike.

Assume for the moment that there is only one type of twin. If we picked out from the entire group of twins those who are most nearly alike, and then compared this group with the remainder, we would, of course, find that the average differences between the twins of the first were much less than the average differences between the twins of the second group. This statistical fact would give us no warrant for concluding that we had two biologically distinct groups. Our problem is to discover whether the mere statistics of differences can give us warrant for such a conclusion.

TABLE 10

MEAN PAIR DIFFERENCES IN SELECTED TRAITS FOR IDENTICAL
AND FRATERNAL TWINS AND FOR SIBLINGS

Selected Traits	Identical	Fraternal	All Twins	Siblings (Like Sex)
Standing heights................	1.7 cm.	4.4 cm.	3.2 cm.	4.5 cm.
Weight........................	4.1 lb.	10.0 lb.	7.1 lb.	10.4 lb.
Binet I.Q.....................	5.9	9.9	7.9	9.8
Head length...................	2.9 mm.	6.2 mm.	4.6 mm.	....
Head width...................	2.8 mm.	4.2 mm.	3.5 mm.	....
Cephalic index.................	.016	.028	.022	....
Total finger ridges.............	5.9	22.3	14.1	....
Total motor score..............	19.3	29.0	24.2	....
Otis I.Q......................	4.5	9.3	7.0	....
Stanford Educational Age........	6.4 mo.	11.6 mo.	9.1 mo.	....
Woodworth-Mathews............	5.3	6.7	6.0	....

If we refer to our biological hypothesis, we get a clue which enables us to make a crucial comparison. The hypothesis is that fraternal twins, or dizygotic twins, are similar biologically to siblings, that is, they develop from separate eggs and have the same genetic relation as have siblings in general. The only difference is that fraternal twins happen to develop at the same time. If we can make allowance statistically for the fact that ordinary siblings are born at different times and that fraternal twins are born at the same time, we ought to find the amount and distribution of differences in the one group similar to the differences in the other. Identical, or monozygotic twins, on the other hand, are presumed to develop from the same fertilized egg. The distribution of differences between such individuals may be expected to be quite different from that of both fraternal twins and siblings.

With these conditions in mind we set about to find a method by which the differences between fraternal twins could be compared with the differences between siblings. We were able to make this comparison for height, weight, and intelligence quotient.

In the case of height and weight it was, of course, necessary to find records of measurements which had been taken at the same age on the members of sibling pairs. It is necessary also, of course, to use like-sex pairs as we did in the case of the twins. It was not, however, necessary to confine the comparison in respect to I.Q.'s to either siblings of the same age or to

TABLE 11

DISTRIBUTION OF PAIR DIFFERENCES IN STANDING HEIGHT OF
IDENTICAL AND FRATERNAL TWINS AND OF SIBLINGS

CM. DIFFERENCE	IDENTICAL		FRATERNAL		ALL TWINS		SIBLINGS (LIKE SEX)	
	No.	Percentage	No.	Percentage	No.	Percentage	No.	Percentage
14–15.9...........	....	....	2	3.8	2	2.0	1	1.9
12–13.9...........	....	....	2	3.8	2	2.0	1	1.9
10–11.9...........	....	....	1	1.9	1	1.0	2	3.8
8– 9.9...........	....	....	5	9.6	5	4.9	5	9.6
6– 7.9...........	2	4	5	9.6	7	6.9	6	11.5
4– 5.9...........	1	2	9	17.3	10	9.8	9	17.3
2– 3.9...........	12	24	9	17.3	21	20.6	11	21.2
0– 1.9...........	35	70	19	36.5	54	52.9	17	32.7
Total........	50	100	52*	99.8	102	100.1	52	99.8
Mean pair difference.....	1.7 cm.		4.4 cm.		3.2 cm.		4.5 cm.	

* Fifty-two pairs of fraternal twins were examined and measured originally and were dealt with statistically before it was found that two of these pairs were unsuitable for some phase of our study because in one case one twin had an infected hand and in the other case one twin had lost three fingers and a part of the palm. These twins were of no use for palm- and fingerprint studies and were not included in any studies involving these data.

those of the same sex since differences in age and sex have only a slight influence on this measure.

The procedure may be illustrated in detail in the case of height. We tabulated the differences in height between members of a pair for identical twins and fraternal twins separately. We then sought cases of brothers or sisters in the records of the University Laboratory Schools whose height had been measured at the same age. The distribution of these differences was made. The three distributions may be compared in Table 11 and in Figure 1.

The first important fact is that the distribution of the differences between twins taken as a whole is radically different from that for siblings. The mean difference in height between twins as shown in Table 10 which gives the mean pair differences, is 3.2; while the mean difference between siblings is 4.5.

This distinction between twins and siblings does not of itself prove that there are two types of twins since it might conceivably be caused by a greater similarity in the environment of twins than of siblings. But if the differences between the twins who have been diagnosed as fraternal are of the same order as the differences between siblings, while the differences between twins who have been diagnosed as identical are much less, the results of the

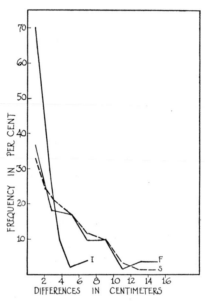

Fig. 1.—Curve of distribution of differences in standing height of identical and fraternal twins and of siblings.

comparisons fit the hypothesis so closely as to constitute some confirmation of it. The mean differences in height are as follows: identical twins, 1.7 centimeters; fraternal twins, 4.4 centimeters; siblings, 4.5 centimeters.

It is clear from an examination of Figure 1 that the distribution of differences for fraternal twins is very closely similar to that for like-sex siblings. It is clear, furthermore, that both these distributions differ radically from that of the differences between identical twins. This also agrees with the hypothesis that identical twins and fraternal twins belong to diverse types and that fraternal twins are essentially siblings.

A similar contrast appears in the correlation coefficients between the heights of members of pairs for the three groups. The correlations, with age partialed out, are as follows: for identical twins, .93±.01; for fraternal twins, .64±.05; and for like-sex siblings measured at the same age, .60±.06. The correlation for fraternal twins is somewhat higher than that for siblings, and the mean difference is slightly less. It is not certain that fraternal twins are significantly more alike than are siblings, but it is possible that they are so. If this difference is statistically significant, it may indicate the effect of a slightly greater similarity in their environments.

TABLE 12

DISTRIBUTION OF PAIR DIFFERENCES IN WEIGHT OF IDENTICAL
AND FRATERNAL TWINS AND OF SIBLINGS

LB. DIFFERENCE	IDENTICAL		FRATERNAL		ALL TWINS		SIBLINGS (LIKE SEX)	
	No.	Percentage	No.	Percentage	No.	Percentage	No.	Percentage
36–39.........							1	1.9
33–36.........			1	1.9	1	1.0		
30–33.........							1	1.9
27–30.........			1	1.9	1	1.0		
24–27.........			2	3.8	2	2.0	1	1.9
21–24.........			2	3.8	2	2.0	2	3.8
18–21.........			3	5.8	3	2.9	6	11.5
15–18.........	1	2	5	9.6	6	5.9	1	1.9
12–15.........			4	7.7	4	3.9	5	9.6
9–12.........	6	12	6	11.5	12	11.8	8	15.4
6– 9.........	7	14	4	7.7	11	10.8	9	17.3
3– 6.........	7	14	13	25.0	20	19.6	11	21.2
0– 3.........	29	58	11	21.2	40	39.2	7	13.5
Total........	50	100	52	99.9	102	100.1	52	99.9
Mean pair difference.....	4.1 lb.		10.0 lb.		7.1 lb.		10.4 lb.	

Similar comparisons for weight are shown in Table 12 and in Figure 2. The same general facts appear in the differences in weight as in those in height. The distribution for the entire group of twins is quite different from that for siblings. The mean difference in weight of twin pairs is 7.1, while that of sibling pairs is 10.4. The curve of distribution for fraternal twins is similar in form to that for siblings, whereas the curve for identical twins is markedly different from the other two. The mean difference in weight between members of identical pairs is 4.1 pounds, as contrasted with 10 pounds for fraternal twins and 10.4 pounds for siblings. The correlation between the weights of members of identical pairs is .917±.01 as contrasted with .631±.06 for fraternal twins and .584±.06 for siblings.

Here again it seems obvious that the fraternal twins and the siblings are essentially alike and that they belong to a different class from the identical twins. The distribution curves for the fraternal twins and the siblings do not resemble each other in detail quite so closely as for height. The dif-

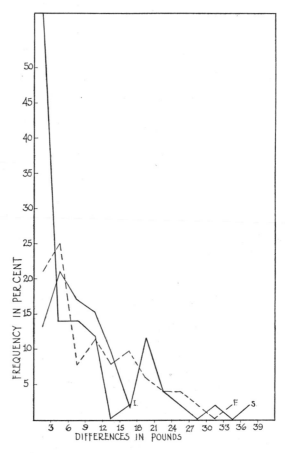

Fig. 2.—Curve of distribution of differences in weight of identical and fraternal twins and of siblings.

ference is probably due to the greater variability in weight than in height and to the fact that it is more subject to the modifying influences of the environment.

The only mental measure for which the comparison of twin differences with sibling differences can be made is the Binet intelligence quotient. The distributions of the differences are shown, as before, in Table 13 and in Figure 3. The mean difference in I.Q. for the entire group of twins is 7.9, and the mean difference for siblings is 9.8. The contrast appears to be somewhat less marked than it is in the case of height and weight. However, the contrast is still evident.

The curves for fraternal twins and for siblings again resemble each other in general form and differ from the curve for identical twins, but the resemblance and the contrast are both somewhat less marked than in the case of the two physical traits. This is true also of the mean differences, which are, respectively, 5.9 points for identical twins, 9.9 points for fraternal

TABLE 13

DISTRIBUTION OF PAIR DIFFERENCES IN BINET I.Q. OF IDENTICAL
AND FRATERNAL TWINS AND OF SIBLINGS

I.Q. DIFFERENCE	IDENTICAL		FRATERNAL		ALL TWINS		SIBLINGS OF (LIKE SEX)	
	No.	Percentage	No.	Percentage	No.	Percentage	No.	Percentage
35–40.........	....	....	1	1.9	1	1.0	....	....
30–35.........	....	....	....	....	....	....	1	2.1
25–30.........	....	....	1	1.9	1	1.0	2	4.3
20–25.........	....	....	2	3.8	2	2.0	2	4.3
15–20.........	1	2	7	13.5	8	7.8	9	19.1
10–15.........	7	14	12	23.1	19	18.6	5	10.7
5–10.........	18	36	12	23.1	30	29.4	9	19.1
0– 5.........	24	48	17	32.7	41	40.2	19	40.4
Total........	50	100	52	100.0	102	100.0	47	100.0
Mean pair difference.....	5.9		9.9		7.9		9.8	

twins, and 9.8 points for siblings. The correlations indicate also the same relations, being for identical twins, .881 ± .02; for fraternal twins, .631 ± .06; and for siblings, .368 ± .07. The greater difference between the correlations for the fraternal twins and the siblings is undoubtedly due to the fact that the I.Q.'s of the siblings are not as much alike as they should be and as they are usually found to be. The correlation between the I.Q.'s of siblings is usually found to be in the neighborhood of .50 or .60. The lower correlation in the case of our group of siblings is doubtless due to the unreliability of the test scores. In a study of the I.Q.'s of a group of pupils of the school attended by the siblings of this study, to whom the test was given twice, the the reliability coefficient was only .615 ± .032, whereas the coefficient which is commonly found is in the neighborhood of .85 or .90.

A number of circumstances conspired to reduce the reliability coefficient for the group from which the siblings were drawn. Their I.Q.'s are nearly all above 100, which reduces their variability. The second tests were commonly given by different examiners, and the interval between the tests was often several years. This caused the earlier and later tests to fall within different areas of the scale. The same circumstances affect the correlation between members of sibling pairs. This stricture does not apply to the I.Q.'s of the twins. Making allowance for the limitations of the data, then, the differences in I.Q.'s reveal the same contrast and similarity as do the measurements of height and of weight.

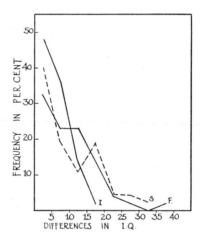

FIG. 3.—Curve of distribution of differences in Binet I.Q. of identical and fraternal twins and of siblings.

To recapitulate. Our data show that the differences between members of fraternal-twin pairs are of the same order as the differences between sibling pairs. On the other hand the differences between members of identical-twin pairs are much less on the average and fall into a different form of distribution. If, now, all twins originated from separate ova, and hence had the same type of biological relation, we should expect the differences between twins to be of the same order as are differences between siblings. This is not the case. The inference is that some twins have a closer genetic relation. When we separate the twins into two classes and find that the twins in the class which by hypothesis are related in the same way as siblings exhibit the same degree and distribution of likeness as do siblings, this fact constitutes confirmation of the hypothesis. It strengthens the view, namely, that identical twins are biologically a distinct group of twins.

c) COMPARISON OF THE DIFFERENCES BETWEEN TWIN PAIRS OF THE
TWO TYPES IN SINGLE TRAITS AND IN COMBINATION OF TRAITS

In the previous section the distribution of differences was used as a means of checking the hypothesis that there exist two distinct types of twins. In the present section this hypothesis will be assumed to have been established,

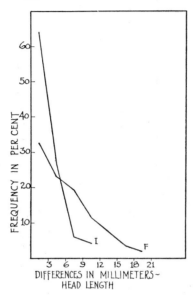

FIG. 4.—Curve of distribution of differences in head length of identical and fraternal twins.

TABLE 14

PAIR DIFFERENCES IN HEAD LENGTH

MM. DIFFERENCE	IDENTICAL		FRATERNAL		ALL TWINS	
	No.	Percentage	No.	Percentage	No.	Percentage
18–21...............	....	....	1	1.9	1	1.0
15–18...............	....	....	2	3.8	2	2.0
12–15...............	....	....	4	7.7	4	3.9
9–12...............	2	4	6	11.5	8	7.8
6– 9...............	3	6	10	19.2	13	12.7
3– 6...............	13	26	12	23.1	25	24.5
0– 3...............	32	64	17	32.7	49	48.0
Total..........	50	100	52	99.9	102	99.9
Mean pair difference.......	2.9 mm.		6.2 mm.		4.6 mm.	

and a comparison will be made between the differences in the various physical and mental traits. In all the traits, except those that have been men-

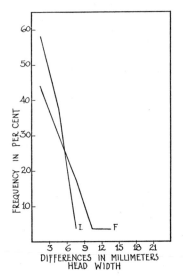

FIG. 5.—Curve of distribution of differences in head width of identical and fraternal twins.

TABLE 15

PAIR DIFFERENCES IN HEAD WIDTH

MM. DIFFERENCE	IDENTICAL		FRATERNAL		ALL TWINS	
	No.	Percentage	No.	Percentage	No.	Percentage
12–15...............	....	....	2	3.8	2	2.0
9–12...............	....	....	2	3.8	2	2.0
6– 9..............	2	4	9	17.3	11	10.8
3– 6..............	19	38	16	30.8	35	34.3
0– 3..............	29	58	23	44.2	52	51.0
Total..........	50	100	52	99.9	102	100.1
Mean pair difference........	2.8 mm.		4.2 mm.		3.5 mm.	

tioned in the previous section, the comparison is only between the identical twins and the fraternal twins. No comparable sibling data are available.

The curves which are to be compared are in Figures 1–10. We may take them up in the order in which they appear in the figures.

The curves for height (Fig. 1) show a very marked difference between the identical group and the fraternal group. This is the sharpest contrast that is exhibited in any of the traits except number of finger ridges. The contrast between the groups in weight (Fig. 2) is perhaps not quite so great as

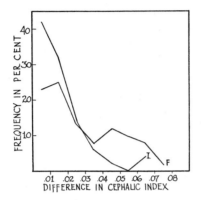

Fig. 6.—Curve of distribution of differences in cephalic index of identical and fraternal twins.

TABLE 16

PAIR DIFFERENCES IN CEPHALIC INDEX

DIFFERENCE	IDENTICAL		FRATERNAL		ALL TWINS	
	No.	Percentage	No.	Percentage	No.	Percentage
.070–.080..........	....	....	1	1.9	1	1.0
.060–.070..........	2	4	4	7.7	6	5.9
.050–.060..........	....	....	5	9.6	5	4.9
.040–.050..........	1	2	6	11.5	7	6.9
.030–.040..........	3	6	4	7.7	7	6.9
.020–.030..........	7	14	7	13.5	14	13.7
.010–.020..........	16	32	13	25.0	29	28.4
.000–.010..........	21	42	12	23.1	33	32.4
Total..........	50	100	52	100.0	102	100.1
Mean pair difference........	.016		.028		.022	

in height, although it is still very marked. The contrast in head length (Fig. 4, Table 14) is not so great as that in height, but there is still a clear differentiation between the two groups. When we come to head width (Fig. 5, Table 15), the situation is very different. While there is still a contrast between the two groups of twins, this contrast is greatly diminished, the

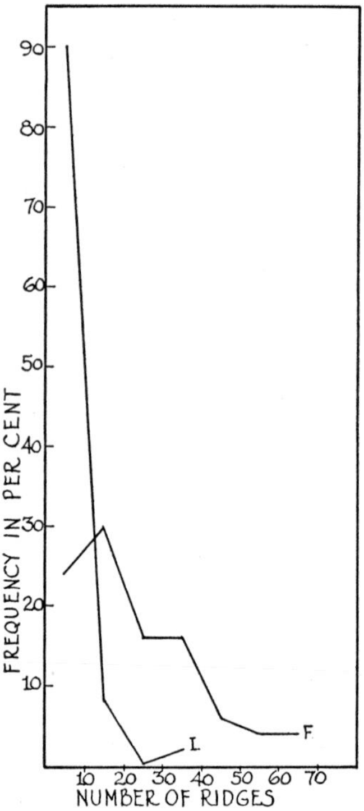

FIG. 7.—Curve of distribution of differences in number of finger ridges of identical and fraternal twins.

TABLE 17

PAIR DIFFERENCES IN TOTAL NUMBER OF FINGER RIDGES

DIFFERENCE	IDENTICAL		FRATERNAL		ALL TWINS	
	No.	Percentage	No.	Percentage	No.	Percentage
60–69..............	....	....	2	4	2	2
50–59..............	....	....	2	4	2	2
40–49..............	....	....	3	6	3	3
30–39..............	1	2	8	16	9	
20–29..............	....	....	8	16	8	8
10–19..............	4	8	15	30	19	19
0– 9..............	45	90	12	24	57	57
Total..........	50	100	50	100	100	100
Mean pair difference........	5.9		22.3		14.1	

differences between the fraternal pairs being less, and the differences between the identical pairs more, than in the case of head length. It would appear that head width is not so definitely determined by heredity as is head

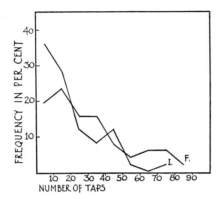

Fig. 8.—Curve of distribution of differences in motor score of identical and fraternal twins.

TABLE 18

PAIR DIFFERENCES IN TOTAL MOTOR SCORE

DIFFERENCE	IDENTICAL		FRATERNAL		ALL TWINS	
	No.	Percentage	No.	Percentage	No.	Percentage
80–90.............	....	....	1	2.0	1	1.0
70–80.............	1	2	3	5.9	4	4.0
60–70.............	....	....	3	5.9	3	3.0
50–60.............	1	2	2	3.9	3	3.0
40–50.............	6	12	4	7.8	10	9.9
30–40.............	4	8	8	15.7	12	11.9
20–30.............	6	12	8	15.7	14	13.9
10–20.............	14	28	12	23.5	26	25.7
0–10.............	18	36	10	19.6	28	27.7
Total..........	50	100	51	100.0	101	100.1
Mean pair difference........	19.3		29.0		24.2	

length, or that it is less reliably measured, or that it is influenced more largely by environment. The contrast in cephalic index (Fig. 6, Table 16) is naturally small since this index is a quotient in which head width is a factor. In finger ridges we have again a trait in which the contrast is sharp (Fig. 7, Table 17). In fact, it is even sharper than is the contrast in height.

Finger ridges evidently constitute a very definite means of determining the proportion of the resemblances between twins which may be attributed to

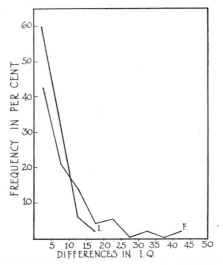

Fig. 9.—Curve of distribution of differences in Otis I.Q. of identical and fraternal twins.

TABLE 19

MEAN PAIR DIFFERENCES IN OTIS I.Q.

I.Q. DIFFERENCE	IDENTICAL		FRATERNAL		ALL TWINS	
	No.	Percentage	No.	Percentage	No.	Percentage
45–50...............	....	....	1	1.9	1	1.0
40–45...............	....	....	....	....	....	....
35–40...............	....	....	1	1.9	1	1.0
30–35...............	....	....	....	....	....	....
25–30...............	....	....	3	5.8	3	2.9
20–25...............	....	....	2	3.8	2	2.0
15–20...............	1	2	2	3.8	3	2.9
10–15...............	3	6	10	19.2	13	12.7
5–10...............	16	32	11	21.2	27	26.5
0– 5...............	30	60	22	42.3	52	51.0
Total..........	50	100	52	99.9	102	100.0
Mean pair difference.......	4.5		9.3		7.0	

heredity. The same sharp contrast appears in the curves for the finger ridges on each hand separately and total number of ridges on both hands. The resemblance of the two types of twins in number of finger ridges, then, may be used as a norm with which to compare the resemblance in other traits.

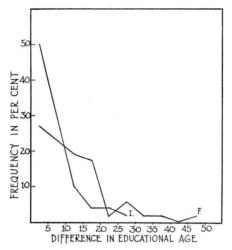

FIG. 10.—Curve of distribution of differences in Stanford Achievement of identical and fraternal twins.

TABLE 20

MEAN PAIR DIFFERENCES IN STANFORD EDUCATIONAL AGE

MONTHS DIFFERENCE	IDENTICAL		FRATERNAL		ALL TWINS	
	No.	Percentage	No.	Percentage	No.	Percentage
45–49..............	....	....	1	1.9	1	1.0
40–44..............	....	....	....	....	....	....
35–39..............	....	....	1	1.9	1	1.0
30–34..............	....	....	1	1.9	1	1.0
25–29..............	1	2	3	5.8	4	3.9
20–24..............	2	4	1	1.9	3	2.9
15–19..............	2	4	9	17.3	11	10.8
10–14..............	5	10	10	19.2	15	14.7
5– 9..............	15	30	12	23.1	27	26.5
0– 4..............	25	50	14	26.9	39	38.2
Total..........	50	100	52	99.9	102	100.0
Mean pair difference.......	6.4 mo.		11.6 mo.		9.1 mo.	

The remaining comparisons are based on measurements of action or behavior rather than measurements of physical dimensions and contours. The first of these is the score on the motor test (Fig. 8, Table 18). The contrast between the two groups is less than in any of the traits in which they have been thus far compared. While some distinction between the two groups of twins still appears, it is only a slight one.

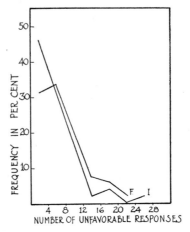

Fig. 11.—Curve of distribution of differences in unfavorable responses on the Wood-worth-Mathews Personal Data Sheet of identical and fraternal twins.

TABLE 21

Pair Differences in Woodworth-Mathews Score

DIFFERENCE	IDENTICAL		FRATERNAL		ALL TWINS	
	No.	Percentage	No.	Percentage	No.	Percentage
24–27................	1	2	....	....	1	1.0
20–23................	....	....	1	2.0	1	1.0
16–19................	2	4	3	5.9	5	5.0
12–15................	1	2	4	7.8	5	5.0
8–11................	8	16	10	19.6	18	17.8
4– 7................	15	30	17	33.3	32	31.7
0– 3................	23	46	16	31.4	39	38.6
Total..........	50	100	51	100.0	101	100.1
Mean pair difference.......	5.3		6.7		6.0	

The curves which show the differences in the Stanford Binet I.Q. and in the Otis I.Q. are shown in Figures 3 and 9, based upon Tables 13 and 19. The differentiation is sharper in the case of the Binet test than in the Otis test. This apparently indicates that the Otis test is somewhat more subject to the influence of experience and training than is the Binet test. Both tests give a somewhat less distinct contrast than do the physical traits of height, weight, and finger ridges; but a distinctly sharper contrast than in the case of head width or cephalic index. The contrast in I.Q.'s is very much sharper than in the motor-ability scores. It would appear that there is large hereditary element in the determination of the intelligence scores but that there is a possibility of its being considerably influenced by environmental factors.

The contrast in the Stanford Educational Age (Fig. 10, Table 20) appears to be somewhat less than in the Otis I.Q. The difference, however, is not great, and the irregularity of the curves makes exact comparison difficult. While the Stanford Achievement Score may be slightly more influenced by environment than the Otis I.Q., the difference cannot be large. The distribution of differences in the Woodworth-Mathews Personal Data Sheet (Fig. 11, Table 21) is nearly the same for the two types of twins. This corresponds to the fact that the correlations in the case of this test are of nearly the same magnitude.

The findings obtained by plotting the distributions of differences as they bear upon the contrast between the identical and fraternal twins may be summarized as follows:

1. There is a close similarity in the distribution of differences in height, weight, and Binet I.Q. of fraternal twins and of siblings, and these distributions are widely different from those of identical twins

2. These facts are taken to be confirmatory of the hypothesis that fraternal twins have the same type of biological relationship as have siblings and that identical twins are related in a different fashion

   Accepting the hypothesis that the identical twins constitute a group in which the biological relation between pairs is such that their heredity is identical, whereas that of fraternal pairs overlaps genetically only in part, the degree of contrast between the distributions of differences in a given trait among the two groups of twins may be taken as an indication of the extent to which that trait is determined by inborn or inherited structure. On this basis comparisons may be made among the various traits—physical and mental.

3. The contrast in the distributions of measures of physical size and contour is, in general, sharper than in distributions of mental traits or of behavior

4. The contrast is sharpest in the number of finger ridges, which is evidently determined almost wholly, if not wholly, by genetic and asymmetry factors, and is not modified by environment.

5. The contrast is somewhat less sharp in height, head length, and weight

6. The contrast in head width and in cephalic index is less sharp still, but this may be due to unreliability of the measurement of head width

7. The contrast in Binet I.Q. is somewhat less than in number of finger ridges, height, weight, or head length, but is the sharpest among the mental traits. The contrast in Otis I.Q. is somewhat less than that in Binet I.Q.

8. The contrast in total score on the Stanford Achievement Test is less than the contrast in the scores on the intelligence tests

9. The contrasts in rapidity of tapping and in score on the Woodworth-Mathews Personal Data Sheet are the least among those traits for which the distributions of differences have been tabulated

THE DISTRIBUTION OF COMPOSITE DIFFERENCES

The preceding comparisons have dealt with single traits or measures. The following comparisons deal with the composites of several traits. We shall first present the composite physical measurements, then the composite mental measurements, and finally the composite of all the measurements—physical and mental. The curves which show the distributions of these composite differences are presented in Figures 12–14. In each case the distributions are shown in the form of a frequency polygon. As indicated in the figures, the distributions of the entire group of twins, and of the identical twins and of the fraternal twins separately, are shown.

Figure 12 and Table 22 show the distribution of the two groups of twins in the composite of five physical measurements. It is evident that the distribution of differences in the two groups is very sharply contrasted. On the other hand, there are a good many pairs among the fraternal twins who differ more than any of the identical twins. There is also a somewhat smaller number of identical twins who are more alike than any of the fraternal twins. Between these two extremes there is also overlapping.

The comparison in the case of four mental tests—mental age, educational age, Woodworth-Mathews score, and the motor test—as shown in Figure 13 and in Table 23 shows much less contrast and much greater overlapping. There is still, however, a contrast between the two groups, and the total distribution curve shows a tendency toward bimodality. A count of the cases, however, shows that eighty-nine of the ninety-nine pairs are within the range of the overlapping between the two groups. This fact would seem to indicate that the mental traits fall in quite a different category from the physical traits.

When the mental and physical traits are combined, the contrast, as shown in Figure 14 and in Table 24 is even sharper than for the physical traits alone. The addition of the mental traits to the composite, while they do not alone distinguish sharply between the two groups, add something to the discrimination which is made by the physical traits. While in the distribution for physical traits alone 46 per cent of the individuals fall within the range of overlapping, in the composite pairs for all traits but 40 per cent fall within this range. The frequency polygon shows a somewhat increased tendency to bimodality than that for the physical traits alone.

The most significant fact which is brought out by these distributions of composite differences is the fact that the physical traits distinguish between the identical and fraternal twins much more sharply than do the mental traits. This difference in the contrast between the two groups on physical

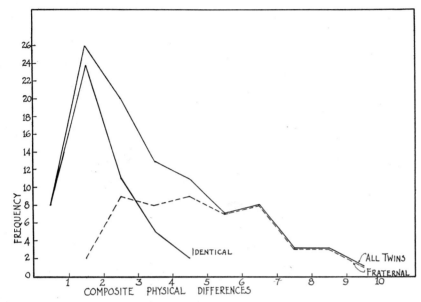

FIG. 12.—Composite physical differences

TABLE 22

COMPOSITE PHYSICAL DIFFERENCES

Difference	Identical	Fraternal	Both
9.0–10.0........	....	1	1
8.0– 9.0........	....	3	3
7.0– 8.0........	....	3	3
6.0– 7.0........	....	8	8
5.0– 6.0........	....	7	7
4.0– 5.0........	2	9	11
3.0– 4.0........	5	8	13
2.0– 3.0........	11	9	20
1.0– 2.0........	24	2	26
0.0– 1.0........	8	....	8
Total........	50	50	100

and mental traits may be due in part to the fact that the measurements of the former are more accurate than those of the latter, but it is hardly likely that this is the sole explanation. It seems probable that either the mental traits are less subject to definite determination by heredity than are the physical traits, and in contrast the mental traits are somewhat more largely

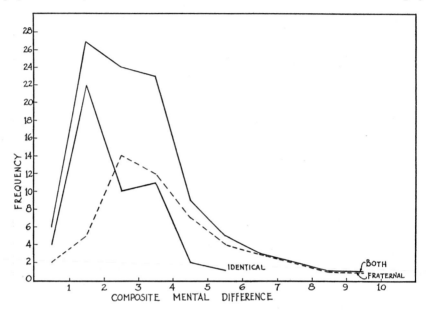

Fig. 13.—Distribution of composite mental differences (mental age, educational age, Woodworth-Mathews score, motor score).

TABLE 23

Composite Mental Differences

Difference	Identical	Fraternal	Both
9.0	....	1	1
8.0	....	1	1
7.0	....	....	....
6.0	....	3	3
5.0	1	4	5
4.0	2	7	9
3.0	11	12	23
2.0	10	14	24
1.0	22	5	27
0.0	4	2	6
Total	50	49	99

influenced by environment, or the inheritance of a mental trait is subject to a different hereditary law than is the inheritance of a physical trait. A

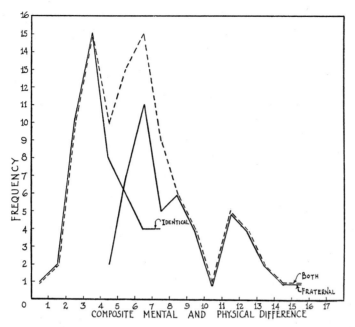

Fig. 14.—Composite mental and physical differences

TABLE 24

TOTAL COMPOSITE DIFFERENCES

Difference	Identical	Fraternal	Both
15.0–16.0........	....	1	1
14.0–15.0........	....	1	1
13.0–14.0........	....	2	2
12.0–13.0........	....	4	4
11.0–12.0........	....	5	5
10.0–11.0........	....	1	1
9.0–10.0........	....	4	4
8.0– 9.0........	....	6	6
7.0– 8.0........	4	5	9
6.0– 7.0........	4	11	15
5.0– 6.0........	6	7	13
4.0– 5.0........	8	2	10
3.0– 4.0........	15	....	15
2.0– 3.0........	10	....	10
1.0– 2.0........	2	....	2
0.0– 1.0........	1	....	1
Total........	50	49	99

most plausible provisional hypothesis would seem to be that behavior and mental ability are more subject to the influence of training and environment than are physical size, form, and features, such as color of eyes, color and texture of hair, etc. It is quite plausible to suppose that the nervous system, which is the physical counterpart of mental traits, of behavior, and of abilities, being more subject to influence by stimulation from the external world, is also more susceptible to variations through such stimulation and through the responses which are made to it.

SUMMARY OF THE CHAPTER

1. A tabulation of the composite measurable physical differences, the observed physical differences, and the differences in palm prints and fingerprints shows:

   a) The 23 of the 100 pairs most alike in composite physical measurements were diagnosed as identical and the 31 least alike were classed as fraternal, the classification being made without a knowledge of the physical measures

   b) The characteristics "appearance of features," "eye color," "hair color," and "shape of ears" are alike or nearly alike in the pairs most alike in composite physical measures and usually different in larger degree in those least alike in composite measures

   c) The palm and finger patterns of the two members of a pair of twins who are much alike in other physical characteristics are usually more alike than are the patterns of the two hands of the same individual

   d) This relative resemblance in palm prints and fingerprints is the most discriminating single measure

   e) The diagnosis based on observation at the time of the examination was practically identical with the final diagnosis based on the entire set of physical measures, being reversed in but 3 out of 100 pairs

2. An inspectional comparison of the distribution of differences of the two types of twins reveals the following facts:

   a) In standing height there is a striking difference between the two types of twins and a striking resemblance between fraternal twins and like-sex siblings taken at the same age

   b) In weight and in Binet I.Q. the contrast between the two types of twins is not so sharp, but fraternal twins and siblings again follow the same trend. In the remaining traits data for siblings are not available. Comparison is made only between the two types of twins

   c) Of the other physical measures, the contrast is greatest for number of finger ridges, least for head width, and intermediate for head length

   d) Of the remaining mental measures, the contrast stands in this order: Otis I.Q., Stanford Achievement Test, tapping test, and Woodworth-Mathews Personal Data Sheet

   e) When measures of the various traits are combined and composite difference curves drawn, the curves of physical differences are more sharply differentiated than are the curves of mental differences

3. The general conclusions which are suggested by these facts are as follows:
   a) The differentiation between two types of twins is in harmony with the distributions of differences
   b) The contrast between identical and fraternal twins is greater in some traits than in others, being greatest in number of finger ridges and, in general, somewhat less in mental than in physical traits. This fact suggests that some traits are more susceptible to environmental influence than others. More precise statistical analysis of these differences will be undertaken in a later chapter

CHAPTER VI

STATISTICAL ANALYSIS OF UNSEPARATED TWINS

CORRELATIONS, MEANS, AND STANDARD DEVIATIONS

a) METHODS OF CORRELATION WITH TWIN DATA

IN CONTRAST with the usual correlation between two variables for a number of individuals, we are here interested in the correlation among the members of a group or class for a single variable such as height. If it were possible to divide our fifty pairs of twins on some basis such as age, putting the older twin for each pair in the same class, we should obtain an "interclass" correlation. Any such basis of classification seems irrelevant, however, in the case of twins, and we shall therefore treat all fifty pairs of twins as belonging to the same class, obtaining what is known as the "intra-class" correlation.

Intraclass correlations are simply obtained by forming a symmetrical or double-entry table. Instead of entering each pair of observations once in such a table, it is entered twice, the co-ordinates of the entries being the same numbers, their order being reversed. Thus, if measurements 62 and 65 are found for a pair of twins, these are entered in the XX' scatter diagram as $X = 62$ and $X' = 65$ and also as $X = 65$ and $X' = 62$. If N is the number of pairs of twins, there will thus be $2N$ entries in the correlation table.

If $\overline{X}$ denotes the mean for all pairs of twins, then

$$\overline{X} = \frac{1}{2N} \sum_{1}^{N} (X + X') ; \tag{1}$$

and the standard deviation, σ, for X or X' is given by

$$\sigma^2 = \frac{1}{2N} \left[\sum_{1}^{N} (X - \overline{X})^2 + \sum_{1}^{N} (X' - \overline{X})^2 \right] . \tag{2}$$

The correlation from the table may then be written in the form

$$r = \frac{1}{N\sigma^2} \sum_{1}^{N} (X - \overline{X})(X' - \overline{X}) . \tag{3}$$

94

An alternate formula may be obtained by the use of the standard deviation of the $2N$ differences $X - X'$ and $X' - X$, denoted by σ_D. It easily follows that

$$r = 1 - \tfrac{1}{2} \frac{\sigma_D^2}{\sigma^2} . \tag{4}$$

In eliminating age from the correlations, the usual first-order partial correlation formula may be used. This may be written in the form

$$r_{xx' \cdot a} = \frac{r_{xx'} - r_{xa} r_{x'a}}{\sqrt{(1 - r_{xa}^2)(1 - r_{x'a}^2)}} . \tag{5}$$

For our twin correlations, however, the values r_{xa} and $r_{x'a}$ are the same, each being taken as the correlation of age with $2N$ twin values of X. The foregoing formula then reduces to

$$r_{xx' \cdot a} = \frac{r_{xx'} - r_{xa}^2}{1 - r_{xa}^2} . \tag{6}$$

In a few cases it was found possible to correct the correlation coefficients for attenuation, using Spearman's formula

$$r'_{xx'} = \frac{r_{xx'}}{\sqrt{r_{x_1 x_2} r_{x'_1 x'_2}}} , \tag{7}$$

where $r_{x_1 x_2}$ and $r_{x'_1 x'_2}$ are reliability coefficients. Since $2N$ cases are again used for these last values, they are equal; and the formula reduces to

$$r'_{xx'} = \frac{r_{xx'}}{r_{x_1 x_2}} . \tag{8}$$

Assuming that age is determined with perfect reliability, corrections for both age and attenuation may be made by combining (8) and (6) in the form

$$r'_{xx' \cdot a} = \frac{r_{xx'} - r_{xa}^2}{r_{x_1 x_2} - r_{xa}^2} , \tag{9}$$

since

$$r'_{xa} = r_{xa} / \sqrt{r_{x_1 x_2}} .$$

In studying the sampling errors of our intraclass correlations, we shall not employ the usual formula $(1 - r^2)/\sqrt{N}$, which assumes a normal distribution of the correlation coefficient. Considering the number of extremely high and low observed correlations and the size of our samples, there is good reason to believe that these distributions are skew. Following Fisher's method,[1] we shall transform the raw correlations by the formula

$$z = \tfrac{1}{2}[\log (1 + r) - \log (1 - r)], \tag{10}$$

where z is distributed very nearly in normal form. The variance of z now is independent of the correlation and depends only upon the size of the sample. The value of this variance is simply given by

$$\sigma_z^2 = \frac{1}{N - \tfrac{3}{2}}. \tag{11}$$

Table 26 gives the transformed values of r from formula (10) with a small corrective factor furnished by

$$\text{Corr.} = +\tfrac{1}{2} \log \frac{N}{N - 1}. \tag{12}$$

b) CORRELATIONS FOR PHYSICAL AND MENTAL TRAITS

The raw intraclass correlations are given in Table 25 for a number of physical and mental traits. Correlations of each variable with age, based on $2N$ cases, and partial correlations with age eliminated by formula (6), are also presented. The two groups include, of course, 50 pairs of identical and 50 pairs of fraternal twins.

It will be noted that the correlations for the nine physical traits are quite high, the values for identical twins ranging from .881 to .966 even with age eliminated. In the case of fraternal twins these nine values are much lower, averaging about .5. This large difference in correlation is undoubtedly due in large measure to the closer genetic relationship of the identical twins.

The next four partial correlations with Binet and Otis tests are approximately .90 for identical twins and .60 for fraternal twins, while the corresponding values for educational age are approximately .90 and .70. It thus appears that for identical twins the partial correlations for physical, mental, and educational traits are about .90, with a slight drop in the case of the latter. For the fraternal twins, however, the corresponding correlations for these three groups of traits are .50, .60, and .70. These last three coefficients are approximately the same as those found for siblings tested at the same or nearly the same age.

The remaining correlations shown in Table 25 are somewhat lower than the foregoing values partly because the tests used were less reliable and

---

[1] R. A. Fisher, *Statistical Methods for Research Workers.* London: Oliver & Boyd, 1930.

partly because the less complex nature of the trait measured may lessen the hereditary resemblance.

TABLE 25

RAW INTRACLASS CORRELATIONS BETWEEN TWINS, CORRELATIONS
OF TRAITS WITH AGE, AND RESULTING
PARTIAL CORRELATIONS

TRAIT	IDENTICAL			FRATERNAL		
	Between Twins	With Age	Partial	Between Twins	With Age	Partial
Standing height............	.981	.849	.932	.934	.902	.645
Sitting height..............	.965	.841	.881	.901	.895	.503
Weight....................	.973	.821	.917	.900	.854	.631
Head length...............	.910	.062	.910	.691	.509	.583
Head width................	.908	.426	.888	.654	.490	.545
Cephalic index.............	.903	.280	.895	.584	− .106	.579
Finger ridges (R)..........	.919	.362	.907	.344	.105	.337
Finger ridges (L)..........	.931	.308	.924	.503	.064	.501
Total finger ridges.........	.953	.346	.947	.463	.083	.459
Total finger ridges omitting one extreme case........	.972	.408	.966	....	....	....
Binet Mental Age..........	.922	.663	.861	.831	.761	.599
Binet I.Q.................	.910	− .491	.881	.640	− .159	.631
Otis score................	.947	.681	.901	.800	.730	.572
Otis I.Q..................	.922	.013	.922	.621	.092	.618
Stanford Achievement:						
Word meaning...........	.923	.674	.859	.804	.742	.563
Arithmetic computation...	.878	.745	.726	.858	.738	.688
Nature study and science..	.905	.765	.771	.885	.818	.653
History and literature.....	.900	.667	.820	.846	.728	.672
Spelling................	.956	.807	.874	.878	.738	.732
Educational Age........	.955	.764	.892	.883	.784	.696
Woodworth-Mathews.......	.562	− .100	.558	.371	− .093	.365
Downey:						
Speed of decision........	.497	.303	.446	.694	.161	.686
Finality of judgment......	.311	− .031	.310	.367	.057	.365
Motor inhibition.........	.513	.009	.513	.575	− .309	.530
Co-ordination of impulses.	.819	.806	.483	.786	.753	.506
Tapping speed—wrist.......	.723	.567	.592	.681	.654	.442
Tapping speed—finger......	.809	.657	.664	.665	.680	.377
Tapping speed—total.......	.814	.636	.688	.689	.705	.382

In order to compare the correlations for identical twins with those for fraternal twins in terms of sampling error, Table 26 has been formed. The raw twin correlations with the transformed z values and corrections by formulas (10) and (12) are presented for comparison. The differences in z value are also given in the next-to-the-last column; and, finally, these values are divided by $\sqrt{2}\,\sigma_z = .2031$, which is the standard deviation of the difference between the two independent z values, $_iz$ and $_fz$. Differences in $_iz - _fz$

TABLE 26

Raw Intraclass Correlations between Twins and Fisher's z-Transformation Given by Formulas (10) and (12)

TRAIT	IDENTICAL		FRATERNAL		DIFFERENCE ($_iz - _fz$)	$\dfrac{_iz - _fz}{\sqrt{2}\,\sigma_z}$
	$_ir$	$_iz$	$_fr$	$_fz$		
Standing height............	.981	2.333	.934	1.699	0.634	3.12
Sitting height.............	.965	2.024	.901	1.488	0.536	2.64
Weight....................	.973	2.156	.900	1.482	0.674	3.32
Head length...............	.910	1.538	.691	0.860	0.678	3.34
Head width................	.908	1.526	.654	0.792	0.734	3.61
Cephalic Index.............	.903	1.498	.584	0.679	0.819	4.03
Finger ridges (R)..........	.919	1.593	.344	0.369	1.224	6.03
Finger ridges (L)..........	.931	1.676	.503	0.563	1.113	5.48
Total finger ridges.........	.953	1.873	.463	0.511	1.362	6.71
Binet Mental Age..........	.922	1.612	.831	1.201	0.411	2.02
Binet I.Q.................	.910	1.538	.640	0.768	0.770	3.79
Otis score.................	.947	1.812	.800	1.109	0.703	3.46
Otis I.Q..................	.922	1.612	.621	0.737	0.875	4.31
Stanford Achievement:						
Word meaning...........	.923	1.619	.804	1.120	0.499	2.46
Arithmetic computation...	.878	1.377	.858	1.296	0.081	0.40*
Nature study and science..	.905	1.509	.885	1.408	0.101	0.50*
History and literature.....	.900	1.482	.846	1.252	0.230	1.13*
Spelling................	.956	1.907	.878	1.377	0.530	2.61
Educational Age.........	.955	1.896	.883	1.399	0.497	2.45
Woodworth-Mathews.......	.562	0.646	.371	0.400	0.246	1.21*
Downey:						
Speed of decision.........	.497	0.555	.694	0.866	−0.311	1.53*
Finality of judgment......	.311	0.332	.367	0.395	−0.063	0.31*
Motor inhibition.........	.513	0.577	.575	0.665	−0.088	0.43*
Co-ordination of impulses.	.819	1.164	.786	1.071	0.093	0.46*
Tapping speed—wrist.......	.723	0.924	.681	0.841	0.083	0.41*
Tapping speed—finger......	.809	1.134	.665	0.812	0.322	1.59*
Tapping speed—total.......	.814	1.123	.689	0.856	0.267	1.31*

* Differences in $_iz - _fz$ less than twice the standard error are regarded as insignificant.

less than twice this standard error have been regarded as insignificant and are indicated by an asterisk in the final column of values.

Insignificant differences in the twin correlations appear for the traits "arithmetic computation," "nature study and science," "history and literature," the Woodworth-Mathews tests of emotional instability, all the Downey will-temperament tests, and "speed of tapping."

The most significant differences in correlation occur in the case of finger ridges, various other physical measurements, and measures of intelligence. The general trend appears to be for greatest difference in correlation for physical traits; next, mental tests; then, achievement tests; and, finally, small differences for measures of temperament and emotionality.

c) DIFFERENCES IN RELIABILITY

Vertical comparisons in Table 26 are not entirely valid, owing to the difference in reliability of the various measurements. It may be assumed that the physical measurements are the most reliable, those of finger ridges being almost perfectly so. For groups other than the present one the reliability of the mental and achievement tests used has been found to be close to .90. It is quite certain that the Downey tests (especially the forms used in the present study) fall far short of .90 in their reliability. Correcting the correlation coefficients for this lack of complete reliability would increase the degree of correlation. The physical correlations would be raised very little if at all, the mental and achievement test correlations would increase somewhat more, while the correlations for temperament and emotional traits would probably be raised considerably.

It would seem probable, then, that if all the coefficients were corrected for attenuation, the correlations of mental and achievement traits for identical twins would be even more like those of physical traits. In the case of fraternal twins the mental and achievement test correlations are already considerably higher than some of the physical, but the difference would be even greater if corrections for attenuation were made.

In order to determine how great a change might be caused by such a correction, reliability coefficients were worked out in a few of the tests. Data were not available for doing this for most of the measurements considered. Table 27 gives the results for four tests. The reliability measures were obtained by correlating the score on the odd items with the score on the even items for the Otis, word meaning, and arithmetic tests. In the case of the tapping test, three trials were given so that the reliability could be obtained by correlating the second trial with the third.

The increase in correlation resulting from these last corrections is not great. For "Otis score," "word meaning," and "arithmetic," the identical correlations are brought closer to .90 by the additional correction for reliability, while the corresponding correlations for fraternal twins are raised only a few points above the correlations with age partialed out. In the case of wrist tapping the change is slight. For such motor tests, therefore, the low values of .592 and .442 are probably due to the relatively simple mental processes involved in such motor tests.

The coefficient 1.010 for Otis score in the case of the identical twins is an illustration of what may happen when very high correlations are corrected by a formula such as (8), which is not truly applicable in such a problem. The reliability of the test in this case is .942, which is slightly less than the correlation of .947 between the twins. In other words, the scores of a pair of twins are more alike than are the scores of the same individual on two forms of the test. The application of formula (8) gives $r = 1.005$, and further correction for age gives $r = 1.010$. Both results are impossible as correlations and indicate that the correction of very high correlations by for-

TABLE 27

SOME CORRELATION COEFFICIENTS CORRECTED FOR ATTENUATION

Test	Group	Correlation between Twins	Reliability Coefficient	Correlation with Age	Corrected for Age Only	Corrected for Age and Attenuation
Otis score.............	Identical	.947	.942	.681	.901	1.010
	Fraternal	.800	.963	.730	.572	.621
Word meaning.........	Identical	.923	.980	.674	.859	.892
	Fraternal	.804	.976	.742	.563	.596
Arithmetic...........	Identical	.878	.924	.745	.726	.875
	Fraternal	.858	.947	.738	.688	.779
Wrist tapping..........	Identical	.723	.962	.567	.592	.627
	Fraternal	.681	.950	.654	.442	.485

mulas like (8) is a doubtful practice. The probable error of the coefficient $r = 1.010$ will, of course, tell us nothing, because for $N = 50$ the usual formula for σ_r is grossly in error for high values of r, and formula (10) is inapplicable.

d) MEANS AND STANDARD DEVIATIONS OF TRAITS

Using formulas (1) and (2), which are based on the two twin groups of 100 cases each, we have computed the means and standard deviations of the traits. These values are presented in Table 28. Differences between the identical and fraternal twins are also shown and marked with an asterisk where the difference is greater than three times its probable error.

It is noteworthy that the identical twins were slightly more intelligent than the fraternal group, with a mean I.Q. approximately five points higher. Neither the mean chronological nor the mental ages of the two groups show

TRAIT	IDENTICAL Mean	IDENTICAL PE_M	FRATERNAL Mean	FRATERNAL PE_M	IDENTICAL σ	IDENTICAL PE_σ	FRATERNAL σ	FRATERNAL PE_σ	DIFFERENCES M_I-M_F	DIFFERENCES $PE_{M_I-M_F}$	DIFFERENCES $\sigma_I-\sigma_F$	DIFFERENCES $PE_{\sigma_I-\sigma_F}$
Age	13 yr. 4.1 mo.	2.4	13–5.4	2.2	34.9	1.70	34.0	1.56	−1.3	3.3	0.9	2.3
Standing height	151.6 cm.	0.87	152.1	1.07	12.9	0.62	16.2	0.76	−0.5	1.4	−3.3*	1.0
Sitting height	79.2 cm.	0.45	79.6	0.52	6.6	0.32	7.8	0.37	−0.4	0.7	−1.2	0.5
Weight	97.9 lb.	1.75	98.6	1.96	25.9	1.24	29.6	1.39	−0.7	2.6	−3.7	1.9
Head length	18.2 cm.	0.05	18.1	0.06	0.81	0.04	0.94	0.04	0.1	0.1	−0.13	0.06
Head width	14.5 cm.	0.05	14.4	0.04	0.69	0.04	0.61	0.03	0.1	0.1	0.08	0.05
Cephalic index	0.795	0.003	0.800	0.003	0.049	0.002	0.038	0.002	−0.005	0.004	0.011*	0.003
Finger ridges (R)	41.8	0.80	38.0	0.86	11.9	0.57	12.7	0.61	3.8*	1.2	−0.8	0.8
Finger ridges (L)	40.8	0.82	36.0	0.94	12.2	0.58	13.9	0.66	4.8*	1.2	−1.7	0.9
Total finger ridges	82.4	1.61	74.0	1.76	23.8	1.14	26.1	1.24	8.4*	2.4	−2.3	1.7
Binet Mental Age	155.9 mo.	2.0	150.5	2.3	29.5	1.41	35.4	1.63	5.4	3.0	−5.9	2.2
Binet I.Q.	101.6	1.2	96.1	1.4	17.3	0.85	15.7	0.71	5.5*	1.6	1.6	1.1
Otis score	44.6	1.4	41.2	1.4	20.7	0.99	21.3	0.99	3.4	2.0	−0.6	1.4
Otis I.Q.	103.7	1.1	99.0	1.0	16.0	0.78	15.8	0.71	4.7*	1.5	0.2	1.1
Stanford Achievement:												
Word meaning	50.1	1.2	50.6	1.3	18.0	0.85	19.9	0.92	−0.5	1.8	−1.9	1.3
Arithmetic computation	107.1	2.1	105.0	2.3	31.2	1.48	35.0	1.63	2.1	3.1	−3.8	2.2
Nature study and science	48.8	1.6	47.0	1.7	23.8	1.13	24.4	1.13	1.8	2.3	−0.6	1.6
History and literature	44.9	1.7	40.3	1.6	24.5	1.20	25.9	1.20	4.6	2.4	−1.4	1.7
Spelling	128.7	3.4	127.8	3.6	50.3	2.40	53.9	2.55	0.9	5.0	−3.6	3.5
Educational Age	13 yr. 4.4 mo.	2.1	13–2.0	2.1	30.5	1.48	32.3	1.48	2.4	3.0	−1.8	2.1
Woodworth-Mathews	14.7	0.55	14.9	0.53	8.2	0.39	8.0	0.37	−0.2	0.8	0.2	0.5
Downey:												
Speed of decision	19.5	0.47	17.9	0.57	7.0	0.33	8.5	0.40	1.6	0.7	−1.5	0.5
Finality of judgment	65.4	2.2	53.7	1.9	31.7	1.56	28.8	1.34	11.7*	2.9	2.9	2.1
Motor inhibition	20.3	1.4	23.2	1.4	20.7	0.99	21.8	0.99	−2.9	2.0	−1.1	1.4
Co-ordination of impulses	50.1	1.3	52.2	1.3	19.8	0.92	19.7	0.92	−2.1	1.8	0.1	1.3
Tapping speed—wrist	163.4	1.7	161.9	1.7	24.6	1.20	26.4	1.20	1.5	2.4	−1.8	1.7
Tapping speed—finger	143.9	1.6	145.1	1.6	23.8	1.13	24.3	1.13	−1.2	2.3	−0.5	1.6
Tapping speed—total	308.1	3.1	307.2	3.3	45.2	2.19	49.2	2.33	0.9	4.5	−4.0	3.2

* Difference greater than three times its probable error.

significant differences, however; so the I.Q. difference is of doubtful importance. We may regard both groups as of average intelligence, judged by the
standards of typical American school children.

It will be observed that the mean educational ages of the two groups are
each a little over thirteen years and agree closely with the corresponding
mean chronological ages. These values furnish further evidence that our
groups are typical children doing normal school work.

Significant differences between groups appear very definitely in the case
of mean number of finger ridges. Identical twins have a larger number of
finger ridges than the fraternal twins. Another significant difference appears in the case of the Downey Test of Finality of Judgment. Here the
mean difference is 11.7 ± 2.9 in favor of the identical group. We have no
explanation to offer for this rather striking result, which is not confirmed
by the remaining Downey tests.

In the case of the standard deviations for the two groups, there is a suggestion of greater variability in sitting height for the fraternal twins. Cephalic index, on the other hand, appears to have greater variability for the
identical twins. It may also be noted that twenty of the twenty-eight standard deviations are larger in the case of the fraternal group. Taken as a
whole, these values suggest a slightly greater variability in trait for fraternal
as compared with identical twins. Statistically unimportant as these differences may be, we have nevertheless taken them into account in the subsequent discussion of individual differences. We do not finally regard them
as important, however. The agreement in homogeneity of the two groups
is about as close as one would expect from two samples of the same population.

e) STANDARD ERRORS OF ESTIMATE

The standard error of estimate given by the formula $\sigma_x\sqrt{1 - r^2}$ has been
computed, using the correlations corrected for age. It will be noted that
the values in Table 29 are much larger for fraternal than for identical twins
because of the lower correlations for the former group. In the last column
of this table the ratio of the standard error for fraternal twins to the corresponding value for identical twins has been given. These ratios are nearly
all greater than one and range from .9 to 4.3. They are, moreover, fairly
consistent for the physical and mental traits, for which the average ratio
is a little over 2.

f) CORRELATIONS OF NUMBER OF FINGER RIDGES

In addition to the three finger-ridge correlations presented in Table 25,
a few other correlations between twins and between the right and left sides
of a given twin are given in Table 30. For these correlations it was con-

sidered that there was a first and a second twin in each pair, the order being determined alphabetically by given name. This made it possible to obtain correlations between the finger ridges on the right hand of the first twin with those on the left hand of the second twin and vice versa. If these correla-

TABLE 29

STANDARD ERRORS OF ESTIMATE

Trait	Identical	Fraternal	Ratio of Fraternal to Identical
Standing height..................	4.68 cm.	12.38 cm.	2.6
Sitting height....................	3.12 cm.	6.74 cm.	2.2
Weight..........................	10.33 lb.	22.96 lb.	2.2
Head length......................	0.336 cm.	0.764 cm.	2.3
Head width.......................	0.317 cm.	0.511 cm.	1.6
Cephalic index...................	0.0219	0.0310	1.4
Finger ridges (R).................	4.69	11.92	2.5+
Finger ridges (L).................	4.45	12.01	2.7
Total finger ridges...............	7.21	23.13	3.2
Total finger ridges (omitting one extreme case)....................	5.43	....	4.3
Binet Mental Age.................	15.00 mo.	28.35 mo.	1.9
Binet I.Q........................	8.19	12.18	1.5−
Otis score.......................	8.98	17.47	1.9
Otis I.Q.........................	6.20	12.42	2.0
Stanford Achievement:			
Word meaning.................	9.22	16.45	1.8
Arithmetic computation..........	21.46	25.40	1.2
Nature study and science........	15.16	18.48	1.2
History and literature...........	14.02	19.18	1.4
Spelling......................	24.44	36.72	1.5+
Educational Age................	13.79 mo.	23.19 mo.	1.7
Woodworth-Mathews.............	6.80	7.45	1.1
Downey:			
Speed of decision...............	6.27	6.18	1.0
Finality of judgment............	30.14	26.81	0.9
Motor inhibition................	17.77	18.49	1.0
Co-ordination of impulses........	17.34	16.99	1.0
Tapping speed—wrist.............	19.83	23.68	1.2
Tapping speed—finger............	17.80	22.51	1.3
Tapping speed—total.............	32.80	45.47	1.4

tions were found to be higher than those between the right hand of the first twin with the right hand of the second and between the left hand of the first and the left hand of the second, it would be an indication of some general asymmetry reversal.

It will be noted that the first four correlations for identical twins are practically the same, ranging from .91 to .93. In the case of the fraternal twins the corresponding four correlations do not differ significantly from one another but are very much lower than the identical coefficients. It thus appears that, whether identical or fraternal twins are considered, there is no indication of a consistent asymmetry reversal. It is to be noted, however, that the reversed likeness is fully as great as the direct.

There is a correlation of .93 between the right and left hands of an individual for the identical group, and exactly the same value is found for the fraternal group. It is therefore apparent that, in the case of number of

TABLE 30

CORRELATIONS OF NUMBER OF FINGER RIDGES

Hand Combinations	Identical	Fraternal
Right of one with right of other..........	.92	.34
Left of one with left of other............	.93	.50
Right of one with left of other..........	.91	.47
Left of one with right of other..........	.93	.40
Total of one with total of other..........	.95	.46
Right of each twin with his left..........	.93	.93

finger ridges, the right hand of an identical twin is as much like the right (or the left) hand of his twin as it is like his own left hand. This is not at all true in the case of fraternal twins.

COMPARISON OF YOUNGER AND OLDER TWINS

a) OTHER STUDIES ON THE RESEMBLANCE OF YOUNGER AND OLDER TWINS

In studying the problem of original nature versus training, Thorndike[2] says, "If now these resemblances are due to the fact that two members of any twin pair are treated alike at home, have the same parental models, attend the same school, and are subject in general to closely similar environmental conditions, then twins should, up to the age of leaving home, *grow more and more alike*, and in our measurements the twins 13 and 14 years old should be much more alike than those 9 and 10 years old" (italics ours), and again on page 2, "the influence of original nature in determining twin resemblances is in proportion to the extent" that the correlation for the younger twins is equal to the correlations for the older twins, while "the influence of environment in determining resemblances is in proportion to

[2] Edward L. Thorndike, "Measurement of Twins," *Archives of Philosophy, Psychology, and Scientific Methods*, No. 1 (September, 1905), pp. 1–64.

the extent" that the correlation for the younger twins is less than the correlation for the older twins.

Thorndike found an average correlation of .83 for the younger twins and .70 for the older twins. He concludes that the difference in these values is insignificant and that nurture can have little influence on the resemblance of twins judged by this method.

In Merriman's[3] study it was also found that, except for teacher ratings, the younger twins were slightly more alike than the older twins. Lauterbach[4] found correlations of about the same magnitude for both of these groups, while Wingfield[5] found average correlations of .782 for the younger twins and .788 for the older twins. He partialed age out of his correlations and allowed for the differing variability of his groups. He concludes (p. 86) that "the evidence obtained from this study of younger and older twins can be said to indicate that older twins are certainly no more alike than younger twins." He also finds (p. 88) that "twins are no more alike in those traits in which they have received much training in school (reading, arithmetic, spelling, literature, etc.) than they are in general intelligence, a trait which is supposedly not directly affected by schooling."

The assumption made by Thorndike (and originally by Galton) that the environment of twins is so similar that we should expect it to make them more alike as they grow older is a debatable one. As twins grow older, their environment may be apparently very similar, but varying influences at home and at school would probably become much more numerous as the twins grow older. The number of similar influences would, of course, also increase as the twins grow older, so that our present question depends upon whether the proportion of similar and dissimilar factors increases as the twins grow older. We may be seriously in error in assuming, as Thorndike appears to do, that the proportion of similar to dissimilar influences increases as the twins grow older. The twins may be living in the same homes, going to the same grades, and studying the same books—all of which would make for an increasing similarity of environment as they grow older. At the same time, however, certain varying influences are also operative, and these are ′ ly to become more numerous as the children grow older. The greater compi ·ty of intellectual and emotional life at the older age would intro-

---

[3] Cur. Merriman, *The Intellectual Resemblance of Twins* ("Psychological Monographs," ·l. XXXIII, No. 5; Whole No. 152). Princeton, N.J.: Psychological Review Co., 1924. ′p. 58.

[4] C. E. L. terbach, "Studies in Twin Resemblance," *Genetics*, X (November, 1925), 525–68.

[5] Alex H. W. ɾfield, *Twins and Orphans: The Inheritance of Intelligence.* London and Toronto: J. M.)ent & Sons, Ltd., 1928. Pp. xii+127.

duce variations in interest, special aptitude, etc. It should also be borne in mind that the actual proportion of truly common experiences in the lives of two children must be very small in relation to the total experience.

If home and school life were a highly controlled laboratory, we might accept Thorndike's hypothesis; but, in view of the complexity of experience, we must view it as a debatable proposition.

Differences and correlations between differences will be determined for twins in the present chapter and compared with those from the studies cited. In order to give a comparable measure of the increasing or decreasing likeness of twins, it is desirable to take into account the changing variability of the groups with age. This will be done in the subsequent comparisons.

b) MEANS AND STANDARD DEVIATIONS FOR
YOUNGER AND OLDER CHILDREN

The fifty pairs of identical twins in the present study were divided into two age groups with the dividing line at age thirteen years and two months.

TABLE 31

TRAIT MEANS FOR THE YOUNGER AND OLDER GROUPS

VARIABLE	IDENTICAL			FRATERNAL		
	Younger	Older	Diff.	Younger	Older	Diff.
Age..........	130.8 mo.	192.4	61.6	126.0	185.4	59.4
Height........	142.5 cm.	161.4	18.9	137.1	162.3	25.2
M.A..........	140.3 mo.	172.2	31.9±3.3	122.6	169.8	47.2±3.7
E.A..........	139.7 mo.	183.2	43.5	132.1	175.6	43.5

The younger group consisted of twenty-six pairs and the older group of the remaining twenty-four pairs. The fraternal twins were divided at age thirteen years and four months into twenty-one younger pairs and thirty-one older pairs.

The mean values for age, height, mental age, and educational age are given in Table 31. It will be noted that the mean increases with age in all four traits and in both groups of twins. In only one of the traits—mental age—is the increase materially different in the fraternal from that in the identical twins. In mental age the increase in the mean is 47.2 ± 3.7 in the case of fraternal as against 31.9 ± 3.3 in the case of identical twins. The excess in the increase for fraternal twins is 15.3 ± 5.0, which is probably statistically significant. We have no explanation of this fact to offer; and it has no direct bearing on the primary comparison, which is the differences between pairs of twins at the earlier and later ages.

The standard deviations for the foregoing groups are presented in Table 32. The significant facts brought out by this table are that for mental and educational age the older groups have a greater dispersion than the younger groups, the differences for these two variables being from three to four times their probable errors. These facts will need to be taken into consideration in comparing the mean differences and correlations for the younger and older groups of twins.

TABLE 32

STANDARD DEVIATIONS OF TRAITS FOR THE YOUNGER
AND OLDER GROUPS

VARIABLE	IDENTICAL			FRATERNAL		
	Younger	Older	Diff.	Younger	Older	Diff.
Age.........	15.7 mo.	15.3	−0.4±1.1	18.2	17.8	−0.4±1.7
Height.......	7.2 cm.	9.7	2.3±0.8	10.4	10.2	−0.2±1.0
M.A.........	21.5 mo.	27.7	6.2±2.4	21.6	30.7	9.1±2.5
E.A.........	16.3 mo.	25.6	9.3±2.1	19.0	27.6	8.6±2.2

c) MEAN DIFFERENCES FOR YOUNGER AND OLDER GROUPS

The mean differences between pair members were next computed for three of the foregoing traits as shown in Table 33.

TABLE 33

MEAN DIFFERENCES BETWEEN TWINS

VARIABLE	IDENTICAL			FRATERNAL		
	Younger	Older	Diff.	Younger	Older	Diff.
Height.........	1.7 cm.	1.6	−0.1±0.3	4.4	4.4	0.0±0.7
M.A...........	7.2 mo.	9.8	2.6±1.3	10.6	19.9	9.3±2.2
E.A...........	5.5 mo.	7.5	2.0±1.1	6.5	15.1	8.6±1.5

In the case of identical twins the mean differences for mental and educational age appear to be insignificantly larger for the older twins. For the fraternal twins, however, these mean differences are significantly larger in the case of the older twins. These mean differences may be expressed as percentages of the common standard deviations taken from Table 32. Thus, the mean difference in the mental age of younger fraternal twins is 10.6/21.6, or .49, while that of older fraternal twins is 19.9/30.7, or .65. The corresponding quotients in the case of educational age of fraternal twins are .34 and .55. Thus the difference is much larger in the older than in the younger group, whether we measure by absolute score difference or in units of standard deviation. Substantially the same results are also obtained if the standard deviation of differences is used as a divisor.

It appears, then, that the difference between identical twins does not increase at all as they grow older in the physical trait of height and that it increases only slightly if at all in mental and educational age. In the case of fraternal twins there is likewise no increase in the difference in height. This seems to indicate that factors producing similarity and dissimilarity are in about the same proportion at younger and older ages. The slight change in the amount of difference in the mental traits in the case of identical twins, furthermore, seems to indicate that, so far as these traits are determined by internal factors, the members of a pair do not diverge to any

TABLE 34

RAW CORRELATIONS BETWEEN TWIN PAIRS

VARIABLE	IDENTICAL				FRATERNAL			
	Younger		Older		Younger		Older	
	r	r_{xa}	r	r_{xa}	r	r_{xa}	r	r_{xa}
Height..........	.924	.600	.958	.561	.847	.802	.827	.712
M.A.............	.880	.375	.918	.573	.749	.384	.677	.606
E.A.............	.853	.428	.917	.367	.895	.479	.760	.631

marked degree. The divergence which we find in the case of the mental traits in fraternal twins, then, may possibly be attributed partly to a differential effect of the environment upon them and partly to the fact that genetically unlike individuals grow increasingly different with age.

d) CORRELATIONS FOR YOUNGER AND OLDER TWINS

The effect of age upon twin differences will next be studied in terms of the correlations for younger and older groups. The raw correlations are presented in Table 34, together with the correlations with age denoted by r_{xa}. As measured by these raw correlations, the identical and the fraternal twins again give contrasting results. In the case of identical twins the older pairs are more alike than the younger pairs in all three traits. In the case of fraternal twins, on the other hand, the older twins are less alike in all three traits, especially in mental age and educational age.

Similar comparisons are next made by partial correlation with age constant and are presented in Table 35. The only coefficients which are probably significantly different are the correlations for mental and educational age in the case of fraternal twins.

TABLE 35

CORRELATIONS BETWEEN TWIN PAIRS (AGE CONSTANT)

VARIABLE	IDENTICAL			FRATERNAL		
	Younger	Older	Diff.	Younger	Older	Diff.
Height......	.88 ± .03	.94 ± .02	.06 ± .04	.57 ± .10	.65 ± .07	.08 ± .12
M.A........	.86 ± .03	.88 ± .03	.02 ± .04	.71 ± .07	.49 ± .09	− .22 ± .11
E.A........	.82 ± .04	.90 ± .03	.08 ± .05	.86 ± .04	.60 ± .08	− .26 ± .09

The differences, −.22 ± .11 and −.26 ± .09, indicate that the older twins are considerably less alike in these two traits, substantiating the results found by the method of mean differences.

The standard errors of estimate are next presented to indicate the effect of taking the variability of the groups into account. These values further substantiate the conclusion already reached that the older fraternal twins are less alike in mental and educational age than the younger twins. The same is true for identical twins, but the differences are hardly significant.

TABLE 36

STANDARD ERRORS OF ESTIMATE

VARIABLE	IDENTICAL		FRATERNAL	
	Younger	Older	Younger	Older
Height........	3.4	3.3	8.5	7.8
M.A..........	11.0	13.2	15.2	26.8
E.A..........	9.3	11.2	9.7	22.1

The foregoing findings are not directly comparable with those of Thorndike, Wingfield, Merriman, and Lauterbach because in the younger-older comparisons made in these studies the identical and fraternal twins have not been separated. The findings, however, are in some respects in harmony with those cited by Thorndike and Wingfield in the first section. The facts brought out in the present study go beyond those obtained by Thorndike and Wingfield in two important respects. First, they distinguish between physical and mental traits, and, second, they distinguish between identical and fraternal twins. The results indicate that neither physical nor mental differences increase significantly with age in identical twins. They indicate further that physical differences behave in the same way in fraternal twins —they do not increase—but that mental differences behave quite differently—they do increase to a marked degree.

e) REGRESSION EQUATIONS FOR DIFFERENCES ON AGE

A still different method of studying the relation of twin-pair differences to age is to note the changing value of these differences as age increases through the whole range. The ideal method would be to study the increase of such differences for the same group of twins at successive ages. In lieu of this impossible procedure we study the foregoing relationship for several groups at different ages by the method of regression.

The variables here considered are pair differences in height, in mental age, and in educational age. The regression equations for estimating these differences from age are as follows:

$$\text{Height} \begin{cases} \text{Iden. } \bar{y} = -\ .008x + 1.82 \\ \text{Frat. } \bar{y} = -\ .028x + 4.78 \end{cases}$$

$$\text{Mental age} \begin{cases} \text{Iden. } \bar{y} = \ .540x + 1.19 \\ \text{Frat. } \bar{y} = 1.385x - 2.67 \end{cases}$$

$$\text{Educational age} \begin{cases} \text{Iden. } \bar{y} = \ .415x + \ .90 \\ \text{Frat. } \bar{y} = 1.150x - 3.89 \end{cases}$$

where x = age for all equations.

It is apparent from these equations that the increase in pair difference with age is most marked in the case of mental age, almost as much so for educational age, and slightly negative in the case of height.

As twins grow older, therefore, we may conclude that there is no tendency for them to become more unlike in such traits as height, but that there is a rather pronounced tendency to become more different in such traits as mental and educational age. This tendency, moreover, is greater in the case of fraternal twins, although the values for the regression coefficients are hardly significantly different. Thus, for mental age we may write $1.385 - .540 = .845 \pm .450$, and for educational age $1.150 - .415 = .735 \pm .364$. These differences in value for the regression coefficients are more than twice their probable errors, so that there is some evidence for significance. In the case of height, on the other hand, the difference between the regression coefficients is $-.020 \pm .134$, which is clearly insignificant. A plot of the foregoing equations brings out the relationships with age very vividly. Again these findings corroborate the results found in the preceding sections. The twins of a pair become less alike in mental ability as they grow older, particularly in the case of fraternal twins.

f) SUMMARY AND CONCLUSION

1. The methods of mean pair differences, correlation, and regression have been employed to study the effect of age upon twin differences.

2. In the case of identical twins there is a slight but hardly significant tendency for the older twin pairs to be less alike than the younger twins in the case of mental and educational age.

3. For the fraternal twins the older pairs have been found to differ significantly from the younger ones in mental- and educational-age differences. In previous studies, where identical and fraternal twins were not separated, it was found that the older twins were not more alike than the younger; but it does not seem to have occurred to some of the foregoing writers that they would have been less alike as found here.

4. In harmony with the findings of Wingfield and Lauterbach, it is found here that twins are not more alike in traits in which they have received training at school than they are in general intelligence.

5. Since it is reasonable to assume that the environment of fraternal twins is less alike than that of identical twins, the decrease in likeness in mental traits of the one type coupled with the maintained likeness of the other is in harmony with the view that such traits are affected by the environment.

THE RELATIVE EFFECT OF NATURE AND NURTURE UPON TWIN DIFFERENCES

a) INTRODUCTION

In the present section we shall attempt to get a measure of the relative effects of nature and nurture factors upon the differences found between members of twin pairs reared within a family. The suggestion for this method arose from the fact that it was possible to separate twins into two categories (identical and fraternal) as shown in chapter iii. By assuming that the former class of twins have identical heredity while the latter do not, we may set up certain formulas for evaluating the relative influence of nature and nurture for fraternal twins reared together.

The term "nature" will be used to refer to the genetic factor while "nurture" will be used to indicate both prenatal and postnatal environment. It would be very desirable to discover some method whereby the effect of postnatal environment alone could be evaluated, but the present data do not afford a basis for such a comparison. The best we can do is to obtain an expression, under certain assumptions, of the relative variance of nature and nurture factors, including in the latter unknown amounts of prenatal and postnatal influences.

One might argue that the postnatal environments of twins reared together is practically identical and that differences found must be attributed to other causes. To this it might be replied that, in the case of both identical and fraternal twins in question, certain preferences in leadership tend to become established, favoring the training of one twin over the other. It is also true that some differences in reading, school training, and social activities do occur. It therefore seems probable that a portion of the factor we have indicated as nurture is made up of postnatal as well as prenatal influences. Whether this portion is large or small, however, must remain for other investigation.

It should also be emphasized that we are dealing with twins reared as members of a family, under conditions which do not permit postnatal influences to operate very greatly on producing differences. Thus a very favorable condition for one twin is likely to be accompanied by a similarly favorable condition for the other twin. In studying the relative effect of nature and nurture by family pairs, we are, therefore, minimizing the influence of postnatal environment. As will be shown later, the relative role of nature and nurture depends not only upon the type of trait but also upon the disparity in external environment. Where such disparity is slight, the relative influence of nurture as compared with nature will be lessened. Our present method and findings are, therefore, very limited, applying only to fraternal-twin pairs reared under quite similar conditions.

The nature, or genetic, factor will be designated as A and the nurture factor as B, while the symbol E will be used to indicate an error due to imperfection in the measurement. The symbol X refers to a trait measurement. Using the front subscripts i and f to refer to identical and fraternal twins, respectively, and using primes to indicate different twins and values of A and B, we may set up the following expressions to illustrate the constitution of these factors as assumed here:

$$\begin{array}{ll} \text{Identical} & \text{Fraternal} \\ _iX = {}_iA + {}_iB + {}_iE & _fX = {}_fA + {}_fB + {}_fE \\ _iX' = {}_iA + {}_iB' + {}_iE' & _fX' = {}_fA' + {}_fB' + {}_fE' \end{array} \Bigg\} \quad (13)$$

It will be noted that the nature of factor A has been assumed to be the same for a pair of identical twins, whereas it has been assumed different for a pair of fraternal twins. The difference in score for a pair of twins will be written as D, the values for identical- and fraternal-twin pairs appearing as

$$\begin{aligned} _iD = {}_iX' - {}_iX = {}_iB' - {}_iB + {}_iE' - {}_iE = {}_iD_B + {}_iD_E \\ _fD = {}_fX' - {}_fX = {}_fA' - {}_fA + {}_fB' - {}_fB + {}_fE' - {}_fE \\ = {}_fD_A + {}_fD_B + {}_fD_E \end{aligned} \Bigg\} \; . \; (14)$$

Thus we conceive of a difference $_iD$ between a pair of identical twins as a function of a nurture difference $_iD_B$ plus errors of measurement; whereas the corresponding difference $_fD$ between a pair of fraternal twins is thought of as a function of a nurture difference $_fD_B$ plus a nature difference $_fD_A$ and errors of measurement.

In a subsequent paragraph we shall consider the additional effect of the factor known as the asymmetry mechanism, which would have a tendency to produce twin differences from neither A nor B as in our setup.

We now seek a formula which will express the relative contributions of the factors A and B in producing observed twin differences, omitting from consideration temporarily the effects of the asymmetry mechanism.

b) FORMULA FOR THE RELATIVE EFFECT OF "A" AND "B" UPON
THE VARIABILITY OF TWIN DIFFERENCES[6]

The formula we now derive is one based on an analysis of the variance (standard deviation squared) of the various twin differences involved. The advantage of the variance measure of variability for such purposes is clear since contributions to a total variance may be expressed in additive form. The present derivation requires some additional symbolism which may be set down as follows:

r = Correlation between X and X', the two members of a twin pair
R = Correlation between D_A and D_B
σ = Standard deviation of a trait for $2N$ cases
σ_D = $\sigma_{(X-X')(X'-X)}$ = Double-entry standard deviation of twin differences, D
σ_A and σ_B = Double-entry standard deviations of D_A and D_B

From equations (14) we may now write

$$_i\sigma_D^2 = {_i\sigma_B^2} \tag{15}$$

and

$$_f\sigma_D^2 = {_f\sigma_A^2} + {_f\sigma_B^2} + 2R\,{_f\sigma_A}\,{_f\sigma_B} . \tag{16}$$

In these last two expressions we have assumed the quantities $_i\sigma_E^2$ and $_f\sigma_E^2$ to be negligible. In a later paragraph we shall give modifications of the formulas by correcting for unreliability of the tests used.

By the use of equation (4) for relating variance to correlation we may write

$$\left. \begin{aligned} \frac{_i\sigma_D^2}{_i\sigma^2} &= 2(1 - {_ir}) , \\[2ex] \frac{_f\sigma_D^2}{_f\sigma^2} &= 2(1 - {_fr}) . \end{aligned} \right\} \tag{17}$$

[6] Karl J. Holzinger, "The Relative Effect of Nature and Nurture Influences on Twin Differences," *Journal of Educational Psychology*, XX (April, 1929), 241–48.

We next set up a function, t^2, involving the variance of D relative to the variance of the trait, viz.,

$$t^2 = \left[\frac{{}_f\sigma_D^2}{{}_f\sigma^2} - \frac{{}_i\sigma_D^2}{{}_i\sigma^2} \right] \div \frac{{}_i\sigma_D^2}{{}_i\sigma^2} . \tag{18}$$

By the use of equations (17), this reduces to

$$t^2 = \frac{(1 - {}_fr) - (1 - {}_ir)}{1 - {}_ir} = \frac{{}_ir - {}_fr}{1 - {}_ir} . \tag{19}$$

This is the desired formula applicable when the errors of measurement due to test unreliability are negligible. The meaning of the function may be shown by substituting values from (15) and (16) in formula (18), whence

$$t^2 = \left[\frac{{}_f\sigma_A^2 + {}_f\sigma_B^2 + 2R {}_f\sigma_A {}_f\sigma_B}{{}_f\sigma^2} - \frac{{}_i\sigma_B^2}{{}_f\sigma^2} \right] \div \frac{{}_i\sigma_B^2}{{}_f\sigma^2} . \tag{20}$$

If ${}_f\sigma^2 = {}_i\sigma^2$ and ${}_f\sigma_B^2 = {}_i\sigma_B^2$, this reduces to

$$t^2 = \frac{{}_f\sigma_A^2 + 2R \,{}_f\sigma_A \,{}_f\sigma_B}{{}_f\sigma_B^2} . \tag{21}$$

If $R = 0$, we finally obtain

$$t^2 = \frac{{}_f\sigma_A^2}{{}_f\sigma_B^2} . \tag{22}$$

Thus t^2 expresses the ratio of the variance of nature differences ${}_fD_A$ to that of nurture differences ${}_fD_B$ under the foregoing assumptions.

These three assumptions will next be considered. The observed ${}_f\sigma^2$ is generally a little, but not significantly, larger than the observed ${}_i\sigma^2$, which makes the value of t^2 from (20) a little smaller than from (22). Next, ${}_f\sigma_B^2$ might be expected to be slightly larger than ${}_i\sigma_B^2$ since there might be a tendency to treat identical twins more alike than fraternal twins and thus accentuate the nurture variance ${}_f\sigma_B^2$ over ${}_i\sigma_B^2$. The effect of such a tendency would be to make the value of t^2 from (20) a little larger than from (22). Thus the errors in these two cases work in opposite directions and would have a tendency to offset each other.

The remaining assumption that $R = 0$ is one frequently made in such problems; but if it is not taken as zero, we may estimate the effect of such correlation by writing (21) in the form

$$t^2 = u^2 + 2Ru \tag{23}$$

where

$$u^2 = \frac{{}_f\sigma_A^2}{{}_f\sigma_B^2}.$$

Now, if there be a correlation between A and B, there will generally be a much smaller correlation between D_A and D_B as given by R. Estimating the maximum value of R as .2 for mental and social traits, $t^2 = u^2 + .4u$ from (23). The estimate of u^2 from this formula is thus too large by the amount .4u. Thus if $u^2 = 16$, $t^2 = 17.6$; if $u^2 = 1$, $t^2 = 1.4$; if $u^2 = .64$, $t^2 = .96$, etc.

The net effect of all three assumptions would appear slight in the case of physical traits, and in the case of mental and social traits the value given by formula (19) will tend to be somewhat larger than the desired ratio given by (22). Since the values from (19) are interpreted as the ratios of nature to nurture differentiating influences, observed values of t^2 from this formula probably weight the nature influences somewhat too heavily.

The first part of formula (19) furnishes another interpretation of the method. If no nurture factor B were operative in the case of identical twins, then the correlation $_ir$ would be 1.00 by our setup. The quantity $1 - {}_ir$ thus measures the effect of the B factor operating alone. In the case of fraternal twins both A and B factors operate in producing differences, and $1 - {}_fr$ measures the combined influence of both. Formula (19) then gives $A + B$ influence less B influence divided by B influence, or A/B influence, in producing twin differentiation expressed in variance.

c) THE PROPORTIONATE EFFECT OF "A" UPON THE VARIABILITY OF TWIN DIFFERENCES

It has been seen that the formula (19) approximates the ratio of ${}_f\sigma_A^2$ to ${}_f\sigma_B^2$. An alternate formula will next be introduced which expresses the proportion of the total unit variance attributable to the nature variability ${}_f\sigma_A^2$. Designating this new measure as h^2, it is apparent from formula (22) that

$$h^2 = \frac{{}_f\sigma_A^2}{{}_f\sigma_A^2 + {}_f\sigma_B^2} = \frac{t^2}{1 + t^2}. \tag{24}$$

Substituting the value of t^2 from formula (19), we find

$$h^2 = \frac{{}_ir - {}_fr}{1 - {}_fr}. \tag{25}$$

A simple example will illustrate the difference between formulas (19) and (25). Let $_ir = .90$ and $_fr = .75$. Then by formula (19) we have $t^2 = 1.5$, which expresses the ratio of $_f\sigma_A^2$ to $_f\sigma_B^2$. From formula (25) we have $h^2 = .60$, which means that 60 per cent of the total differentiating variance was due to nature. These two results express the same fact in different form. If 60 per cent of the variance was due to A, then 40 per cent was due to B, and the ratio is 1.5, as by formula (19). In the following tables we shall give both forms of expressing the contribution of $_f\sigma_A^2$ and $_f\sigma_B^2$ to the total variance.

d) THE PROBABLE ERRORS OF t^2 AND h^2

The probable error of t^2 from formula (19) may be derived by differentiating and reducing in the usual way. We assume here that $_ir$ and $_fr$ are uncorrelated. The resulting formula for t^2 is

$$PE_{t^2} = .6745 \frac{1 - _fr}{1 - _ir} \sqrt{\frac{(1 + _ir)^2 + (1 + _fr)^2}{N}}, \tag{26}$$

and for h^2 we have similarly

$$PE_{h^2} = .6745 \frac{1 - _ir}{1 - _fr} \sqrt{\frac{(1 + _ir)^2 + (1 + _fr)^2}{N}}. \tag{27}$$

N is taken as the number of twin pairs involved.

The distributions of t^2 and h^2 for extreme values are probably not normal, and formulas (26) and (27) must be used with caution. So far, two good mathematicians have failed to obtain even fair approximations to the required distributions.

e) VALUES OF t^2 AND h^2 FOR VARIOUS TRAITS

Before considering other factors and assumptions which are concerned in the interpretation of t^2 and h^2, we shall next present a table of values based on correlations corrected for age by the method of partial correlation. The basic correlations have been reproduced from Table 25 in the section on "Methods of Correlation with Twin Data."

From Table 37 it appears that from 75 to 90 per cent of the difference variance is attributable to nature for physical traits. In the case of intelligence the values of h^2 range from .65 to .80, so that on the average nearly three-fourths of the variance in intelligence is attributable to nature. For the Stanford achievement tests, which are also intelligence measures in part, the value of h^2 from the total score is .64. In the case of "arithmetic computation" the value of h^2 is only .12 $\pm$ .20, which is probably insignificant. This also suggests that training accounts for nearly all the observed variance in computation skill. For "spelling," however, $h^2 = .53$, which indicates that nature and nurture have been about equally effective in producing variation in this trait. If these last two values approximate even roughly the true ratios of nature and nurture factors, the implication would appear to be that training plays a far more important role in producing good computers than in producing good spellers among twins.

TABLE 37

VALUES OF t^2 AND h^2 FROM CORRELATIONS CORRECTED FOR AGE

Trait	$_i r$	$_f r$	t^2	PE_{t^2}	h^2	PE_{h^2}
Standing height............	.932	.645	4.22	1.26	.81	.05
Sitting height..............	.881	.503	3.18	0.96	.76	.05
Weight....................	.917	.631	3.45	1.07	.78	.05
Head length..............	.910	.583	3.63	1.10	.78	.05
Head width...............	.888	.545	3.06	0.95	.75	.06
Cephalic index............	.895	.579	3.01	0.94	.75	.06
Finger ridges (R)..........	.907	.337	6.13	1.58	.86	.03
Finger ridges (L)..........	.924	.501	5.57	1.53	.85	.04
Total finger ridges........	.947	.459	9.21	2.37	.90	.02
Binet Mental Age.........	.861	.599	1.88	0.68	.65	.08
Binet I.Q.................	.881	.631	2.10	0.74	.68	.08
Otis score................	.901	.572	3.32	1.04	.77	.05
Otis I.Q..................	.922	.618	3.90	1.17	.80	.05
Stanford Achievement:						
Word meaning..........	.859	.563	2.10	0.72	.68	.07
Arithmetic computation...	.726	.688	0.14	0.26	.12	.20
Nature study and science..	.771	.653	0.52	0.35	.34	.15
History and literature....	.820	.672	0.82	0.43	.45	.13
Spelling................	.874	.732	1.13	0.52	.53	.11
Educational Age........	.892	.696	1.81	0.68	.64	.09
Woodworth-Mathews.......	.558	.365	0.44	0.28	.30	.14
Tapping speed—wrist.......	.592	.442	0.37	0.28	.27	.15
Tapping speed–finger.......	.664	.377	0.85	0.38	.46	.11
Tapping speed—total.......	.688	.382	0.98	0.41	.50	.11

Comment on some of the remaining values in this table will be made in connection with subsequent correction factors.

f) THE EFFECT OF TEST RELIABILITY UPON VALUES OF t^2 AND h^2

Returning to the equations (14), it will be noted that the unreliability of the measures is expressed by the quantities $_i D_E$ and $_f D_E$, which were temporarily neglected in the foregoing analysis. In the present section the effect of these errors upon values of t^2 and h^2 will be estimated.

If we employ Spearman's correction formula

$$r'_{xx'} = \frac{r_{xx'}}{r_{x_1 x_2}} \qquad (8)$$

to give an approximation to the true correlation free from the unreliability of measurements, we may hope to get truer values of t^2 and h^2 from such corrected coefficients. As noted in section a, corrections for both age and unreliability may be effected by applying the single formula

$$r'_{xx' \cdot a} = \frac{r_{xx'} - r_{xa}^2}{r_{x_1 x_2} - r_{xa}^2},$$

(9)

where $r_{xx'}$ is the raw correlation coefficient, r_{xa} the correlation with age, and $r_{x_1 x_2}$ the reliability coefficient. It was not possible to obtain reliability coefficients for many of the traits studied, but the necessary coefficients for four[7] tests were obtained and are presented in Table 38.

TABLE 38

CORRELATIONS AND RELIABILITY COEFFICIENTS FOR FOUR TRAITS

TRAIT	RAW CORRELATIONS $r_{xx'}$		RELIABILITY COEFFICIENTS $r_{x_1 x_2}$		CORRELATIONS WITH AGE r_{xa}	
	Iden.	Frat.	Iden.	Frat.	Iden.	Frat.
Otis score..............	.947	.800	.942	.963	.681	.730
Word meaning............	.923	.804	.980	.976	.674	.742
Arithmetic computation.....	.878	.858	.924	.947	.745	.738
Wrist tapping............	.723	.681	.962	.950	.567	.654

Upon working out the corrected correlation from the values in this table, we find that $_i r'_{xx' \cdot a}$ for "Otis score" has the value 1.01 from formula (9) and $_i r'_{xx'}$ the value 1.005 from formula (8). This suggests that these correction formulas, which are the best available, overestimate the corrected coefficients for high correlations. We shall, however, present the remainder of the corrected coefficients with resulting t^2 and h^2 values for the reader's consideration. These values are presented in Table 39.

From Table 39 it will be observed that the rise in h^2 after correcting for unreliability as well as age is not great. Thus for "word meaning" h^2 is raised from .68 to .73, while for "wrist tapping" it is raised from .27 to .28. In the case of "arithmetic computation" h^2 is raised from .12 to .43, however—a value which is probably significant. Unfortunately, the reliability of the spelling test was not known, but the original value of $h^2 = .53$

[7] Since these tables were completed, correlations for quality of handwriting were obtained, corrected for reliability of rating. The values of t^2 and h^2 from these corrected coefficients were 3.11 ± 1.01 and .757 ± .06, respectively. (See chap. vii.)

(Table 37) would probably be raised to about .7 if the unreliability were available, and the greater dependence upon nature of spelling variation as compared with computation variation appears as before.

In a good many of the traits, such as height and weight, the unreliability of the measurements is so slight that it may be assumed to have negligible

TABLE 39

CORRELATIONS CORRECTED FOR AGE AND UNRELIABILITY WITH
RESULTING VALUES OF t^2 AND h^2 FOR FOUR TRAITS

TRAIT	CORRELATIONS CORRECTED FOR AGE AND UN-RELIABILITY		VALUES FROM CORRELATIONS CORRECTED FOR AGE		VALUES FROM CORRELATIONS CORRECTED FOR AGE AND UNRE-LIABILITY	
	Iden.	Frat.	t^2	h^2	t^2	h^2
Otis score..............	1.010	.621	3.32	.77	Indeterminate	Indeterminate
Word meaning............	.892	.596	2.10	.68	2.74	.73
Arithmetic computation.....	.875	.779	.14	.12	.77	.43
Wrist tapping............	.627	.485	.37	.27	.38	.28

effect upon the values of t^2 and h^2. In other traits, such as those measured by Woodworth-Mathews tests, the unreliability is probably large, and the resulting t^2 and h^2 are doubtless much too small.

g) THE ASYMMETRY FACTOR

As pointed out in chapter iv, an asymmetry may be regarded as an inequality of the two bilateral halves of a so-called bilaterally symmetrical organism, due to some mechanism favoring one side over the other. In the case of a pair of identical twins which have been regarded as arising from a single zygote, an observed difference of some character may be thus due in part to the asymmetry mechanism. In the case of a pair of fraternal twins which arise from two zygotes, the asymmetry mechanism will have no effect upon a twin difference, provided the measure used includes both halves of the single individual. Thus the difference in total finger ridges on both hands of a pair of identical twins may be in part due to the asymmetry mechanism, whereas the corresponding difference for a pair of fraternal twins is clearly independent of any such asymmetry.

In order to note the effect of the asymmetry mechanism upon the foregoing formulas we shall first set up one fundamental equation introducing this new factor, which we designate as M. We shall assume (tentatively) that M operates additively with B in the case of identical-twin pairs and that its influence is independent of B. One setup of twin differences will then appear as follows:

Identical   Fraternal

$${}_iD = {}_iD_B + M + {}_iD_E \qquad {}_fD = {}_fD_A + {}_fD_B + {}_fD_E$$

Omitting the quantities D_E from this consideration and assuming ${}_i\sigma_B = {}_f\sigma_B$, ${}_i\sigma = {}_f\sigma$, and $R = 0$ as before, we have

$$_Mt^2 = \frac{{}_f\sigma_A^2 - \sigma_M^2}{{}_f\sigma_B^2 + \sigma_M^2}. \tag{28}$$

This value of t^2 is clearly smaller than the desired ratio ${}_f\sigma_A^2/{}_f\sigma_B^2$.

Similarly, we find

$$_Mh^2 = \frac{{}_f\sigma_A^2 - \sigma_M^2}{{}_f\sigma_A^2 + {}_f\sigma_B^2}. \tag{29}$$

Here, also, the observed value of h^2 from formula (29) is smaller than the desired value ${}_f\sigma_A^2/({}_f\sigma_A^2 + {}_f\sigma_B^2)$.

From the foregoing analysis we would then conclude that, if our values of t^2 and h^2, calculated by formulas (19) and (25), are of the form (28) and (29) with M operative, they minimize the effect of the nature factor truly indicated by (22) and (24). In other words, if the asymmetry mechanism operates as assumed above, then the nature factor has a greater influence in determining observed twin differences than our formula and table of values (Table 37) indicate. We may thus tentatively regard these observed values of h^2 as lower limits of the true values of the ratios of nature to nurture difference measured by variance, but this tendency may be offset by other factors as described below.

h) SUMMARY OF CHIEF FACTORS WHICH MAY AFFECT t^2 AND h^2

Taking ${}_f\sigma_A^2/{}_f\sigma_B^2 = u^2$ as the desired ratio to be measured by t^2, we may list the various factors considered as affecting this ratio together with their direction of influence:

Factor	Assumed	Probable	Comparison of t^2 and u^2
1. Observed variance of trait...............	${}_f\sigma^2 = {}_i\sigma^2$	${}_f\sigma^2 > {}_i\sigma^2$	$t^2 < u^2$
2. Variance of nurture difference............	${}_f\sigma_B^2 = {}_i\sigma_B^2$	${}_f\sigma_B^2 > {}_i\sigma_B^2$	$t^2 > u^2$
3. Correlation between D_A and D_B..........	$R = 0$	$R > 0$	$t^2 > u^2$
4. Asymmetry mechanism....................	$M \neq 0$	$M > 0$	$t^2 < u^2$
5. Reliability of the test....................	$r_{x_1x_2} = 1$	$r_{x_1x_2} < 1$	$t^2 < u^2$

A similar table could be made for h^2 and $_f\sigma_A^2/(_f\sigma_A^2 + _f\sigma_B^2)$. It will be observed that factors (2) and (3), if operating as probable, assign to the observed t^2 a value larger than the desired u^2, while the remaining three factors operate to give t^2 too small a value for u^2. To what extent these factors counteract one another is problematical. The influence of (1) and (2) we believe to be slight; and, since they act in opposite directions, their net effect might be regarded as negligible. Factor (5) may be taken into account by the use of the corrections for unreliability of the test. When this is done, there remain only factors (3) and (4) as having appreciable influence; and these act in opposite directions. In the case of a mental trait there is reason to believe that the correlation between D_A and D_B may be appreciable since children of better intelligence live in homes with better surroundings. For such a trait it also seems reasonable to assume that the asymmetry factor M would have slight influence. We would therefore conclude that the t^2 and h^2 values from coefficients corrected for age and test unreliability are probably somewhat larger than the desired values.

Taking Binet Mental Age as an example, we may estimate its reliability as .98 (a value found in several other studies). We find the value of h^2 is raised from .653 to .688, or t^2 from 1.88 to 2.21. Next, assuming that $R = .2$, the value of u^2 for $t^2 = 2.21$ is 1.69. If the portion of h^2 attributable to the asymmetry factor be estimated as .03, the adjusted value .718 gives an estimated u^2 of 2.55. The average of 1.69 and 2.55 is 2.12, which is slightly less than the observed value of t^2, 2.21. The foregoing estimate of M is, of course, hypothetical and is introduced merely to show the effect upon t^2 for such magnitudes.

For the tabled values presented in this chapter the combined effect of the foregoing five factors is probably slight, and its direction is difficult to estimate. Further experimental study on such effect is desirable, but we would conclude tentatively that our values of t^2 and h^2 are approximately correct and useful.

CHAPTER VII

RESEMBLANCE IN HANDWRITING OF IDENTICAL AND FRATERNAL TWINS REARED TOGETHER

THE handwriting of a relatively mature individual is highly characteristic. This is shown by a series of facts. One can commonly recognize the handwriting of one's acquaintances. Bank clerks identify checks by means of the signature of those who draw them. Experts in the art of identification can determine the authorship of specimens of handwriting even when they have been disguised.

There seems to be some evidence, furthermore, that the characteristic appearance of an individual's handwriting is not the result of accident but is, in part at least, an expression of the nature of his nervous organization. Several facts support this conclusion. The characteristic appearance of a person's handwriting appears also in writing which he produces by other members of the body than the hand, for example, the foot. Again, there appears to be some hereditary resemblance between the handwriting of parents and children or of other relatives. Finally, there seems to be some basis for the claim of graphologists that a person's general character is expressed in the form of his handwriting, though the specific signs which are regarded by graphologists as indicating particular characteristics, and even the character traits themselves, may be in large part fanciful. The fact that we cannot yet trace exactly the relationship between the forms of handwriting and the individual's general character or behavior does not warrant us in doubting the evidence that some such relationship exists.

If it is true that the individuality of handwriting is an expression, even in a general way, of the individual's nervous organization, it is natural to look to handwriting as one of the marks of the genetic resemblance between twins and other relatives. Four previous investigations have dealt with the handwriting of twins. Kramer and Lauterbach[1] in 1928 reported a comparison of the quality and speed of handwriting of twins and siblings. The quality was measured by the use of the Kansas City Handwriting Scale. The correlations are presented in Table 40. It will be seen that the correlations in the case of like-sex twins, which include the identical twins, are higher than those for opposite-sex twins and that those for opposite-sex twins are of the general order of those for siblings or possibly somewhat higher. These

---

[1] Emily Kramer and Charles E. Lauterbach, "Resemblance in the Handwriting of Twins and Siblings," *Journal of Educational Research*, XVIII (September, 1928), 149–52.

facts appear to indicate that degree of resemblance in speed and quality of handwriting corresponds to closeness of genetic relationship and to support the hypothesis that these characteristics of handwriting are, to some extent, at least, an expression of genetic character. The possible environmental factors which might produce the resemblances found are the example or teaching of parents and the kind and quality of teaching in schools which are attended alike by the different members of a family. These factors would probably affect twins in about the same way, whether they were of the same or of the opposite sex. Such factors, therefore, do not appear to explain the higher correlations for like-sex than for unlike-sex twins. They might affect siblings somewhat differently if the members of a pair differed much in age

TABLE 40

COEFFICIENTS OF CORRELATION BETWEEN THE SCORES OF VARIOUS GROUPS OF SIBLINGS AND TWINS AS MEASURED BY THE KANSAS CITY HANDWRITING SCALE (FROM KRAMER AND LAUTERBACH)

Group	Number of Pairs	Quality	Rate
Siblings:			
Brothers............	25	.46	.27
Sisters..............	32	.24	.09
Brother-sister........	44	.13	.16
Twins:			
Brothers............	69	.69	.82
Sisters..............	74	.68	.84
Brother-sister........	61	.37	.37

and so, for example, attended different schools. If they did, and if their effect was appreciable, the correlations for siblings should be significantly lower than for those for unlike-sex twins. This does not appear to be the case. All the correlations may be, and probably are, due in part to the similarity in education and environment of members of the same family, whether twins or siblings. The greater similarity in the handwriting of like-sex twins and of unlike-sex twins or siblings would seem to be assignable partly to the difference in genetic relationship, partly, perhaps, to a general sex difference in neatness and interest in details, and partly to a purely conventional difference in attention to quality.

In connection with our own study of twins we secured a specimen of handwriting from each individual. The specimens of handwriting of the members of each twin pair were compared by two methods—first, by scoring them on a handwriting scale, and, second, by matching them according to their general appearance. The results from the first method are thus comparable with those of Kramer and Lauterbach.

. Each specimen of handwriting was scored independently by three scorers, using the Kansas City Handwriting Scale as a basis for rating. The average reliability coefficients for the three raters for 49 pairs of identical twins was $_ir_{x_1x_2} = .745$; the corresponding reliability coefficient for 51 pairs of fraternal twins was $_fr_{x_1x_2} = .733$. The reliability of scoring handwriting for both types of twins was thus practically the same.

Next, the correlations between the scores of identical twin pairs were obtained. The average of the three raters was $_ir_{xx'} = .691$. The corresponding average correlation for fraternal-twin pairs was $_fr_{xx'} = .516$. Correcting these last two coefficients for unreliability, we obtain from formula (8)

$$_ir'_{xx'} = \frac{.691}{.745} = .928$$

and

$$_fr'_{xx'} = \frac{.516}{.733} = .704 .$$

The values of t^2 and h^2 from the corrected handwriting correlations may be of interest. We find

$$t^2 = \frac{_ir - _fr}{1 - _ir} = 3.11 \pm 1.01$$

and

$$h^2 = \frac{_ir - _fr}{1 - _fr} = .757 \pm .06 .$$

These last two values correspond closely to those for the majority of physical and mental traits as reported in chapter vi.

Two other studies—Galton's and our own—deal with another aspect of the writing of twins. In both cases the feature of handwriting which was studied was its general appearance—its individuality, the sum total of characteristics which enable us to identify the handwriting of an individual amid all the variations which occur from time to time, and to distinguish it from that of other individuals. We might, perhaps, expect identical twins to resemble each other especially in this characteristic in somewhat the same way as they resemble each other in facial appearance, and to a greater degree than in speed or quality. But such is not the case.

Galton's[2] findings on this point are summarized in the following quotation:

Most singularly, the one point in which similarity is rare is the handwriting. I cannot account for this, considering how strongly handwriting runs in families, but I am sure of the fact. I have only one case in which nobody, not even the twins themselves, could distinguish their own notes of lectures, etc.; barely two or three in which the handwriting was indistinguishable by others, and only a few in which it was described as closely alike. On the other hand, I have many in which it is stated to be unlike, and some in which it is alluded to as the only point of difference. It would appear that handwriting is a very delicate test of difference in organization—a conclusion which I commend to the notice of enthusiasts in the art of discovering character by the handwriting.

Our own experiment gives conclusive support to Galton's observations. We made two comparisons, both of which were designed to determine

TABLE 41

DEGREE OF SIMILARITY OF THE WRITING OF PAIRS OF IDENTICAL
AND FRATERNAL TWINS AS JUDGED BY TWO RATERS

RATING	RATER H			RATER F		
	Identical	Fraternal	Total	Identical	Fraternal	Total
3.............	13	12	25	12	13	25
2.............	27	33	60	33	34	67
1.............	9	7	16	5	5	10
Total.....	49	52	101	50	52	102

whether the handwriting of pairs of identical twins was more alike than that of fraternal twins.

The first comparison was made independently by the experimenters H and F. The two specimens written by each pair of twins were examined and were rated as being "much alike," "moderately alike," or "unlike." The three classes were designated by the numbers 3, 2, and 1, respectively. The raters did not know whether the specimens were written by identical or fraternal pairs. After the writing of all the pairs was rated in this way, the ratings were tabulated to see whether the specimens written by identical pairs were judged to be more alike than those written by fraternal pairs. Table 41 shows that they were not.

The distributions of the ratings by the two raters are remarkably similar.

[2] Francis Galton, *Inquiries into Human Faculty and Its Development.* New York: Macmillan Co., 1883. Pp. 220.

Rater H judged the writings of 13 identical and 12 fraternal pairs to be alike, whereas Rater F judged the writings of 12 identical and 13 fraternal pairs to be alike. If the ratings of the two judges are averaged, exactly the same number of writings of the two types are judged alike, namely, 12.5 identical and 12.5 fraternal. Likewise, there is no significant difference in the number of specimens written by identical and fraternal twins which are judged to be unlike.

To investigate the matter still further, one of the experimenters made a different and more laborious comparison. An assistant divided the papers into six groups. Each group contained the writings of from 16 to 18 twin pairs. The groups were formed by first making three groups according to age and then by dividing each age group according to sex. The purpose of

TABLE 42

THE PERCENTAGE OF PAIRS OF WRITINGS OF IDENTICAL AND FRATERNAL
TWINS WHICH WERE CORRECTLY MATCHED

| Type of Twin Pair | Age Group | | | | | | All Ages | | |
| | Younger | | Middle | | Older | | Boys | Girls | Both Sexes |
	Boys	Girls	Boys	Girls	Boys	Girls			
Identical..........	00	50	20	100	11	11	6	18	24
Fraternal.........	29	12	50	42	33	12	17	14	31
Both.............	12	31	33	56	22	12	23	33	27

the grouping was, first, to get groups of manageable size, and, second, to get groups of papers that would not differ greatly on account of the age or sex of the writers.

The papers of each group were then shuffled, and the experimenter undertook to match those that had been written by twin pairs. The method was, by comparing the various specimens with one another, to put together those pairs that seemed to be most alike. The matchings were then tabulated to see whether pairs of specimens written by identical twins were put together more frequently than those written by fraternal twins.

Table 42 shows that a larger number of the writings of fraternal pairs were matched than of identical pairs, the percentages being 31 and 24, respectively. This confirms the evidence of the rating method to the effect that the writings of identical twins are no more alike in general appearance than are the writings of fraternal twins.

Before attempting to interpret these somewhat divergent findings, we may refer to a graphological study by Seeman and Saudek[3] of the handwriting of three pairs of identical twins reared together, one of them being a pair of Siamese twins. This study is hardly comparable to the other modern studies reported in this chapter since it did not include a comparison of identical with fraternal twins. The comparisons, moreover, are made in part by the observation of objective features of the writing and in part by means of the special technique of graphology, which cannot be duplicated or even adequately judged by one who is not initiated into its mysteries. The objective features include speed and fluency, regularity, pressure, size and proportion, arrangement on the page, spacing and detailed letter forms. The character traits which are inferred by graphological interpretation include such characteristics as self-control, self-confidence, spontaneity, carefulness, conventionality, self-consciousness, exhibitionism, conservatism, and the like. What the authors did was to list the similarities and differences in objective characteristics and in character traits as judged by an examination of the handwriting. In one pair they find rather important differences; in the second pair, minor differences; and in the third pair, very little difference. They conclude:

In view of the foregoing analyses of twin personalities, it appears obvious that as every individual natural object is unique in some respect from every other individual of its species, so even that most identical of Nature's creatures—the monozygotic twin—must yield to her inexorable wish to vary. Therefore, whether it be through the more or less effectual shaping instrument of disease, accident, endocrinal or vasomotory function, reflected differences of environment or diverse experience of life through sensation, feeling, enjoyment or suffering, an accumulation of gradual and minute differences seems to be expectable in the alteration and integration of every individual congregation of innate, or hereditary, human material.

SUMMARY

Both Kramer and Lauterbach's study and our own indicate that the handwriting of identical twins is somewhat more alike than is that of fraternal twins in terms of general quality. The studies are not directly comparable since Kramer and Lauterbach did not classify their pairs into identical and fraternal but rather into same-sex and opposite-sex. An exact comparison of the correlations is therefore not possible. The greater similarity in the handwriting of the identical twins, however, appears in both studies. Beyond this general fact our own study indicates that the ratio of heredity to environment in determining general quality of handwriting in fraternal twins is about three to one, with heredity the larger factor.

[3] Ernest Seeman and Robert Saudek, "The Self-Expression of Identical Twins in Handwriting and Drawing," *Character and Personality*, I (December, 1932), 91–128.

The studies by Galton, by Seeman and Saudek, and our own, dealing with those features of handwriting which give it its individuality and character, suggest that a lesser contrast exists between the two types of twins in these features than in general quality. Galton and the present writers find no evidence of a resemblance in individuality which can be ascribed to identical heredity as contrasted with partly common heredity, and Seeman and Saudek find considerable similarity but also considerable divergence. It appears that many of the subtler characteristics of handwriting are not determined by heredity but are due either to chance or to the influence of the environment, or to a combination of the two. If this is true of handwriting, it is probably true of other forms of behavior or expressions of personality. Further analysis of resemblance and difference in handwriting will be presented in connection with the case studies of the separated pairs of identical twins.

PART III

STUDY OF NINETEEN PAIRS OF IDENTICAL TWINS
SEPARATED IN INFANCY

INTRODUCTION

A S INDICATED in chapter ii, this study is divided into two main sections. The first section, dealing with the comparison of fifty pairs of identical and fifty pairs of fraternal twins reared together, has been presented in Part II. Part III will present the result of the other section of the study, which deals with an analysis of the likenesses and differences of nineteen pairs of identical twins reared apart. The resemblances between these twins will be compared, so far as data are available for such comparison, with the resemblances between identical twins reared together. They will also be correlated with differences in the environment.

Two chapters (chaps. viii and ix) are devoted to the life-histories of these twins separated in infancy, to a minute description of their physical characteristics and the evidence that they are identical, and to a number of interesting stories of their experiences, particularly of the way they met, which illustrate their striking similarity. These chapters give a concrete picture of the nineteen pairs of twins which gives the basis for understanding the more abstract analysis of the results of measurement which follow. Accompanying all of the case studies except one are photographs. In this case, however, because the film was spoiled in developing, we are unable to publish a photograph.

Chapters x and xi present the results of these measurements first in the form of case studies. The limitations of case studies are recognized by the authors, but it is believed that they yield certain types of evidence which fall through the meshes of statistical formulation and that they are useful when taken in conjunction with more generalized treatment.

Chapter xii presents the statistical analysis which the authors have been able to make of the data of the separated cases, and chapter xiii presents a general summary and interpretation of the entire study.

CHAPTER VIII

GATHERING THE SEPARATED CASES; PROOFS OF MONOZYGOCITY AND DEGREE OF SEPARATION

WHEN we began our studies of twins reared together we had not at all contemplated any attempt to secure cases of identical twins reared apart. During the course of our studies of twins reared together, however, it became obvious that this material alone gave only an incomplete picture of the roles of heredity and environment and that it badly needed to be supplemented by a study of identical twins reared apart.

In the faint hope of possibily securing information about as many as four or five cases of such twins, one of us (Newman) wrote a short article about our studies of twins in which an urgent appeal was made for information about any cases of identical twins reared apart. Among the scores of replies to this request were four or five that seemed promising. Incidentally, it might be intimated that this matter of opening up the channels for public correspondence is not without its drawbacks. Letters were received from scores of proud mothers of twins and from twins themselves telling how similar they were, how utterly different, or how remarkable in various ways. Though nearly all these letters were from twins that had been reared strictly together, replies had to be sent to each, explaining that our studies of twins reared together were complete. Many persons wrote merely because they were interested in twins and had some questions they wanted to ask. The commonest questions had to do with whether one member of a twin pair is likely to be sterile or whether one twin is not usually subnormal in one way or another. Such letters had also to be answered. Other communications were more to the point but still irrelevant to our needs. Many cases were reported of non-identical twins reared apart, even twins of opposite sexes, and several cases of apparently identical twins were reported who had been separated too late for our purposes. One type of information obtained in those days which has recently borne fruit had to do with three cases of identical twins reared apart who at that time were too young to take standard intelligence tests. These cases were kept track of by occasional correspondence until they reached the age of eleven or twelve years. During the last year these postponed cases have all been examined.

The first case studied by us of identical twins reared apart gained considerable publicity through no fault of ours, for the twins themselves gave their photograph and their life-stories to an enterprising local reporter, who sent his news story to an American newspaper, from which it was copied far and wide. Since our name and address were given, we were again deluged with all sorts of letters from twins and about twins, a few of which furnished valuable clues.

The second pair of separated twins studied by us desired publicity in the hope that it might be the means of bringing them information about their unknown parents. So a little story with a cut of the twins was given to Chicago newspapers. This brought a further deluge of letters—some of value but most of no scientific significance. After completing the study of three cases, further effort was postponed until our return from six months abroad. During this period one of our best cases—one that had been definitely arranged for—was very unfortunately lost through the untimely death of one of the twins. This was discouraging, but we picked up the thread of correspondence, tracing down some of the more promising clues. It should be understood that not all information sent in by correspondents was fruitful. In some cases the clues led only to disappointment and failure. One man wrote us that he had heard that the wife of Mr. Blank of his town had a twin sister from whom she had been separated since infancy. The husband of this lady, when asked for information, proved to be unwilling to have the case investigated because of possible undesirable revelations. Assurances that all information would be confidential were without effect, so this case was given up. An elderly lady wrote that she used to know a woman of about her own age who was a twin separated in infancy from her sister. Inquiry revealed that this lady had died years ago. A Canadian broker wrote, saying that he and his twin brother were just the kind of twins we wanted, but most of his letter was taken up with an account of certain mining properties, the stocks of which were then selling at a ridiculously low figure. He urged us to take advantage of this very unusual opportunity. Our reply, failing to show any interest in mining stocks, though plenty of interest in the twin situation, remained unanswered, and even a follow-up letter expressing mild interest in stocks, which we were unfortunately at the time unable to take advantage of, failed to elicit any reply. A pair of maiden-lady twins in South Carolina wrote that they would gladly offer themselves at the altar of science for any sort of experiment if we would support them for the years during which they were made use of. A somewhat more reasonable offer came from a charitable organization, which was willing to give us a pair of identical-twin orphans a few weeks old, whom we could then separate and bring up in environments as different as we might wish. This seemed to us a fine opportunity, but the thought of having to wait twelve years for them to reach an age suitable for testing, and in the meantime acting as scientific parent to a pair of twins, would have been enough to dissuade us, even without the refusal of our better half to countenance any such wild scheme.

To come back to the actual gathering of cases, it has been intimated that newspaper publicity of a discreet sort had brought some results. Four or five cases were secured for study in this way. But newspapers were far less effective than radio. Two radio talks were given on national hookups, and information from that source came in very rapidly. We thus got into correspondence with about ten new cases—all apparently of the desired type. It was one thing, however, to locate cases but quite another and much more difficult one to bring the cases to Chicago for study. Three cases, otherwise satisfactory, were too far away from us to make such a study feasible. In one of these cases a man wrote that his twin brother, from whom he had been separated at four years, was now in Denmark and did not speak English. Apart from the prohibitive expense of bringing this man from Denmark, it would have been impossible to give him any of the mental tests we have been using. In another case one twin lived in Alaska and the sister in California. This case might have been managed by a Californian, but the distances were too great for us. In still another case the twins were separated by the whole width of the American continent, and, moreover, neither twin could leave her job long enough to come to Chicago unless we would pay their salaries during their absence. Most of the other cases, however, after considerable correspondence and offers of inducements of one sort or another, have finally come to us. In two cases we had to go to them, but this is not so satisfactory, for we work better in our own quarters and with our full corps of specialists.

The one most important factor in our ultimate success in securing the last nine cases within a few months was the Century of Progress Exposition. Pair after pair, who had previously been unmoved by appeals to the effect that they owed it to science and to society to permit us to study them, could not resist the offer of a free, all-expenses-paid trip to the Chicago Fair. For a time we had a pair every week-end, and once, inadvertently, two pairs on the same week-end. So we are grateful to the Fair for enabling us to reach our goal of twenty cases[1]—a number far exceeding our earlier hopes. No one who has not tried to get together many cases of identical twins reared apart can realize the amount of sustained effort required. Yet we believe this collection is worth the effort. It is not merely, in all probability, representative of the types of situations that might be found in a larger collection but it is very nearly the entire available population of such cases within a thousand

---

[1] Whenever twenty cases are mentioned in this chapter the one reported by Muller is included. Cf. H. J. Muller, "Mental Traits and Heredity," *Journal of Heredity*, XVI (1925), 433–48.

miles of Chicago. We have at the present time no further promising clues. All the good cases known to us have been studied. On this account, if for no others, we have decided to let this be our definitive collection of cases. Another generation of students of twins may pick up another ten or twenty cases of such separated twins, but we feel that our task for the present is accomplished.

PROOFS OF THE MONOZYGOCITY OF THE SEPARATED PAIRS

Because of the great expense involved in bringing these separated twins to Chicago, no chances were taken that any of them might prove to be fraternal twins. In every case an affirmative answer to the following questions was required before twins were asked to come to us for study:

1. Are you or have you been at some time so strikingly similar that even your friends or relatives have confused you?

2. Do you yourselves believe that you are far more alike than any pair of brothers or sisters you know of?

3. Can you send us a good photograph of yourselves, taken together in about the the same positions?

In all of our nineteen cases these questions were answered in the affirmative, and in every case the photographs, sometimes several for one pair of twins, showed such striking similarity that we could be fairly sure on the ground of the photographs alone that they were monozygotic twins.

After the twins arrived they were examined in great detail as to genetic correspondences, and in not a single case has there been a marked genetic discrepancy between the two members of any pair. We looked for and frequently found concordances in many rare and peculiar characteristics, such as moles and other birthmarks, eye defects, finger and toe peculiarities, strange habits, and other oddities.

In addition, it should be said that, in eighteen out of nineteen of our own pairs, the palm and finger patterns would in themselves have afforded sufficient evidence of monozygocity for one familiar with these materials. In our Case II, however, the dermatoglyphic method of diagnosis would have been inconclusive; but this pair was one of the most strikingly similar of our twins and showed so many other evidences of monozygocity that the somewhat inconclusive evidence from palm prints and fingerprints was overruled. It might be said that there were a few cases of identical twins reared together in which the palm-print and fingerprint evidence taken alone was also inconclusive but not contradictory of a monozygotic diagnosis.

On the whole, it would be fair to say that our collection of nineteen pairs of identical twins reared apart average as similar physically as those reared together and can be as definitely diagnosed as monozygotic as were the latter.

In a good many of our pairs reared apart the real cause of their discovering each other was their very striking similarity. In these cases, where the twins were either unaware that they were twins or else had lost track of each other, they had discovered or rediscovered each other because a close acquaintance of one had encountered the other and had mistaken the latter for the former. Some of these first meetings between long-separated twins have been highly dramatic and are to be described in chapter ix. This method of discovering each other seems to us to be sufficient guaranty in itself that such twins are monozygotic, but no reliance is placed on this circumstance unless the twins meet all the other requirements of monozygocity previously applied in the diagnosis of identical twins reared together. In general, it may be said that our collection of identical twins reared apart constitute a selected group, from which any doubtful cases have been excluded before an invitation was extended to them to appear in Chicago for study. One case was excluded because the twins wrote: "A good many people think we are identical twins, but we ourselves do not think we are so very much alike." Another case failed to meet our requirements because one of the twins wrote that, while they look very much alike so that they were sometimes mistaken for each other, they were "as different as can be in disposition, and I am almost as much like my older sister as I am like my twin." These two cases may have been monozygotic, but the uncertainty was too great for us to advance the rather large amount of money required for their transportation.

In spite of the care taken by us to exclude all cases of separated twins about whose monozygocity there was any doubt, we shall not neglect to muster all the additional evidences of monozygocity that we have at our disposal, for, unless these twins are surely monozygotic, this whole study is worthless.

a) THE SIMILARITY METHOD OF DIAGNOSIS OF MONOZYGOCITY

The same methods of diagnosis have been used as for the twins reared together, and the criteria used may be found in chapter iii (p. 35). When the twins have been found to correspond almost exactly in a great many separately inherited genetic characters, such as hair color, hair form, hair texture, eye color and shape, ear shape and set, features, shape and arrangement of teeth, form of hands and fingers, shape of fingernails, general body build, and, in addition, exhibit correspondences in a number of unusual peculiarities, we might be satisfied that they are monozygotic; but we have gone even farther in order to make the diagnosis doubly sure. The procedure may again be reviewed.

The final check on monozygocity, after all the ordinary methods have been favorable, involves the detailed study of palm prints and fingerprints.

There are nine elements in each palm and five elements in each set of fingers of each hand, making for the two hands twenty-eight units for comparison. It is a general rule, with very few exceptions indeed, that, when homologous items are compared item for item, there is greater interindividual resemblance than intraindividual resemblance. Stated in another way, this means that in nearly all cases of twins which on other grounds seem to be unquestionably monozygotic, there is greater resemblance between one hand of one twin and one of the hands of the other twin than between the two hands of the same twin. This correspondence between the two individuals may involve a comparison of the two right hands, or the two left hands, or it may involve a comparison of right hand of twin A with left hand of twin B, and left hand of twin A with right hand of twin B. The first type of correspondence is far more frequent than the second, but there are not a few cases where the mirror-image type of correspondence is closer than same-sided correspondence. In comparing interindividual correspondences with intraindividual correspondences, we chose the closer type of interindividual correspondence, whether it be same-sided or opposite-sided. If cross correspondences are numerically greater than internal correspondences, we consider this fact strongly confirmatory of a previous monozygotic diagnosis. There are, however, two types of rare cases in which this criterion fails to work satisfactorily. The first consists of cases where all four hands of the two twins are so much alike that it is difficult to formulate any differences between them. The second consists of cases where none of the four hands is very much alike, again making comparison difficult. The third type is rather common and consists of cases in which three hands are about equally alike and one is different. Only in such cases do we ever find exceptions to the rule that cross resemblances are closer than internal resemblances.

In Table 43 will be seen the data of cross correspondences for our nineteen pairs of identical twins reared apart. When a plus (+) sign is used with a numeral such as +8 or +3, it means that on comparing the twenty-eight items of palm and finger patterns, there are eight or three more correspondences between the two individuals than the sum of the two intraindividual correspondences.

It will be noted that eighteen out of nineteen of our cases show plus (+) totals ranging from 8 to 1, while only one pair of twins, Case II, shows a minus (−) total. An examination of this one case shows that the palmar formulas of twin G are exactly the same for her two hands, a very unusual situation; also that all ten fingers of twin E are simple ulnar loops, which are the commonest by far of all finger patterns. The lack of marked peculiarities and the abundance of the commonest types of pattern units in this pair of twins, coupled with the almost total lack of bimanual asymmetry in one individual, render this case exceptional. The cross-correspondence rule works best where there are somewhat unusual features in the dermato-glyphic patterns and is likely to fall down in those cases where the patterns are too ordinary to make comparison significant. When all is said, however, our Case II fails to meet the dermatoglyphic test for monozygocity as laid down in our own rule. But a failure to meet this one requirement of mono-zygocity does not weigh very heavily in this case, for on all other grounds this is one of the most conclusive of the twenty cases of separated twins. In this case the twins knew nothing of each other's existence until they were twenty-one years old, and they found each other through one of them being mistaken for the other. Moreover, they are so extremely similar in a multi-tude of unusual characters that the experienced student of twins would at once diagnose them as monozygotic. While they were with us, we could dis-tinguish them only by their costumes and were obliged repeatedly to ask them which was which.

b) STOCKS'S FINGER-PATTERN TEST OF MONOZYGOCITY

Percy Stocks, of the University of London, published in 1930 *A Biometric Investigation of Twins and Their Brothers and Sisters.* In this elaborate sta-tistical study of about 230 pairs of twins of all sorts, he deals critically and exhaustively with methods of diagnosing monozygotic and dizygotic twins and searches for a simple single criterion that will serve to identify mono-zygotic twins. If twins meet with the ordinary requirements of bodily re-semblance, he finds in fingerprints a simple method of testing monozygocity. His method is as follows: He compares numbers of similar patterns found on the ten fingers of the two hands of the two twin individuals.

A pair of fingers were classed as similar when they were not merely of the same class (arch, whorl or loop) but so much alike as regards general configuration, in-clination of axes, position of deltas and numbers of ridges, as to make them appear the same to casual examination without actually counting the ridges or looking for minutiae.

This test was easily applied to our nineteen pairs of separated identical twins and may be easily repeated by the reader on reference to Table 43.

Stocks found that all twins that on the basis of their combined resem-blances are classifiable as monozygotics show not less than six corresponding fingers alike between the two individuals—a number greater than, or at least equal to, the total resemblances between opposite hands of the same in-dividual. He

counted for each pair of twins the number of correspondences, α, β, and γ, defined as follows:

α = Number out of the ten sets of corresponding fingers of the same-sided hands of the pair which presented similar patterns

β = Number out of the ten possible sets of correspondences either on the same-sided hands of the pair, or, failing that, on the opposite-sided hands of the pair

γ = Number out of the ten possible sets of corresponding fingers of the opposite hands of each individual of the pair which presented the patterns

In each case β should equal or be greater than γ.

Since he found no sex differences in fingerprints, a comparison between the fingers of opposite-sexed pairs should give the range of resemblance likely to be found in dizygotic twins in general. He found that no opposite-sexed pairs had more than six fingers alike and that only three out of fifty-two opposite-sexed pairs had as many as six correspondences.

To make a long story short, it could be concluded that the possession of seven or more correspondences would make monozygotic diagnosis sure and that as many as six would be considered as proof of monozygocity, provided that the heights and three out of four head measurements do not differ more than the standard deviation for the respective measurements corrected for age.

Applying this rigid test to our data on identical twins, we have gone a little farther than Stocks in formulating the different types of patterns, for we have distinguished seven types of whorls, designated W, Wu, Wr, Wlu, Wlr, Wdu, and Wdr; four types of loops, U, Ua, R, and Ra; and two types of arches, A and A^t. We have also taken into account the size, shape, and height of patterns. In another place we shall compare the twins on the basis of number of ridges in the patterns.

Reference to Table 43 will show that, of our nineteen pairs of separated twins, two showed 10 (the maximum) correspondences, five showed 9, five showed 8, three showed 7, three showed 6, and one showed 4. These average 7.7 correspondences per pair and are therefore well over the minimum requirement as a group. Four pairs, however, show less than 7 correspondences—Cases II, V, XIV, and XVIII.

Case II is the same pair that failed to meet the general dermatoglyphic requirement and was discussed above. Most of the failure to meet the previous requirement is involved in the shortage of fingerprint correspondences, so we need not dwell on this case further.

Case V meets the general dermatoglyphic requirement and happens to be a pair who were first brought together through one's being mistaken for the other. Also, in palmar dermatoglyphics, there is almost perfect mirror-image correspondence, the right hand of each resembling the left of the other, whereas the right and left hands of the same individual are quite different in both twins. These twins were in their youth so similar in every way that one frequently substituted for the other at her place of employment without exciting the least suspicion. The number of correspondences being six out of a possible ten would neither prove monozygotic origin nor disprove it. It is a border-line matter, as Stocks shows statistically.

Case XIV shows only six correspondences and is therefore on the border line. In this case, again, there is almost perfect mirror-image correspondence in palm patterns, with decided differences between the opposite hands of the same individual in both twins. They were also brought together for the first time through one's being mistaken for the other in a distant city.

Case XVIII constitutes the only real exception. These twins show only four correspondences, according to our formulation. Yet dermatoglyphic comparisons as a whole show greater cross resemblance than internal resemblance and therefore reinforce the monozygotic diagnosis based on general genetic correspondences. There are also only four corresponding fingers between the two hands of the same individuals, so that cross correspondences at least equal intraindividual correspondences. The photographs of these twin men show a correspondence of the closest kind, and they seemed to us, when we met them, to be even more similar than they appear in the photograph. In addition, one is right-handed, the other fully left-handed; one has clockwise hair whorl, the other a partially counterclockwise hair whorl. They both have a nearly blind left eye that tends to cross; and in both the nails are bitten down to the quick. Their physical measurements are all very similar. There can be no doubt about the monozygotic diagnosis of this pair, although they fail by a slight margin to meet Stocks's finger-pattern criterion.

c) FINGER-RIDGE COUNT CRITERION

The ridge counts were made in the same way as for our twins reared together. The counts for the two hands separately and for the total of the two hands of each individual are given in Table 43. The difference in totals between two members of a pair range from 0 to 13. Of these, 2 show no difference, 5 show a difference of 1 point, 1 a difference of 2 points, 4 a difference of 3 points, 2 a difference of 4 points, 3 a difference of 6, 1 a difference of 8, and 1 a difference of 13 points. All but the last are very close and well within the usual range of identical twins reared together. Even the 1 with 13 points difference is less different than several of our cases of identical twins reared together. This pair (Case XII) meets easily all the other criteria of monozygocity and must be classed as true "identical" twins.

The average difference for the whole 19 pairs is 3.5 points, which is almost the same as for our 50 pairs of identical twins reared together, which averaged 3.74 points difference—a remarkably close correspondence.

d) ASYMMETRY REVERSALS

The presence of asymmetry reversals in handedness, hair whorl, and palm and finger patterns and rare peculiarities of an asymmetrical sort are not in themselves definite criteria of monozygotic origin, but they are very common accompaniments of monozygotic twinning. When they occur, they serve as additional evidence for monozygocity.

In the twenty pairs of identical twins reared apart twelve out of forty individuals (30 per cent) are left-handed to some marked degree. This means, since in one pair both twins are left-handed, eleven out of the twenty zygotes involved produced pairs that exhibit left-handedness. This percentage is 15 per cent higher than was present in our identical twins reared together and reinforces our contention that left-handedness is much commoner in identical than in fraternal twins. On the other hand, reversed or partially reversed hair whorls occur in only seven out of thirty-eight individuals of the identical twins reared apart. In Muller's case the hair-whorl condition was not recorded. It occurs in 18.4 per cent of the individuals and in the products of 36.8 per cent of the zygotes involved. This occurrence is a little less frequent than in our identical twins reared together, where there were reversed hair whorls present in 40 per cent of the pairs. It should be said, however, that none of the reversed whorls was fully reversed. Apparently, reversed hair whorls are much less common among native Americans than among the Europeans that Bernstein worked with, for we have found reversed hair whorls in only 15.5 per cent of two hundred individuals chosen at random, and half of these were left-handers in which one might expect more individuals with reversed hair whorls. The 18.4 per cent of reversed hair whorls in these identical twins is higher per individual than in a fair sample of the singly born population, and more than twice as numerous on the zygote basis as in the latter.

Six pairs show extensive reversal and mirror-imaging of the whole palm patterns, and there are many cases of mirror-imaging of one or two pattern elements. There is but one case showing complete mirror-imaging in finger patterns and three cases of partial mirror-imaging.

A good many pairs show mirror-imaging in eye defects, tooth anomalies, in master-eye, in a number of anthropometric measurements, and in motor and strength tests of the two hands. These items will be brought out in connection with individual cases.

Contrary to what some writers have thought, we do not consider asymmetry reversals taken by themselves as evidence of monozygocity; but we do consider that their occurrence in twin pairs showing many other indications of monozygotic relationship strongly supports their claim to be classed as true identical twins.

In conclusion, let us reiterate that, so far as methods of diagnosis of mono-zygotic twins are reliable at all, all the twenty cases very easily meet the requirements. There is not even one doubtful case, whereas there were two slightly doubtful cases among our identical twins reared together.

TIME, DURATION, DEGREE OF COMPLETENESS, AND DISTANCE OF SEPARATION

It would be a very simple matter to collect a large number of cases of identical twins who were reared together up to adult age and then were separated more or less completely. It not uncommonly happens, for ex-ample, that identical-twin girls live together until one or both marry and then live completely separate lives. In the case of male identical twins, also, it frequently happens that they are separated when sent away to different colleges or when they obtain positions in different places and remain apart from then on. Doubtless, even in these cases some differences in mental, temperamental, and physical condition might be induced by marked differ-ences in environment, for in some of our cases of identical twins reared apart there are evidences that marked environmental differences did not come into play until adult age had been reached, yet such differences had a defi-nite effect. As a parallel study to our studies of identical twins separated in infancy it would be of great value to investigate twenty or more cases of identical twins separated much later in life. We would recommend such a study to anyone ambitious enough and competent enough to carry it through.

a) AGE OF TWINS AT TIME OF SEPARATION

In order, however, to eliminate from our studies the possibility that simi-lar or identical environments during childhood might tend to cast twins in the same mold and thus bring about similarities, we decided at the outset to study only those cases of identical twins that were separated in infancy. Several cases came to our attention in which the separation occurred at the ages of eight to twelve years, but such cases appeared to us at the time to be of little value and were not followed up.

We have adhered consistently in eighteen out of nineteen cases to the rule that the separation must have occurred in real infancy, but we weak-ened a little in the nineteenth case. This case, which had been on our list for some time, was finally accepted in order to round out the second block of ten cases (the first block of ten including Muller's case). In this pair, our Case XIX, the twins were separated at six years, somewhat late for our purposes; but we had information that the environments of the twins had been so markedly different since separation that we decided to add the case to our collection. In justification of this apparent relaxation of our standards, it might be said that we had not a single clue as to the existence of any more cases, so, if we were to round out our second block of ten cases, it was this case or none. Moreover, it seemed to us that a marked difference in environment with a relatively late separation might be about as good for our purposes as an earlier separation with no marked contrast in environments. After all, the human organism should be still plastic after six years of age and therefore susceptible to modification by real differences in the environment. Positive differences in the environment, therefore, seemed for our studies more important than mere separation, no matter how relatively late such separation had begun.

b) DURATION OF SEPARATION

The actual ages when separated range in our twenty cases from two weeks to six years. Table 44 gives the data as to time, duration, and degree of completeness of separation. Twelve out of twenty cases were separated before the end of the first year of life, five cases were separated during the second year, one during the third year, one during the fourth year, and one during the seventh year. The duration of separation ranged from 11 to about 53 years, the actual durations being: 11, 12, 12, 13, 16, 17, 18, 19, 19, 22, 26, 27, 28, 29, 32, 33, 34, 34, 35, and 53 years. These periods of separation include a large part of the periods of infancy, childhood, and youth in all cases, and in several of the cases the first meeting did not occur until the twenties or thirties. There is no apparent correlation between the extent of the periods of separation and the extent of mental, temperamental, and physical differences found.

c) DEGREE OF COMPLETENESS OF SEPARATION

The separated twins differed greatly in the degree of completeness of separation during the critical period. In a number of cases the separation was complete for a long period after they first parted company. In other cases there has been visiting at intervals throughout the entire period, or there has been at least some communication during that period.

The most extreme instances of complete separation are those in which twins had never heard of each other's existence until they were brought together by some curious freak of circumstances. There are six such cases. In several cases the twins have always been known to each other, but there has been visiting between them only at long intervals. Most of the cases are of this sort. Two of the pairs, Cases IV and IX, are cases where the twins lived very close together and saw each other frequently, though living in different families and in different environments.

It is a question whether complete separation is in itself an important factor when there are involved no pronounced differences in the environment.

TABLE 44

TIME OF SEPARATION, LENGTH OF SEPARATION, AND DEGREE OF COMPLETENESS
OF SEPARATION IN 20 PAIRS OF IDENTICAL TWINS REARED APART

Case	Time of Separation in Months	Duration of Separation in Years	Degree of Completeness of Separation
M.'s......	0.5	32	Separation complete until 18 years. They met for a short time and have been apart again for 14 years but have corresponded more or less
I.........	18	18	Separation complete until about a year before tests were given. Had lived together for a year before tests were given
II........	18	19	Separation complete until they met at 20 years of age. Had lived together 7 years when tests were given
III........	2	22	Separation complete. Had seen each other only once prior to taking of tests
IV........	5	29	They have been acquainted and have visited back and forth at intervals all their lives
V.........	14	33	Separation complete until 16 years old. Spent a year together when they were 20 but have lived apart except for occasional visits for the 18 years since then
VI........	ca. 36	ca. 13 until first meeting, about 40 years since	Separation complete from 3 to 16 years of age. Since then they have lived mostly apart but have visited a good deal and were living together when examined at the age of 58 years
VII........	1	13	Have had a day or so together about once a year for the last 5 years
VIII.......	3	16	Only a few short visits have broken into an otherwise complete separation
IX........	ca. 6	ca. 19	Living only a few miles apart, they have seen a good deal of each other and attended the same high school for 3 years
X.........	ca. 11	ca. 12	Met first at 5 years and have had only a few short visits together. Both lived in Chicago until 7 years old, but R moved away some distance at that time. Visits have been infrequent since then
XI........	18	28	Separation complete except for visits at long intervals. Some correspondence
XII........	ca. 18	34	Separation complete until nearly 30 years of age, when they met for the first time. Since then they have seen each other often during the last 5 years
XIII.......	Less than 1	17	Complete for 13 years but have visited at long intervals during the last 4 years
XIV.......	6	34	Complete until their first meeting at 24 years. Since then they have tried to spend a few weeks together each year and have corresponded
XV........	ca. 6	ca. 27	Complete until their first meeting at 24 years of age. Only short visits together since then

TABLE 44—*Continued*

Case	Time of Separation in Months	Duration of Separation in Years	Degree of Completeness of Separation
XVI.......	Very early infancy	*ca.* 11	Complete except for visits of an hour or so two or three times a year, during recent years
XVII......	*ca.* 25	*ca.* 12	Complete except for occasional short visits one of the longest being when they were examined
XVIII.....	Less than 12	*ca.* 26	Complete except for rare short visits. Had never spent a night together before they came to Chicago for examination
XIX.......	*ca.* 72	*ca.* 35	They spent 6 months studying nursing together when they were 17 years old, 11 years after their separation. Since then they have lived rather far apart and have seldom seen each other

Complete separation of a pair of twins guarantees that they shall have in common none of the random and casual experiences of childhood and shall have no friends and acquaintances in common, but it does not preclude the possibility that they may have been brought up in environments and lived through experiences which, if not specifically, at least generically, are the same. That more or less visiting between separated twins does not tend to vitiate the experimental aspects of separation is shown by the examination of Case IV, where the twins lived only a few miles apart and saw each other frequently. This pair turned out to be one of the most different mentally, temperamentally, and physically; while some of our cases that were absolutely separated, but in whom the environmental factors were not very different, turned out to be very similar in these respects.

All this goes to show that mere separation is ineffective in producing differences and that, only when marked differences in the environment occur, are twins likely to show differences of a significant sort.

d) DISTANCE OF SEPARATION

There is a great deal of difference among our cases as to the extent of geographic separation involved. The greatest distance of separation was found in Case I, where A was reared in England and O in Canada; while in Case IX, the two boys lived in homes only three miles apart. In between these extremes there were many intermediates, ranging from about a thousand miles to about eight miles. The question arises as to whether actual distance apart is a significant factor in producing differences in twins. Great distances apart may be associated with differences in climate or differences in customs and mores, but this has not been especially true for many of our cases if we may judge by the differences produced. While in

Case I the distance apart did involve both climatic and social differences of considerable degree, other cases involving great distances apart, such as Cases XIV and XV, have not involved very marked differences in environment. On the other hand, some of the cases in which the actual geographic separation was very slight, such as Cases IV and XVIII, in which the twins lived only a few miles apart, the differences were among the greatest found. It appears then that mere distance apart, unless accompanied by marked differences in environment, has no particular influence. In conclusion, then, it appears certain that separation in itself is not a factor of consequence except as it is accompanied by marked differences in some one or more features of the environment. Even though separation may be rather incomplete, environmental differences that are real and large have a marked effect. It should be possible, without very completely separating identical twins, to subject them to markedly different educational and social environments and thus learn more fully what effects are produced by different environments working on a common heredity.

CHAPTER IX

HUMAN-INTEREST STORIES AS TOLD BY TWINS

IN OUR interviews and sometimes extensive correspondence with the separated twins there came to light a number of rather interesting human-interest stories that we believe should be told, even though they may not in all cases represent the exact facts. These stories may be taken for what they are worth as part of the data that may influence one's judgment as to personality resemblances and differences. Some of the events related in this chapter may have had a significant influence upon the characters of the twins and may therefore be important. Because of their subjective tone, however, we have decided to omit these stories from the more objective data presented in connection with the individual case studies.

For obvious reasons some of these stories are more or less disguised, though the essential facts are not distorted.

THE STORY OF ED AND FRED

The most interesting feature of this story is the remarkable parallelism in the lives of these twins in spite of the fact that they lived without knowledge of each other's existence for twenty-five years. They were both reared as only children by childless foster-parents, both being led to understand that they were own children. Though they lived a thousand miles apart, they had about the same educational experience, and both found employment as repair men in branches of the same great telephone company. They were married in the same year and each had a baby son. Each owned a fox terrier dog named Trixie. According to their statements, both of them from early boyhood on were obsessed with the idea that they had a brother who died and often stated this to their playmates.

The story of their discovery of each other's existence is almost stranger than fiction. When Ed was twenty-two he was accosted by a jovial fellow who had just come from a distant city to work in Ed's department. "Hello Fred! How's tricks?" he inquired. Ed explained that he was not Fred and denied that he knew the newcomer, but the latter was hard to convince, declaring that Ed was trying to cover up his identity. Soon afterward another man accosted him as "Fred" and stated that if he was not Fred Blank he was exactly like a fellow of that name with whom he had recently worked in a distant city. Ed was by this time rather disturbed about the matter and told his parents about it. Reluctantly, the parents were forced to admit

147

that Ed was an adopted son and that he was one of a pair of twins, the other of whom had been adopted by a couple who lived in their home town but with whom they were not acquainted. They also revealed the fact that when the twins were small boys they had attended school together for a short time and that the other children had often noticed their close resemblance. It occurs to us that this early association of the twins may have led to the above-mentioned mutual feeling about a brother who had died.

Needless to say, Ed lost no time in getting in touch with Fred. The latter was out of work at the time and came to visit Ed. It was during this time that we succeeded in inducing them to come to Chicago to see the Fair and, incidentally, to be examined. Their visit with us was made even more interesting to them and to us by reason of a confusion of dates which resulted in their coming to us at the same time as a pair of young women twins, Ethel and Esther, whose story comes next in this series. The two pairs of twins became great friends and were much impressed by the similarity in the circumstances that led to their discovery that they were twins. The visits to the Fair were made together, each young man taking one of the young women. When they walked about, people were startled to see one couple walking ahead and a duplicate couple following behind. Everywhere they went they attracted attention and enjoyed the sensation they created. On one occasion they attended a side show featuring a pair of Siamese twins and, according to their statement, stole the show, attracting more attention than the exhibits.

THE STORY OF ETHEL AND ESTHER

These twins were also brought up to consider themselves as own children, and it was only when they had reached the age of eighteen or so that the fact of their adoption was revealed. When Esther was told of her adoption, she was also informed that she had a twin sister somewhere. Try as she might, she was unable for several years to get any news about her sister, but at last she received a letter from an old friend who was visiting in a distant city telling of meeting a young woman who was the image of Esther. At the first opportunity Esther, with her recently adopted baby daughter, journeyed to this distant city, and the twins were brought together. On comparing notes about birthplace and birthdays, etc., there was no question about their twinship. A strong mutual affection sprang up between them, and they have ever since managed, in spite of limited funds, to spend a week or so together every year.

These young women were most co-operative in furthering our studies of them and were highly appreciative of the attention paid them by the twins Ed and Fred. When they left for their homes, they expressed to us their feeling that their experience here had constituted the high light in their lives.

THE STORY OF EDITH AND FAY

As in the two previous cases, these twins were reared as own children by foster-parents who were unacquainted. Naturally, neither girl knew of the existence of a twin sister. Their first meeting was brought about under somewhat dramatic circumstances. Edith was employed as a clerk in her foster-father's store. One day a salesman, waiting for an opportunity to see the proprietor, caught sight of Edith and, hurrying over to her, surprised her by calling her "Fay" and asking her how she happened to be working in this town so far from home. Edith, suspecting a flirtation, denied any acquaintance with the young man. The latter persisted in his conviction that she must be Fay R. or her exact double. Edith's father, on being asked about the matter, remembered that, when he had adopted Edith, he had been told that there was a twin sister named Fay. It turned out that this twin sister was a near neighbor and friend of the young salesman, and, as soon as he could bring it about, a meeting between the twins was arranged. Edith, waiting for the train on which Fay was expected to arrive, had a strange experience. "I saw myself getting off the train!" she exclaimed to us. During this first visit they were very happy together, for a great mutual affection seemed to mature at once. They were so much alike that they continually impersonated each other, changing clothes and modes of dressing their hair so as to enhance their exchanges of personality. Photographs taken during this first visit attest their close similarity. Even their voices, their peculiarities of walking, and their mannerisms were and still are strangely similar, although they had been entirely apart for sixteen years. Four years after this first visit the twins began a much longer visit together, for Edith moved to Fay's town and secured employment there. During this period one twin sometimes substituted for the other without employers suspecting any such exchange of personalities. This happy year together was brought to a close by Edith's marriage and consequent removal to another town. Edith's happy and carefree life became much harder, while Fay's life remained much the same, although she soon followed Edith's example and married. The rest of their story is told elsewhere.

THE STORY OF ELEANORE AND GEORGIANA

The remarkable feature of the first meeting of these twins was the purely fortuitous circumstance that brought it about. Neither of the girls knew that they were twins, and apparently the foster-parents knew nothing about the twin condition. When she was twenty years old Eleanore had occasion to take a bus trip to another city. The bus stopped to take on a passenger from a convent, and a Catholic sister got on board and sat down beside Eleanore. As soon as she was seated, the sister seemed to recognize Eleanore as one of her former pupils. When Eleanore denied ever having attended the convent, the sister informed her that a girl, named Georgiana, who looked exactly like Eleanore, had attended the convent a few years before. Eleanore, who had never known a real relative, suspected that she and Georgiana might be sisters, for they had the same surname. Georgiana was soon located. She was a schoolteacher in a city not far from Eleanore's home. On comparing notes, it was found that their birth certificates corresponded exactly as to day, place, and circumstances leading to adoption. Georgiana gave up her teaching position to come to Eleanore's city and to start a new kind of life similar to that of her sister. One is now a doctor's assistant, the other a dentist's assistant, and their offices are in the same building. Both now consider themselves as very suitably employed. They both find that their work is exactly adapted to their capacities and temperaments. This fact alone indicates their similarity in personalities.

THE STORY OF THE TWO PAUL HAROLDS

In another connection these twins are referred to by the initials of their surnames, for their given names are identical. No one knows how it happened that both boys were called Paul Harold. It could hardly be a mere coincidence. An unsupported hypothesis may, however, be offered. It seems not unlikely that, when the first baby was taken, the foster-parents were given a name from the record, and in some way the name was not checked. When the second foster-parents took the other twin away, it is probable that they were also told that their baby had been named Paul Harold. It was strange when the twins were with us to hear them address each other mutually as Paul. The two Pauls knew nothing of each other's existence until Paul C. happened upon an old paper in the bottom of his trunk that proved to be a birth certificate and showed that he had a twin brother. By persistent effort and the use of some detective ability, Paul C. finally located Paul O., and they arranged to spend the Fourth of July together. In contrast with most identical twins, these boys were not particularly cordial toward each other. Apparently, one was too much of a city boy and the other too much of a country boy for mutual approval. When they were here with us, we were surprised to find them acting more like mere acquaintances than like twin brothers brought together after twenty years' separation.

THE STORY OF ALICE AND OLIVE

This is the only case among all those studied in which the twins were separated from each other by the extent of an ocean. Both Alice and Olive were born in London, England. Alice remained in London until about a year before we began to study the case, while Olive was brought to Canada at a very early age. Since the essential features of the life-histories of these twins is told in the detailed case study, we shall in this place merely mention a personal unpleasantness which arose out of our study. Because of the difficulties involved in entering the United States, it was decided to send Mrs. Mitchell, an experienced assistant, to Canada to give the tests and secure the data. Had we realized that other cases of separated identical twins were to come, we should have made a greater effort to have the twins come to Chicago.

Unfortunately, this case received more newspaper publicity than was desirable, though we must admit that it resulted in the discovery of several other cases. After the publication in the *Journal of Heredity* of studies of the first three cases, a newspaper writer, on the false pretext of an interview with one of us (Newman), published a garbled account of these studies in a Sunday supplement. In this account he grossly exaggerated the differences found between Alice and Olive, much to the former's disadvantage. While there were only twelve points I.Q. difference between them, this writer gave the impression that Olive was very bright and Alice quite stupid. Naturally, this was seriously resented. Assuming that we were responsible for this libel, Alice secured a lawyer who threatened to start a suit for damages. After considerable difficulty the matter was adjusted, but for a time things looked a bit serious. In this place we wish to assert as strongly as we can that even the raw scores of the tests show Alice to be a person of good average intelligence, though her showing was not so good as that of Olive. This difference is explained as due to two probable causes—the marked difference between English and Canadian courses of study for girls and the fact that the tests were designed for American students and were therefore not quite fair for an English girl. A very fine letter from Alice in which she points out these and other reasons for her unfavorable showing goes far to correct any previous possible wrong impression as to her intelligence. She is really much more intelligent than the test scores indicate.

THE STORY OF HELEN AND GLADYS

The first meeting of twins Helen and Gladys had in it some elements of human interest. These women had been separated in early infancy, and, although Helen had long known she had a twin sister somewhere, she had no clue as to where she might be. The strange thing about the case is that through devious paths they had gravitated to the same city and were both well established there when they crossed each other's trails in the following curious fashion. Helen was a grade schoolteacher in a large city school. Among her favorite pupils was a little girl who was very fond of her teacher and always greeted her with a happy smile. One morning the little girl did not smile and appeared to be downcast. On inquiry it appeared that she thought she had seen Helen the night before at a concert in a distant part of the city. She had said "Hello!" and smiled at her teacher but had received not so much as a sign of recognition. When Helen denied that she had attended the concert at all and insisted that the pupil must have mistaken someone else for her teacher, the little girl would not be convinced. She asserted that the lady she saw was exactly like Helen and felt that she could not have been mistaken, for she knew her teacher so well. Helen at once suspected that the person in question must be her long-lost twin sister. She went to the part of the city where the concert had been held and found a number of people who had been in attendance. The result was that one person was found who knew Gladys and recognized at once her close resemblance to Helen. So they were soon brought together and had a happy reunion after a complete separation of twenty-eight years. The extreme difference in their life-experiences is described in the detailed study of the case in chapter x.

THE STRANGE FIRST MEETING OF KENNETH AND JERRY

These boys had been reared in complete ignorance of each other's existence. Our information about these twins came from a schoolteacher who had formerly been one of our students in the University of Chicago and knew of our interest in twins. In her first letter she told us that, when she was visiting a teacher friend in another city, she met a boy who bore the most remarkable resemblance to one of her own pupils at home. So impressed was she that she decided to get the two boys together. So she brought the boy Jerry from her school to visit Kenneth, the boy in her friend's school. When they were placed side by side, the two boys were indistinguishable. Inquiry showed that both were adopted, had the same birthday, the same birthplace, and the same parents, so that they had to be identical twins.

While this was one of the first cases that came to our knowledge, we had despaired of being able to make use of it, for Kenneth's grandmother would not hear of his coming to Chicago, which she considered a dangerous place to visit. After several years, however, renewed effort on our part, together with the inducement of a free trip to the Fair, broke down all resistance, and we were able to study the case.

THE STORY OF JOHN DOE AND RICHARD ROE

In this story of a hypothetical twin case there is contained certain information that is of importance. What it is the intelligent reader must discover for himself. These twins were reared in the same general community but were separated by social barriers. The foster-parents of the twins were quite different in their social attitudes. John's foster-father brought him up to be industrious and respectable, while Richard's foster-father was neither industrious nor respectable. The result was that John grew up to be a good, steady, respected citizen, while Richard early got into bad company, has lived a very irregular life, and has had several difficulties with the laws of the land, which he has had to expiate in appropriate ways. Because of the vastly different social outlooks of the two foster-families, the twins have been kept consistently apart, hardly ever seeing each other, though aware of each other's existence almost all their lives.

CONCLUDING REMARKS

We have chosen to recount the human-interest features of nine of our nineteen cases of twins reared apart. Most of the other cases contain material that exhibits certain more or less romantic aspects. Hardly any of the cases are what could be regarded as lacking in human interest. In fact, a story-writer could doubtless find plenty of data in every one of the nineteen cases for a good story. Unfortunately, however, we are sadly lacking in skill as a teller of stories. All we have attempted to do is to set down the bare facts of a few of the more striking cases. In so doing we feel that we have gone as far as would be appropriate for a study such as this. Some day, perhaps, some of these stories may be written by a pen more skilled than ours.

In conclusion we feel inclined, in view of the strange circumstances that led up to the first meeting of several of these separated twins, to venture the highly original remark that "it's a small world after all."

CHAPTER X

CASE STUDIES

EACH of our nineteen cases of identical twins reared apart is written up as a case study. The first nine cases have already been published by one of the authors (Newman) in nine different numbers of the *Journal of Heredity*.[1] In some respects these published case reports give more detailed information than is deemed necessary for present purposes. Should anyone desire this additional information, it is readily obtainable by reference to the *Journal*. A few mistakes were made in presenting the data in these case studies, corrections of which are made in the present volume. The main discrepancy between the published case studies and the present report has to do with the scores of the International Test. It was found advisable to rescore all the papers on this test, using a revised method of scoring uniform for all cases. Formerly, different methods of scoring had been used by different scorers.

The earlier reports were written as the cases came in. The number of cases with which each case could be compared, therefore, was limited to the cases which had preceded it. The statement of the significance of a given amount of difference was therefore necessarily more tentative than are the present statements, which are based on a comparison of each pair with the entire nineteen. To quote from one of the earlier reports: "In any case, it would be fatal to generalize on matters of such importance on the basis of one case or even a few."[2] This is particularly true of the comparisons of differences on the personality tests which had not been given to the fifty pairs reared together. This will explain a few seeming contradictions between this report and the earlier ones. Where they exist, the conclusions of the present report have been weighed with especial care, and they represent the mature judgment of the authors.

Should anyone at any time wish more detailed information with reference to any of the numerous tests given, such information is available, for all data are filed in the archives.

Muller's interesting case, the first case of identical twins reared apart to be reported, will not be redescribed here, for it has been rather fully discussed by several writers.

[1] H. H. Newman, "Mental and Physical Traits of Identical Twins Reared Apart," *Journal of Heredity*, XX (1929), 49–64, 97–104, 153–66; XXIII (1932), 3–18, 297–304, 369–77; XXIV (1933), 209–14; XXV (1934), 55–60, 137–43.

[2] *Ibid.*, XX (1929), 104.

CASE I. TWINS ALICE AND OLIVE

These twin girls born in London, England, were nineteen years old when examined. They had been separated on account of the death of the mother when they were eighteen months old and did not meet again for about seventeen years. They had been living together in Olive's home for one year when they were examined.

EDUCATIONAL CAREERS

Alice had lived all her life up to eighteen years of age in London and had secured her education there. She had nine years of schooling in London at a girls' school, finishing the required course when she was fourteen. After that she took an eighteen-month business training course. She did poorly in school until she was eleven years of age, after which she improved greatly, averaging above 90 in her courses. She has worked in business offices for the last three years or more. Quantitatively, her schooling amounted to a completion of ninth grade in our schools, plus a business course. Qualitatively, according to her own statement, her work was very different from that in Canadian schools. In the first place, the curriculum was largely practical, including domestic science, art, and other courses designed especially for girls, and lacked many courses required in Canadian and American schools. In the second place, during the World War education was seriously interrupted. Alice also claims that the tests were American in tone and did not give her quite a fair chance.

Olive was brought to Canada when she was eighteen months old and has lived since then in a rather small but attractive Ontario town. She had the full equivalent of our grade-school course and one-half of the high-school course. The Canadian educational system is the equal of that generally found in the United States. She stood first in her class when she completed grade school, her grades having always been above 90. Her two years in the collegiate institute, the equivalent of our high school, were devoted to the commercial course, which involves a good deal of general as well as commercial work. She finished her business course when she was sixteen and has been employed in offices ever since. It should be said that Alice missed eight months of schooling when she was eight, had to repeat the year, and finally skipped the last year of grade school to enter high school.

There was thus no appreciable difference in the number of years of schooling experienced by these twins, but qualitatively the difference was rather marked, partly as the result of differences in curriculum and partly the result of serious disturbances resulting from wartime conditions in London, which from Alice's account must have been serious.

PLATE I

CASE I, ALICE (*left*) AND OLIVE AT NINETEEN YEARS OF AGE

The social environmental differences were fairly large as to the general character of the communities, the social position of the families, and the internal family relations. The contrast between a home in a congested district of London and a small Ontario town (population about eighteen thousand) is obvious and needs no comment. Alice was reared in a family with four older girls, the real daughters of the family, so she received relatively little special attention. The foster-family of Alice belongs to the lower middle class and is a little less well off financially than the foster-family of Olive. Alice has been interested in church activities for several years. She has had very little interest in men and has had no love affairs.

Olive was reared as an only child by rather indulgent foster-parents, who are said to have "spoiled" her. Her home has been relatively large and well furnished, and the family has a social status above the average in the town. She, too, for years has been interested in church matters. She has never been much interested in boys or men, seeing them only at church socials and in business.

At birth Alice was very weak, and it was thought she might not live. She probably had the less favorable prenatal environment, which gave her a poor start in postnatal life. Some months after birth, however, she improved in health and has been rather healthy all her subsequent life. At five years she had scarlet fever, and in the two succeeding years, measles and whooping cough. She has suffered a good deal with tonsillitis and bronchitis; and, since she came to Canada, she has had some rheumatism, probably resulting from diseased tonsils, for she has not had a tonsillectomy.

Olive was much stronger at birth. She had measles at seven, chicken pox at eight, and diphtheria at nine. She has also suffered from tonsillitis and bronchitis, associated with rheumatism, even though she had a tonsillectomy at nine years of age.

During the war Alice claims to have suffered from meager and restricted diet and to have grown thin, while Olive had no such experience. It probably is better for the health in general to live in an attractive small town than in the heart of London.

On the whole, it appears that Olive was favored over Alice by postnatal physical environments.

These scores which are presented in Table 45,[3] taken at their face value, indicate more than the average difference between Alice and Olive (as compared with all our separated pairs) in the tests of ability (intelligence and

[3] The ratios which are given in the last column of this table and the similar tables in the other case studies are assembled in the reference table, No. 46.

TABLE 45

TEST RECORD AND ENVIRONMENTAL RATING OF PAIR NO. 1
(ALICE AND OLIVE)

Test	Alice	Olive	Diff.	Ratio of Diff. to Mean Diff.*
Stanford-Binet:				
M.A.	13–7	15–6	23 mo.	1.49
I.Q.	85	97	12	1.46
Otis S.-A.:				
Score	32	50	18	. . . .
I.Q.	90	108	18	2.25
Percentage right	55.6	81.3	25.7	1.79
Otis Advanced:				
M.A.†	. . . .	. . . .	. . . .	I.Q.† . . . . .
I.Q.†	. . . .	. . . .	. . . .	. . . .
American Council score	77	143	66	2.44
International score	79	123	44	2.83
Stanford Achievement:				
Reading age	16–8	18–4	20 mo.	. . . .
Arithmetic	11–11	15–9	46	. . . .
Nature study and science	13–2	15–4	26	. . . .
History and literature	14–0	15–7	19	. . . .
Language usage	16–8	17–11	15	. . . .
Dictation	18–1	18–6	5	. . . .
Total	15–1	16–8	19	1.17
Downey:				
Total	39	53	14	1.53
Pattern difference	. . . .	. . . .	. . . .	1.16
Woodworth-Mathews:				
Number of neurotic traits	17	18	1	.20
Pressey Emotions:				
Total crossed out	154	150	4	.08
Deviations	51	55	4	.82
Kent-Rosanoff:				
Number of common responses	94	95	1	.10
Average frequency	120	110	10	.25
Number of identical responses	18	18‡	. . . .	. . . .
Average of all tests	. . . .	. . . .	. . . .	1.26
Environmental rating:				
Educational	. . . .	. . . .	15	.99
Social	. . . .	. . . .	27	1.51
Physical	. . . .	. . . .	19	1.20

* The ratios in this column of the table, and in the last columns of similar tables in the other case studies, are given in Table 46.

† Omitted.

‡ Ratio to mean, 1.25.

Ratios of Score Differences on Tests to the Average Difference of the Group

CASE	STANFORD-BINET M.A. (M = 15.42)	STANFORD-BINET I.Q. (M = 8.21)	OTIS S.-A. I.Q. (M = 8.00)	OTIS S.-A. Percentage Correct of Those Attempted (M = 14.36)	STANFORD ACHIEVEMENT (M = 16.26)	PSYCH. EXAM. (THURSTONE SCORE) (M = 27.06)	INTERNATIONAL TEST (M = 15.53)	WOODWORTH-MATHEWS Number of Neurotic Traits (M = 5.00)	KENT-ROSANOFF Number of Common Reactions (M = 9.63)	KENT-ROSANOFF Average Frequency of Response (M = 39.42)	PRESSEY EMOTIONS Total Number Crossed Out (M = 47.16)	PRESSEY EMOTIONS Number of Deviations (Idiosyncrasy Score) (M = 4.89)	DOWNEY WILL-TEMPERAMENT Total Score (M = 9.16)	DOWNEY WILL-TEMPERAMENT Pattern Difference (Average of Differences on Parts) (M = 1.98)	TOTAL	AVERAGE RATIO FOR 14 TRAITS
I	1.49	1.46	2.25	1.79	1.17	2.44	2.83	.20	.10	.25	.08	.82	1.53	1.16	17.57	1.26
II	1.49	1.46	1.88	3.11	2.34	*	1.87	1.60	1.66	.96	1.55	1.64	.33	1.46	21.35	1.64
III	.19	.24	1.25	.25	.98	1.00	.84	.40	.21	.76	2.04	1.23	.66	.86	10.91	0.78
IV	2.20	2.07	1.75	1.30	2.09	2.59	.52	1.00	.10	.23	.76	.61	2.62	1.52	19.36	1.38
V	.45	.49	.38	.47	.37	.37	.06	.60	.62	1.32	.36	.61	.11	1.46	7.67	0.55-
VI	.97	.97	.25	1.79	.25	*	.32	0	1.87	.84	.66	.41	.44	.66	9.43	0.73
VII	.13	.12	.50	.92	.12	.55	.39	.40	5.61	1.40	.30	.61	1.86	1.16	14.07	1.01
VIII	1.82	1.83	1.88	2.01	.80	1.44	1.93	1.60	.83	1.88	.76	4.91	1.64	1.06	24.39	1.74
IX	.65	.73	.62	.67	.49	1.26	.52	.80	1.25	1.05	1.42	0	.11	.66	9.23	0.66
X	.52	.61	1.00	.64	1.17	.18	0	.60	.62	.38	.70	1.02	1.09	1.26	9.79	0.70
XI	2.98	2.92	1.50	.29	4.24	3.25	2.90	0	.83	.18	1.44	2.45	3.06	1.46	27.50	1.96
XII	.84	.85	.12	.36	.86	.11	0	.20	0	1.47	1.82	0	1.75	.96	10.34	0.74
XIII	.06	.12	.38	.60	.43	2.14	.77	1.00	.73	1.29	.45	1.02	.11	.96	10.06	0.72
XIV	.19	.12	1.25	1.69	1.05	.26	.58	4.40	.31	2.74	.83	1.84	.22	.61	14.25	1.02
XV	.26	.12	1.00	.50	.12	.07	1.80	.80	.93	.71	1.23	.61	.76	1.36	11.50	0.82
XVI	.19	.24	.38	.17	.06	.18	.19	.60	2.80	1.88	1.36	.61	.55	.30	9.51	0.68
XVII	1.10	1.22	0	0	0	.41	1.16	2.20	.21	.84	.91	1.02	.98	.81	10.86	0.78
XVIII	2.33	2.31	2.50	2.17	2.15	.67	2.25	1.20	.31	.71	.93	0	.11	.66	18.30	1.31
XIX	1.10	1.10	.12	.28	.31	.07	.06	.40	0	1.12	1.40	.20	1.09	.66	7.91	0.57
Total	18.96	18.98	19.01	19.01	19.00	16.99	18.99	19.00	18.99	19.01	19.00	19.00	19.02	19.04	264.00	

* Omitted.

achievement), and less than the average difference in the personality measures, with the exception of the Downey test. It should be noted that the differences in the ability tests are all in the same direction, which makes the superiority of Olive quite certain, so far as the tests are valid. It is worth noting that while Olive is superior to Alice on each part of the Stanford Achievement Test, the sisters are alike in the tests on which they do better or worse than children in general. Both are relatively higher in reading, language usage, and dictation (spelling) than in arithmetic, nature study and science, and history and literature. In spite of the difference in their education, then, they resemble each other in the pattern of their abilities.

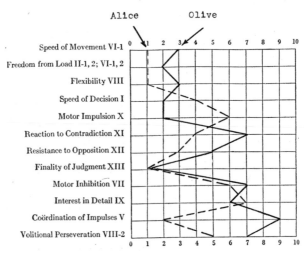

Fig. 15.—Downey Individual Will-Temperament Test profiles

Olive's higher total score on the Downey test is due to her higher scores on speed and fluidity, on reaction to contradiction and resistance to opposition (aggressiveness), and on co-ordination of impulses and volitional perseveration. She is, according to the test, more rapid, aggressive, self-controlled, and persistent. These characteristics appear to have some relation to her intellectual superiority.

The similarity in the scores on the other personality tests in some measure covers up differences which appear from a detailed examination of the responses. For example, in the Woodworth-Mathews test, while each gave approximately the same number of unfavorable responses (17 and 18), less than half the unfavorable responses given by the two were the same, namely, 8. Alice made 9 unfavorable responses which Olive did not make, and Olive made 10 which Alice did not make. In other words, though both are about equally nervous, they are nervous about different things. One, but not the other, has felt like running away or jumping off a high place or has had dreams about her family, about robbers, or about being dead; only one gets so angry she sees red, is made sick by some kind of food, cannot stand the sight of blood, etc. Their reactions are far from identical.

The responses on the Kent-Rosanoff test may be analyzed to find out not only the similarity in terms of the commonness of the responses given by the twins but also to determine how far they gave the same responses. The sisters gave 18 identical responses out of the 200 given by both together. Does this indicate a high or low degree of similarity in their particular mental associations?

The significance of the number of identical responses could be determined if we could establish two points. The first is the number of identical responses that would be given by two persons picked at random who gave responses of the same frequency as those given by the twins in question. The second is the number of identical responses that would be given by the same person on two different occasions. These two points would represent, respectively, zero resemblance and maximum resemblance in associations which are due to the individual mental constitution.

The first determination is possible but, for the present at least, is impracticable because of the amount of labor involved in calculating the necessary probabilities. The second, however, has been estimated by experimental procedure. The number of identical responses will, in each case, be compared with this figure.

One technical difficulty confronts us in the use of repeated tests of the same individuals. This is the fact that memory may produce some identity in response. We shall attempt to take some account of this factor.

The Kent-Rosanoff test was given twice to twenty-seven pupils, fifteen girls and twelve boys, ranging in age from twelve to seventeen years. The second test was given five weeks after the first one. The number of identical responses to the 100 words varied from 10 to 63 in the different individuals, the mean being 40.9 $\pm$ 1.83, with an S.D. of 11.2. The number of identical responses is thus two and one-half times as many as in the case of this pair of twins.

We cannot determine how many of the identical responses in the case of the same individuals are due to memory; but we can perhaps determine whether memory is the sole or even the chief factor. If memory is the sole factor, the number of identical responses should not be affected by the frequency with which these responses are given by people in general. That is, one would be as likely, perhaps more likely, to remember a response which is not commonly given than one which is, on the principle that a single unfamiliar experience is more likely to be remembered than a familiar one. A check was made by comparing the general frequency or commonness of the identical and the non-identical responses. The mean frequency of the identical responses was found to be 20.75 ± .31 (S.D., 15.00). The mean frequency of the non-identical responses, on the other hand, was, on the first test, 8.95 ± .175 (S.D., 10.40), and on the second, 10.25 ± .172 (S.D., 11.20). This seems to indicate that the repetition of the same responses was due in large measure to the tendency of the mind to run along the same association channels on successive occasions and that this tendency is more

TABLE 47

TOTAL NUMBER OF WORDS CROSSED OUT, NUMBER OF DEVIATIONS, AND
NUMBER MARKED BY BOTH AND BY ONE ALONE
ON THE PRESSEY X–O TEST

TEST	WORDS CROSSED OUT		DEVIATIONS		NUMBER MARKED BY BOTH	NUMBER MARKED BY ONE ALONE
	Alice	Olive	Alice	Olive		
Test I: Unpleasant words........	47	37	12	6	30	24
Test II: Words associated in mind with given word........	41	49	14	17	28	34
Test III: Things thought wrong....	54	56	12	14	48	14
Test IV: Worries................	12	8	13	18	4	12
Total................	154	150	51	55	110	84

frequently found manifested in common than in uncommon associations. We should probably make some allowance for memory, then, but not very much.

Perhaps it is fair to estimate that the tendency of these identical twins to follow the same associations is about half as great as that of the same individual at different times. Since these twins were brought up apart, this is a high degree of similarity. Unfortunately, we cannot compare it with that of identical twins reared together.

The data are not at hand for making as complete an analysis of the responses on the Pressey test. However, we can show that, although the total number of words crossed and the total number of deviations are very similar, the particular responses differ rather widely. This is shown in Table 47.

It is evident from this table that the very similar totals are made up of largely different particular responses. The significance of this similarity is therefore somewhat reduced. The larger difference in the idiosyncrasy score, .82 of the mean difference, perhaps more nearly expresses the real difference in emotional temperament.

The analysis of the detailed responses of Alice and Olive on the Woodworth-Mathews, Kent-Rosanoff, and Pressey tests shows that, while the summary scores differ by small amounts, the responses are by no means identical. They are not the kind of responses that would be made by the same person on two different occasions, though they are very much more alike than those that would be made by two persons picked at random. Certainly, at least, this is true of twins who have been separated. The exaggerated statements of the identity of twins that are sometimes found in the literature—that they are the same person living in two bodies or that they are like two clocks set to keep time and to run down exactly together—are not true. Certainly, at least, the near-identity of reactions is not maintained when the circumstances of life are unlike.

The upshot of this detailed analysis, which will not be repeated so fully in the case of the other pairs, is that, while a large difference in the summary scores given in Table 47 indicates a marked difference in personal reactions, a small difference does not indicate identity of reactions. In fact, it may conceal rather marked differences.

In chapter vii a review of statistical studies of similarity in handwriting and a report of a statistical examination of the handwriting of our own twins are given. Several graphological studies of the handwriting of identical twins are also reviewed. We, the authors of the present study, are not prepared to make a graphological interpretation. In fact, we do not regard the graphological interpretation as yet scientifically established, although we regard it as probable that certain features of handwriting are the expression of somewhat general characteristics of the personality. We shall therefore content ourselves mainly with making a comparison of the appearance of the handwriting of our pairs of twins and drawing inferences concerning the type of movement which was used in producing the writing. If we go beyond this, it will be only to suggest occasional inferences of the more obvious sort concerning general features of personality that are suggested by the nature of the movements revealed by the writing.

HANDWRITING

As shown in the dictation exercise of the Stanford Achievement Test, Olive's writing is light flowing, somewhat inclined to flourishes, with rather long beginning and ending strokes, full loops and fairly light pressure.

PLATE II

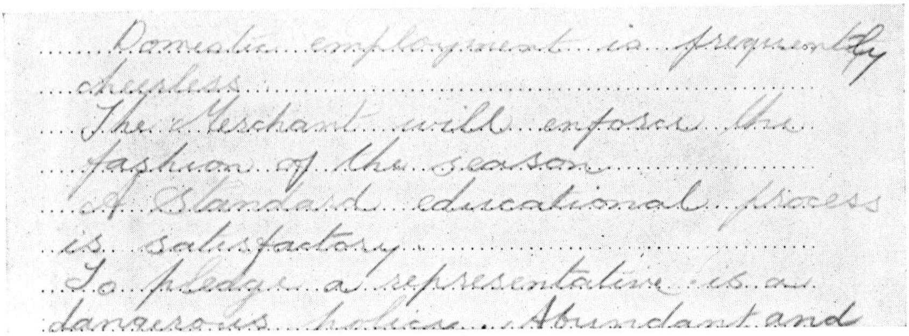
Domestic employment is frequently cheerless
The Merchant will expose the fashion of the season
A Standard educational process is satisfactory
To pledge a representative is a dangerous policy. Abundant and

Handwriting of Alice, Case I

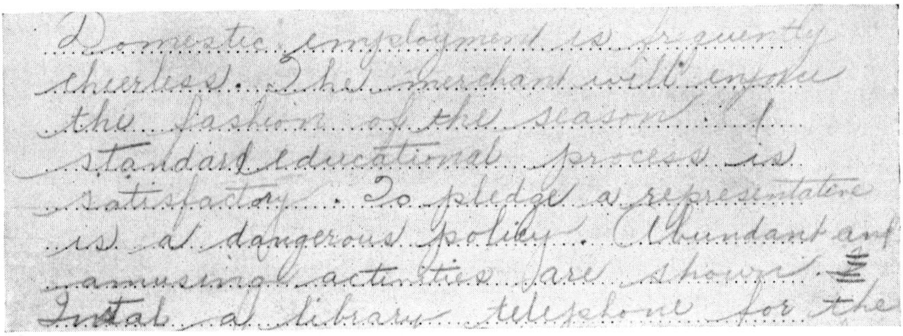
Domestic employment is frequently cheerless. The merchant will expose the fashion of the season. A standard educational process is satisfactory. To pledge a representative is a dangerous policy. Abundant and amusing activities are shown. Instal a library telephone for the

Handwriting of Olive, Case I

Alice's writing, on the other hand, is heavy, restrained, and economical of strokes. Many loops are not completed. Of course, there are differences in letter form which are not significant. Both sisters form the letters clearly and legibly. Both write a rather round style. These differences suggest that Alice is more inhibited in her reaction than is Olive. The difference in the form of some of the letters is, of course, purely conventional. Examples of this are the capital A and the small t at the end of a word. Other differences, however, are due entirely to individual habit. For example, Olive completes the lower loops, usually with an extra flourish, while Alice omits the loops at the end of words, making the down stroke with much pressure and usually ending abruptly. The crossing of the t is made differently. Olive places the stroke nearly in the proper place, while Alice places it to the right of the upright stroke. This is taken by Saudek to be a sign of speed. The pressure and general cramped appearance of Alice's writing, however, suggest a slower, less fluent movement than that of Olive, and the difference in the crossing of the t may possibly be conventional. Possibly this indicates that Alice, like Olive, is naturally disposed to fluent movement but that this disposition, in her case, has become inhibited by convention. This is probably as far as speculation should go.

PHYSICAL RESEMBLANCES AND DIFFERENCES

In the original report on these twins attention was called to the fact that these girls were alike in a considerable series of physical traits, in which there is little or no correspondence among their seven sibs. Using the Muller method of computation, it was determined that there is only one chance in two thousand that these twins are dizygotic.

There is extremely close correspondence in hair color and texture, eye color, ears, teeth, complexion, features, hands, feet, etc. There is about 0.7-inch difference in height. The head length of Alice was 17.5 centimeters; that of Olive, 17.9 centimeters. The head width of Alice was 13.6 centimeters; that of Olive, 13.8 centimeters. Olive weighed 102 pounds; Alice, $92\frac{1}{8}$ pounds. This rather large difference in weight gives Olive the advantage in all circumferential measurements of body regions. It is a large difference for such small persons and reflects a rather marked difference in the physical condition of the two girls, Olive being about normal for her height and Alice rather definitely thin and underweight. It is difficult to decide whether this difference is a carry-over from a prenatal handicap or is the result of postnatal environmental differences. In this connection it should be recalled that they have had one year of similar food and have lived together in the same house. Olive is right-handed and Alice is left-handed. This reversal of asymmetry is reflected in the palm patterns.

SUMMARY

These sisters were reared under rather widely different circumstances. The physical conditions probably differed considerably, due partly to the fact that the war caused more privation in England than in America. The general social environment is rather widely different in the old and the new world. The education, while about the same in duration, probably differed a good deal in content.

The sisters are very similar, if not identical, in those physical features which are most clearly ascribable to genetic factors. There is no doubt that they are monozygotic. The chief difference is in weight and the corresponding circumference measures. The reversal of asymmetry is probably the accompaniment of the twinning process.

The tests reveal a marked and consistent difference in mental ability in favor of Olive, who probably had the better education. In all but one of the personality tests the general summary scores are closely alike, but a good deal of difference occurs in the detailed responses. On the Downey Will-Temperament Test there is a rather large difference in total score, corresponding to the difference in mental ability. Some difference in personality is suggested by the differences in handwriting. There is also some difference in facial expression and in observable manner, Olive being somewhat freer, more spontaneous, and disposed to take the initiative.

Since Olive's superiority in ability is attested by five different measures, there can be no doubt of its existence and of its substantial amount. The fact that the difference in ability is correlated with a difference in environment strongly suggests that the environment is at least partly responsible for it. The close similarity in the tests of personality indicates close native resemblance. In fact, the personality tests themselves reveal greater similarity than is suggested by an observation of the sisters' personality as revealed in social intercourse. Apparently these differences, like those in ability, have been brought about by a different social environment acting on natures which are fundamentally alike.

On the whole, then, quite marked differences in ability and somewhat less pronounced differences in personality appear, and it seems probable that these differences are in considerable measure due to differences in the environment. The magnitude of these differences should, of course, not be exaggerated. In ability, to be sure, the sisters are less alike than are the average siblings or fraternal twins. In personal appearance, manner, and general behavior, however, they are probably more alike than the average siblings or fraternal twins, though in these respects we do not have good objective basis for comparison. In general, it seems safe to say that this pair exhibits greater difference in ability than in personality.

CASE II. TWINS ELEANORE AND GEORGIANA

These young women, twenty-seven years old when examined, were born in New York City and were left in an orphanage without any information about the parents. They were adopted by two sets of foster-parents. Eleanore was adopted when eighteen months old and Georgiana when twenty months old, neither family knowing that their adopted child was a twin. The twins were brought together at the age of twenty-one by a fortunate incident that is related in chapter ix. For nearly twenty years they were entirely unknown to each other, although they lived not very far apart—one in Indiana and the other in Michigan. They had lived and worked together for over five years when we examined them.

EDUCATIONAL CAREERS

Eleanore went to school in a medium-sized Indian city. When she had completed the fifth grade, she was greatly needed at home as an aid to her invalid foster-mother and left school. This was the last of her formal schooling. No further scholastic work was carried on at home, but at eighteen Eleanore became an assistant to a dentist and has had occasion to learn a good deal about that profession. She must have received some intellectual training from this work, for she is known to be very efficient.

Georgiana, because of the death of her foster-mother less than two years after she had been adopted, was placed in a Roman Catholic school when she was six and continued her education in this institution until she completed the eighth grade. The last year of her grade school was spent in a girls' boarding-school in Detroit. She continued through a full high-school course in the same school, studying music along with the regular academic courses and completing the full music course in four years. She then took a course in normal school lasting three years. It was during this period that the twins first met. After finishing normal school, Georgiana moved to Eleanore's home city and there taught in the parochial school. She also gave piano lessons in the evening. For two and a half years prior to our examination of the twins Georgiana had been a doctor's assistant in the same building where Eleanore was a dentist's assistant. Both seem to consider their present very similar work ideally suited to them.

There is, therefore, a difference of ten years of schooling, to say nothing of musical education, between these twins. This is the second largest educational difference we have found among our separated twins.

SOCIAL ENVIRONMENTS

The cultural and economic status of the two foster-homes was much the same, but Georgiana lost her foster-mother when she was three and one-

PLATE III

CASE II, ELEANORE (*left*) AND GEORGIANA AT ABOUT TWENTY-FIVE
YEARS OF AGE

(The differences in position and lighting in the photograph make them appear less
similar than they really are.)

half years old and her foster-father when she was eight years old, so her home life was of short duration, most of her life being spent in girls' schools. Eleanore was reared in the family of rather elderly people along with a foster-brother and a foster-sister, respectively nineteen and twenty-one years older than herself. Both of these foster-sibs married and left home when Eleanore was about eight. The foster-father was a business man in fairly comfortable circumstances. Neither he nor his wife had received much education, the wife being completely illiterate. Eleanore worked in a shirt factory for several years before obtaining her present position as assistant to a prominent dentist.

PHYSICAL ENVIRONMENTS

There seems to have been no notable differences in physical environments. Neither has had any serious illnesses. They have lived in essentially the same part of the country, and their food and living conditions offer no contrasts. The only difference that might be classed as physical is that Georgiana has done a good deal more manual work than Eleanore, though her work has never been very burdensome.

PHYSICAL RESEMBLANCES AND DIFFERENCES

These twins belong to that group of identical twins that are practically indistinguishable in appearance. They are now about as similar as the most similar of our identical twins reared together. Georgiana was about an inch taller and weighed five pounds more than Eleanore, that is, she is just a size larger physically. The head width of Eleanore is 14.2 centimeters; of Georgiana, 14.1 centimeters. The head length of Eleanore is 17.7 centimeters; that of Georgiana, 17.75 centimeters. Both have the same almost black, naturally wavy hair, somewhat coarse, and with scattering white hairs. The crown whorl is clockwise in both. Both are fully right-handed. The eye color was light reddish brown in both. All four ears are nearly identical—long, narrow, and flat. Lower front teeth have a pronounced overbite in both, and the median line of the tooth row is distinctly on the left side in both. The teeth are rather regular and in equally good condition. The palm-print formulas, alone, would strongly support a monozygotic diagnosis, for the two left palms are far more similar than is either to her own right palm. The same is true for the fingerprints of the two right hands. The total ridge-count values of finger patterns are: Eleanore, 79; Georgiana, 82—a very close correspondence.

Thus, there is no greater difference physically between these twins than would be expected in identical twins reared together.

TABLE 48

TEST RECORD AND ENVIRONMENTAL RATING OF PAIR NO. 2
(ELEANORE AND GEORGIANA)

Test	Eleanore	Georgiana	Diff.	Ratio of Diff. to Mean. Diff.
Stanford-Binet:				
M.A.	10–6	12–5	23 mo.	1.49
I.Q.	66	78	12	1.46
Otis S.-A.:				
Score	11	26	15	....
I.Q.	69	84	15	1.88
Percentage right	29.7	74.3	44.6	3.11
Otis Advanced:				
M.A.	9–10	14–1	51	....
I.Q.	32	83	51	....
American Council score*	....	....	....	
International score	69	98	29	1.87
Stanford Achievement:				
Reading age	11–4	15–11	55 mo.	....
Arithmetic	8–6	10–11	29	....
Nature study and science	12–0	12–8	8	....
History and literature	10–7	12–9	26	....
Language usage	11–2	15–7	53	....
Dictation	12–1	16–9	56	....
Total	10–11	14–1	38	2.34
Downey:				
Total	56	59	3	.33
Pattern difference	....	....	2.9	1.46
Woodworth-Mathews:				
Number of neurotic traits	18	26	8	1.60
Pressey Emotions:				
Total crossed out	159	232	73	1.55
Deviations	58	50	8	1.64
Kent-Rosanoff:				
Number of common responses	79	95	16	1.66
Average frequency	105	143	38	.96
Number of identical responses	24	24†	....	....
Average of all tests	....	....	....	1.64
Environmental rating:				
Educational	....	....	32	2.12
Social	....	....	14	.78
Physical	....	....	9	.57

* Omitted.
† Ratio to mean, 1.67.

The differences on all the tests of ability, including intelligence and educational achievement, are consistently in favor of Georgiana, who had the superior education. The ratios of the differences on the intelligence tests are somewhat lower than the ratio of the rating of educational opportunity, while the ratio on the Stanford Achievement Test is somewhat larger. The significant general fact is that all the differences in ability are in the same direction as the difference in education and that they are at least half again as large as the average differences of all nineteen pairs.

That the superiority of Georgiana cannot be ascribed merely to the possession of information or to facility in the use of language is shown by an analysis of the test scores. The difference on the International Test, which is a nonlanguage test and does not include materials taught in school, yields one of the largest differences. Many of the tests of the Stanford-Binet Scale passed by Georgiana and failed by Eleanore utilize materials which are not to be found in the school. School work can be thought to prepare for the passing of these tests only on the assumption that the mental operations which are required in passing them are facilitated by the work of the school. Examples of such tests are the "ball and field" test, requiring one to trace the path he would follow to find a ball lost in a circular field; the "dissected sentences" test, requiring one to put a jumbled list of words into an order which makes sense; "repeating digits backward"; "interpretation of pictures"; and the "code" test, requiring one to translate a sentence into a simple code made of lines and figures.

The very large difference in the percentage right on the Otis test is due to the fact that, whereas the sisters attempted nearly the same number of items, Eleanore made 26 errors against Georgiana's 9. The difference in the scores is therefore not due to a difference in speed of performance but rather of accuracy.

The Otis Group Intelligence Scale, Advanced Examination, was not given to the whole group of twins. It is more difficult than the Otis Self-administering Test and yields the large difference of 51 months, or 51 points, in index of brightness—an index somewhat like the I.Q.

On the Stanford Achievement Test the greatest differences are on the language tests, reading, language usage, and spelling (dictation); and the smallest difference is in nature study and science, in which field Eleanore's reading may, perhaps, have partly made up her deficiency in schooling. However, Georgiana is superior on all parts of the tests. Both make their highest score in spelling and their lowest in arithmetic, which suggests a similarity in pattern of endowment.

On the Downey Will-Temperament Test the total scores are similar, but the difference in pattern is rather marked. The greatest differences are in speed of movement, freedom from load, and finality of judgment, in which Georgiana makes the larger score; and reaction to contradiction and resistance to opposition, in which Eleanore's score is larger. According to Dr. Downey's interpretation, this means that Georgiana is more rapid and uninhibited in her actions and that Eleanore is more aggressive.

The difference on the Woodworth-Mathews test is greater than the average, Georgiana revealing more neurotic symptoms than Eleanore. Since

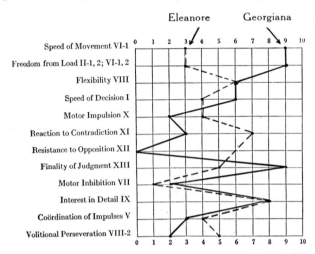

FIG. 16.—Downey Individual Will-Temperament Test profiles

the correlations in chapter xii do not indicate any relationship between score on this test and any of the three features of the environment, we cannot attach any general significance to the fact that the twin with more schooling shows more neurotic symptoms. It is possible, however, that in this particular case the schooling was of such a nature as to induce neurotic symptoms. It is also possible that other unknown features of the environment are responsible. Of the 18 possible identical responses, 12 are actually identical. Both twins make somewhat larger scores than the average, which is 15. They differ from the average in the same direction.

The difference in the responses of Eleanore and Georgiana on the Pressey Test of the Emotions is rather marked, the difference in both the number of words marked and the number of deviations from common responses being about one and one-half times the mean difference. It may be sig-

nificant that Eleanore deviates more from the common mode of responding
in both the free-association test and this test. Since Eleanore marks fewer
words altogether in every part of the test, the greater number of uncommon
responses she makes is the more striking. It is not true for the group as a
whole that the one with more education gives more uncommon responses.
The difference in this case may be due to some special factor in the environment or to a native difference. Georgiana appears to have more dislikes,
fears, worries, and neurotic symptoms than Eleanore, but her attitudes are
more conventional.

TABLE 49

TOTAL NUMBER OF WORDS CROSSED OUT AND NUMBER OF
DEVIATIONS ON THE PRESSEY X–O TEST

TEST	WORDS CROSSED OUT		DEVIATIONS	
	Eleanore	Georgiana	Eleanore	Georgiana
Test I: Unpleasant words..................	32	46	13	15
Test II: Words associated in mind with given word.........................	28	47	10	7
Test III: Things thought wrong.............	53	75	15	12
Test IV: Worries.........................	46	64	20	16
Total.........................	159	232	58	50

The number of identical responses on the Kent-Rosanoff test is rather
high, namely, 24; though it is still well below the number of identical responses given by the same person at different times (41). It indicates a good
deal of community in thought processes. Notwithstanding this, the sisters
differ about as much as do the entire group of twins in the average frequency
of their responses and more than the group as a whole in the number of common responses they give. In general, the large difference in education does
not seem to have produced an unusual difference in the association of ideas.
The one with more education, Georgiana, gives more common responses
than does Eleanore; but this fact may not be significant since, for the group
as a whole, there is a small negative correlation between frequency of responses and amount of education.

PLATE IV

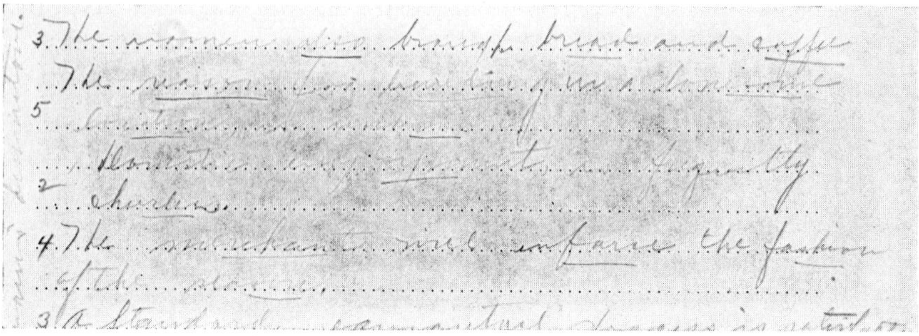

HANDWRITING OF ELEANORE, CASE II

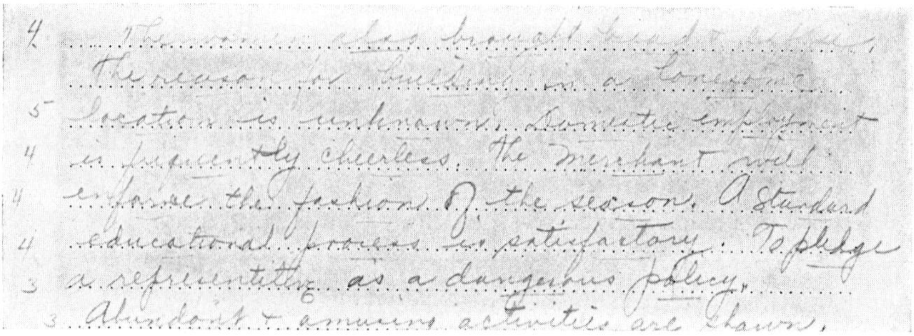

HANDWRITING OF GEORGIANA, CASE II

HANDWRITING

It is evident from an examination of the handwriting of Eleanore and Georgiana that there is not much superficial resemblance beyond what might be expected to result from similar instruction. The two would never be confused. In Georgiana's writing the letters are more complete and better formed, while in Eleanore's there is an economy of strokes which causes some letters to be slurred over and some strokes, particularly in the loops, to be omitted. Georgiana's writing is more decidedly feminine in style than Eleanore's. She appears to have exerted less pressure. Both are regular in slant, fairly fluent, and both extend the lower loops into the line below. In spite of these similarities, the differences appear to be the more striking and to suggest marked differences in personality and modes of behavior. One is tempted to venture the suggestion that Georgiana's writing indicates greater conventionality and hence agrees with the Kent-Rosanoff and Pressey tests, but this is perhaps too speculative a suggestion.

SUMMARY

In physical appearance, and in all physical characteristics except height, the twins are remarkably similar. The difference in height, 1.1 inches, is common among identical twins reared together. No marked contrast in physical environment appears to have existed. Under these conditions genetic identity has produced two individuals who are practically identical in physical traits.

In general intellectual ability and in general scholastic attainment Georgiana is decidedly superior to Eleanore. Expressed in terms of years, the difference ranges from two to four years. The difference is greatest on the most difficult test. It is nearly as great on the intelligence tests as on the educational tests. While the scores on the nonverbal test cannot strictly be compared with the others, since it is not standardized in terms of mental age, the difference on it appears to be fully as marked as on the verbal tests. Georgiana, then, who received the more education, is markedly and consistently superior to Eleanore in intellectual ability.

On the tests of will-temperament and emotion the responses of the twins are far from identical. In will-temperament Georgiana is more rapid and unrestrained in movement but less aggressive. The sisters gave themselves markedly different self-ratings. Georgiana's free associations resemble those of people in general more closely than do those of Eleanore. The twins gave the same word in response more often than would pairs of persons picked at random, but most of their responses differ. Some similarity in association of ideas is indicated, but there is also marked difference.

In the two tests of emotions the responses of the sisters differed widely.

Georgiana appears to be the more emotional and also the less stable of the two. In the Woodworth-Mathews test the number of unfavorable responses and a good many of the particular responses were different. The difference in emotional reaction, as measured by the tests, is rather marked. The handwriting differs markedly in general appearance, and an analysis shows that it differs in important essential features. On the whole, the differences on the tests of personality seem to be nearly as great as those on the ability tests.

In the present case Eleanore left school and remained at home for several years. She began to work in an office at eighteen years of age. Georgiana, on the other hand, lived in a Roman Catholic boarding-school for several years and then took a normal-school course. Subsequently, she taught school and gave music lessons. It is quite conceivable that this difference may have caused large differences in personality, though specific relations are not obvious. The differences in ability, however, are larger than the differences in personality, as in the first pair.

The interpretation of the differences in personality in relation to differences in the environment is not so clear as that of the differences in ability. The whole problem will be discussed at the close of the case studies. In the meantime, the differences themselves may be described in comparison with the differences in the whole group, and such relations with the environment as seem obvious may be noted.

CASE III.   TWINS PAUL C. AND PAUL O.

These young men, twenty-three years of age when examined, were born in a small Illinois town. Paul C. was nursed and cared for by his mother until he was two months old, when he was adopted by Mrs. C. of a near-by city. Paul O. was kept until he was five months old and then put in a Chicago orphanage, from which he was taken almost at once by Mr. and Mrs. O., who lived in a small rural town in Illinois. The two foster-families knew nothing of each other, and neither knew that their adopted child was a twin. By a curious circumstance Paul C. learned from some family papers that he had a twin brother, and after a long search located him and had one visit with him before we examined them. The story of their meeting is told in chapter ix. The separation of these twins was complete from infancy to manhood.

EDUCATIONAL CAREERS

Paul C. lived in the small town where he was born until he was thirteen years old, attending school there. When he was in the eighth grade he moved to a larger town, where he lived for two years and started high school.

PLATE V

CASE III, PAUL C. (*left*) AND PAUL O. AT TWENTY-THREE
YEARS OF AGE

Before he had finished the first year, however, he moved to a medium-sized Michigan city where he completed high school, being graduated at the age of eighteen. For two years after graduation he worked in the business office of a furniture factory. Having a liking for this kind of work, he took a ten months' course in a commercial and technical school. For eighteen months he was employed in office and sales work with a Grand Rapids furniture firm. At the time when he came here for examination he had just finished a three months' course in accounting at a South Bend business college.

Paul O. has never lived very long in one place. His foster-father is a telegraph operator and has been moved about from one small place to another. Paul O.'s environment has been strictly rural. He attended grade school in three different villages. He took the whole high-school course in the rural town where he now lives, being graduated at the same time as Paul C. During the year after graduation Paul O. traveled a good deal in the western states and entered the engineering school of Iowa State College. Finding the work there, especially mathematics, too difficult, he gave it up before the year was over and returned to his home to become assistant postmaster, a position he has occupied for the last three years.

Quantitatively, it appears that Paul C. has had about seven months more schooling than Paul O. and in larger, if not better, schools. The difference is not great.

SOCIAL ENVIRONMENTS

There are some contrasts of note between the social milieus of these twins. Paul C. has had much experience in city and business life since he was thirteen, while Paul O. has had an exclusively rural environment. Paul C. was brought up as an only child, while Paul O. was reared with a foster-brother and foster-sister several years younger than he. He has always been treated as one of the family. The economic status of the two foster-families was much the same, Paul C.'s foster-father being a painter and paper hanger, and Paul O.'s a telegraph operator. There are few, if any, cultural influences in either home.

PHYSICAL ENVIRONMENTS

Climatic conditions have been much the same, and there have been no marked contrasts in the living conditions of the two homes. Paul C. was rather sickly as a baby. He did not learn to walk until he was two years old. He had measles at two and chicken pox at twelve but seems to have had no serious illnesses. He has taken systematic exercise and is now strong and healthy. Paul O. was the stronger baby of the two and was the one the mother preferred to keep. He had scarlet fever and mumps almost simultaneously when he was eleven, measles at nine, and a light attack of smallpox at fifteen. Tonsils and adenoids were removed at sixteen. His disease record is distinctly worse than that of Paul C.

One might assume that country life, even if it involved no active farm work, would be just as healthy as life in cities, but Paul O. is not in as good physical condition as Paul C. at this time.

PHYSICAL RESEMBLANCES AND DIFFERENCES

While the facial appearance of these twins is less similar than that of the average of identical twins reared together, they meet all the requirements of monozygocity unusually well. There is less than $\frac{1}{2}$-inch difference in height, Paul C. being the taller. Paul C. is over 10 pounds heavier and much better developed muscularly. They are both right-handed and have clockwise hair whorl. The head length of Paul C. is 18.6 centimeters; that of Paul O., 18.4 centimeters. The head width of Paul C. is 15.3 centimeters; that of Paul O., 14.8 centimeters. Thus, Paul C. has the larger head. The eye color of both is red brown. The hair is medium brown, soft, straight, and is thinning in front in both, but Paul O.'s hair is distinctly thinner than Paul C.'s. The skin is equally fair and clear in both. All four ears are strikingly similar. The teeth are regular and very similar, Paul C. having three and Paul O. two lower molars filled. The features are very similar except that Paul C. keeps his eyes less wide open and has a firmer set to his mouth. The dermatoglyphics are in themselves sufficient for monozygotic diagnosis. The two left palms are extremely similar as are also the two rights, but there is considerable difference between the two hands in each individual. The same is true for the finger patterns of the two left hands. The ridge-count total of Paul C. is 102; that of Paul O., 105—a very close correspondence for such high numbers.

Thus, the only notable physical differences between these twins are a distinct superiority of Paul C. in physical condition (reflected in body weight and muscularity) and in facial expression.

TESTS OF ABILITY

On the tests of general mental ability and educational achievement Paul C. is superior with the exception of one, the Stanford-Binet. On this test the difference is negligible since it is less than the average difference on repeated tests of the same individual. Paul C. failed on two tests of repeating digits, which Paul O. passed, but was superior in vocabulary. On the three other intelligence tests Paul C. is consistently superior. This is true on most of the parts of the tests, two of which are divided into parts, as well as on the tests as a whole. Paul C. is also superior on each part of the Stanford Achievement Test except arithmetic, on which Paul O. is superior by six

TABLE 50

TEST RECORD AND ENVIRONMENTAL RATING OF PAIR NO. 3
(PAUL C. AND PAUL O.)

Test	Paul C.	Paul O.	Diff.	Ratio of Diff. to Mean Diff.
Stanford-Binet:				
M.A.	15–11	16–2	3 mo.	.19
I.Q.	99	101	2	.24
Otis S.-A.:				
Score	52	42	10	....
I.Q.	110	100	10	1.25
Percentage right	81.6	78.0	3.6	.25
American Council score	101	74	27	1.00
International score	160	147	13	.84
Stanford Achievement:				
Reading age	18–1	16–3	22 mo.	....
Arithmetic	15–1	15–7	6	....
Nature study and science	17–6	16–1	17	....
History and literature	15–9	15–4	5	....
Language usage	18–6	15–4	38	....
Dictation	17–6	16–2	16	....
Total	17–1	15–9	16	.98
Downey:				
Total	55	61	6	.66
Pattern difference	....	....	1.7	.86
Woodworth-Mathews:				
Number of neurotic traits	13	15	2	.40
Pressey Emotions:				
Total crossed out	161	257	96	2.04
Deviations	51	45	6	1.23
Kent-Rosanoff:				
Number of common responses	98	100	2	.21
Average frequency	163	133	30	.76
Number of identical responses	29	29*	....	....
Average of all tests	....	....	....	0.78
Environmental Rating:				
Educational	....	....	12	.79
Social	....	....	15	.84
Physical	....	....	12	.76

* Ratio to mean, 2.02.

months. The ratios of superiority on these tests are approximately one, indicating a difference about equal to the average. That Paul C.'s superiority is not due primarily to speed is shown by the fact that he is more accurate on the Otis Self-administering Test. It would probably not be correct to infer that the equality on the Binet test indicates equality in native ability, whereas the superiority on the other tests is due to better education. Such an inference is confused by the fact that the International Test is probably as much a measure of native ability as is the Binet test. We shall probably have to content ourselves with the statement that the burden of evidence points to a superiority on the part of Paul C. and that this superiority agrees with the fact that he has had somewhat more education and has lived in a somewhat more stimulating environment.

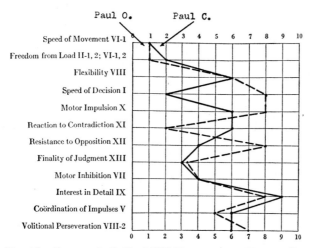

FIG. 17.—Downey Individual Will-Temperament Test profiles

TESTS OF PERSONALITY

The patterns of behavior represented by the Downey Will-Temperament Test, the profiles of which are shown in Figure 17, are more alike than for the separated twins as a whole, both in the total score and in the pattern itself. Both young men, to follow Dr. Downey's interpretation, are rather slow and deliberate, rather careful and interested in details, and only moderately aggressive. On only three of the subtests is there a marked contrast. Paul O. is more rapid in making decisions. He also resists opposition more vigorously but, paradoxically, does not react so strongly to contradiction. We can offer no very plausible explanation of this difference. On the whole, the similarities are the more numerous and striking.

On the Woodworth-Mathews test the total number of unfavorable responses agrees very closely, but the particular unfavorable responses made by each differ widely. The agreement and difference are as follows:

Responses both favorable	50
One favorable and the other unfavorable.....	22
Both unfavorable........................	3
Total...............................	75

Some of the unfavorable symptoms reported by Paul O. but not by Paul C. are that he feels that nobody loves him, his feelings are easily hurt, he gets cross over very small things, and he has a hard time making up his mind about things. On the other hand, Paul C. reports the following unfavorable symptoms not reported by Paul O. He has a habit of twitching his head, neck, or shoulders, feels that nobody quite understands him, lives a make-believe life, is bothered by a feeling that things are not real, and has many headaches. These are all commonly recognized neurotic symptoms. They do not appear to fall into clearly distinguishable classes. What might be significant, if we could discover it, would be the kind of situation which produces these symptoms. The particular symptoms of emotional conflict may not be particularly significant. Our conclusion is that, so far as this test goes, the brothers do not differ greatly in emotional reactions.

The Pressey Test of the Emotions gives a different picture from the other three tests of personality. This test appears to indicate a striking difference between the brothers in their emotional reactions. The number of items which Paul C. marked is below the median of college students in all four divisions of the test, whereas Paul O.'s score is approximately at the upper quartile in three of the four, and his total score is about at the upper quartile. The details are shown in Table 51.

In Test II, "words associated with a given word," the boys are similar, both rating low in number of words so associated. The scores of 34 and 38 fall in the lowest quartile.

In "unpleasant words," Test I, Paul C. is slightly above the twenty-fifth centile, while Paul O. is considerably above the seventy-fifth. Paul O. is unpleasantly affected by eighty of the one hundred words given, including "roar," "failure," "tremble," "dirty," "nervous," "unfair," "influence," "black," "whisper," "sneeze," "small," "giggle," "queer," and "sticky."

In "things thought wrong," Test III, Paul C. is close to the twenty-fifth percentile, while Paul O. is close to the seventy-fifth. Things Paul O. considers wrong but Paul C. does not are begging, flirting, spitting, anger, suspicion, dulness, fussy, childish, sporty, snob, graft, worry, divorce, fighting, betting, and boasting.

Paul C.'s "worries," Test IV, number considerably less than Paul O.'s, 29 being in the lowest quartile, while 55 is at the seventy-fifth percentile point.

TABLE 51

TOTAL NUMBER OF WORDS CROSSED OUT AND NUMBER OF
DEVIATIONS ON THE PRESSEY X–O TEST

TEST	WORDS CROSSED OUT		DEVIATIONS	
	Paul C.	Paul O.	Paul C.	Paul O.
Test I: Unpleasant words................	34	80	13	8
Test II: Words associated in mind with given word.........................	34	38	9	9
Test III: Things thought wrong............	64	84	13	11
Test IV: Worries........................	29	55	16	17
Total........................	161	257	51	45

TABLE 52

ANALYSIS OF THE RESPONSES TO TEST I

Type of Reaction	Paul C.	Paul O.
Disgust........................	16	21
Fear...........................	8	21
Sex............................	7	16
Self-feeling....................	3	22
Total......................	34	80

Further analysis of Tests I and IV show the nature of the "unpleasant words" and of the "worries."

Since the list is made up of twenty-five words of each type, it appears that Paul O. is most affected by the "self-feeling" words, while Paul C. is least affected by that type. Paul O. appears to have more fears than Paul C., and to be somewhat more affected by sex words.

Paul O. is evidently more neurotic and melancholic than Paul C. Some examples of Paul O.'s associations in Test II are: death—welcome, living—

bare, wish—die, sleep—worry. These seem to bear out the indications of Test IV regarding melancholy.

Their associative responses, as brought out by the Kent-Rosanoff Free Association Test, are rather similar (see Table 50). The number of common responses and the average frequency of responses differ less than do the nineteen pairs on the average. The number of identical responses, 29, is high. It is not far from the number of identical responses that might be given by the same person taking the test twice. The evidence of the free-association test, then, points to a rather marked similarity in the pattern of thought of these twins.

The tests of personality present a rather confused picture and one hard to reconcile with the impression made by the young men on the observers. The Downey test and the Woodworth-Mathews test yield very similar

TABLE 53

ANALYSIS OF THE RESPONSES TO TEST IV

Type of Personality Indicated	Paul C.	Paul O.
Suspicious (paranoid)	4	4
Jumpy (neurotic)	5	13
Self-conscious (shut-in)	7	10
Melancholic	6	16
Hypochondriacal	7	12
Total	29	55

scores. The similarity in pattern on the Downey test is rather striking. The Kent-Rosanoff test elicits a large number of identical responses, and the commonness of responses is rather similar. The greatest difference is in the Pressey test, which seems to indicate that Paul O. is distinctly less stable and more emotional. The difference in handwriting may be largely conventional, but it suggests more self-consciousness on the part of Paul O. and to this extent agrees with the Pressey test.

The observers describe the social behavior of the brothers in these words: "Paul O. impresses the observer as having an affable, free, and unrestrained manner, whereas Paul C. is constrained, taciturn, and might almost be thought to be sullen." Again, "Paul C. impresses one as more dignified, more reserved, more self-contained, more unafraid, more experienced, and less friendly." On the other hand, one of the observers reports that "Paul O. is more unstable emotionally." This judgment agrees with the Pressey test. Taking the tests and observations together, it appears that the differences in personality are somewhat greater than the differences in ability but that they are, on the whole, moderate in amount. The tests do not agree very closely with the observations as to kind of differences which do exist, and this somewhat minimizes their significance.

HANDWRITING

The handwriting of Paul C. and Paul O., as reproduced in Plate VI, shows marked differences. Paul O. has two styles of writing. One is a highly formal, somewhat ornate, and self-conscious style. It is more clearly represented in a letter written to one of the investigators than in the test (see Pl. VII). It will be noted that this writing is slightly backhand, that the letters are all carefully drawn, and that some of the capitals approach the ornate. There are a number of variations in the method of writing the same letters, as though the writer were thinking about the forms instead of writing from habit. Note the variation in the final *t*, the lower loops, and the initial *T*. The highly variable character of Paul O.'s ordinary writing may be explained by the influence of this formal style, conflicting with a more fluent style developed as a result of the demands of the writer's daily work as an assistant postmaster. He starts out in his rather formal style of vertical writing but soon lapses into a more fluent sloping style. Throughout the page there is frequent oscillation between the two styles.

Paul C.'s writing shows nothing of this vacillation. It is uniform, straightforward, unaffected, and fluent. However, it is not so fluent as to show neglect of details. While the letters are not formed with excessively close adherence to the conventional forms, each letter is completed, and there is no slurring-over of the letters in the haste to push ahead. The activity is poised and consistent.

The difference is one which might well have been produced by different experiences operating to influence the personality of two persons originally very similar.

SUMMARY

The picture presented by these twin brothers is somewhat involved, but upon analysis several rather definite outlines emerge. Paul C. has had somewhat better educational advantages and has, perhaps, had a somewhat more stimulating social environment. In ability he shows consistent superiority on all the tests except the Stanford-Binet. The difference is about the same as the average difference of all nineteen pairs, with the one exception.

Some of the personality tests suggest close similarity and some rather marked difference. The contradiction, as between the Woodworth-Mathews and the Pressey tests, does not seem readily explicable. However, there are indications of certain rather marked differences in personality, or at least in behavior, as shown in the Pressey test and in the handwriting, which cannot be explained away. These indications of difference are supported by the observation of the manner and social behavior of the young men. It appears reasonable to conclude that there is a basic close similarity in the organic groundwork of personality but that either environment or variations in the developmental process have produced certain differences in the end result.

PLATE VI

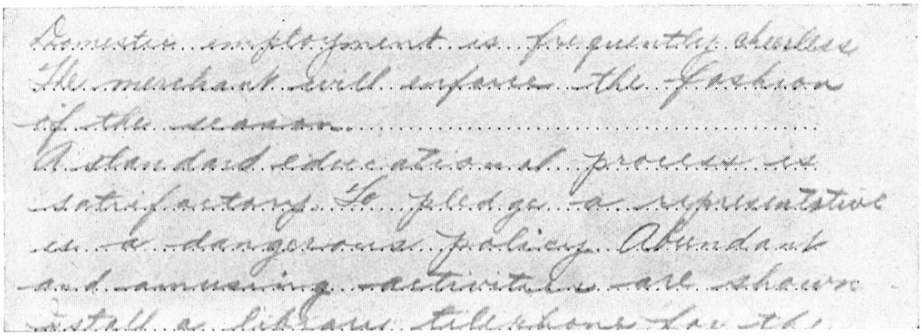
Domestic employment is frequently cheerless
The merchant will enforce the fashion
of the season.
A standard educational process is
satisfactory. To pledge a representative
is a dangerous policy. Abundant
and amusing activities are shown
Install a library telephone for the

Handwriting of Paul C., Case III

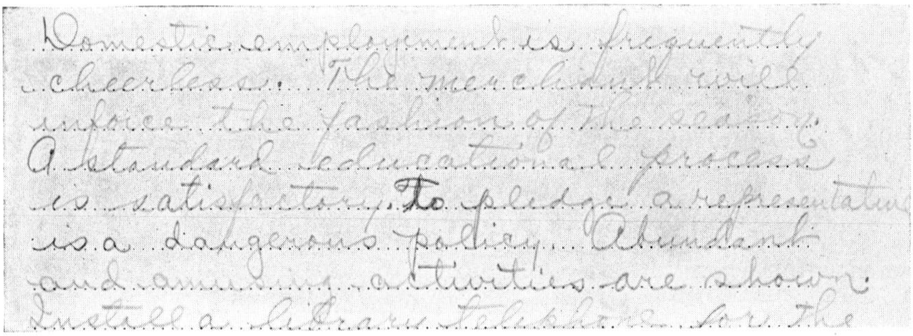
Domestic employment is frequently
cheerless. The merchant will
inforce the fashion of the season.
A standard educational process
is satisfactory. To pledge a representative
is a dangerous policy. Abundant
and amusing activities are shown:
Install a library telephone for the

Handwriting of Paul O., Case III

PLATE VII

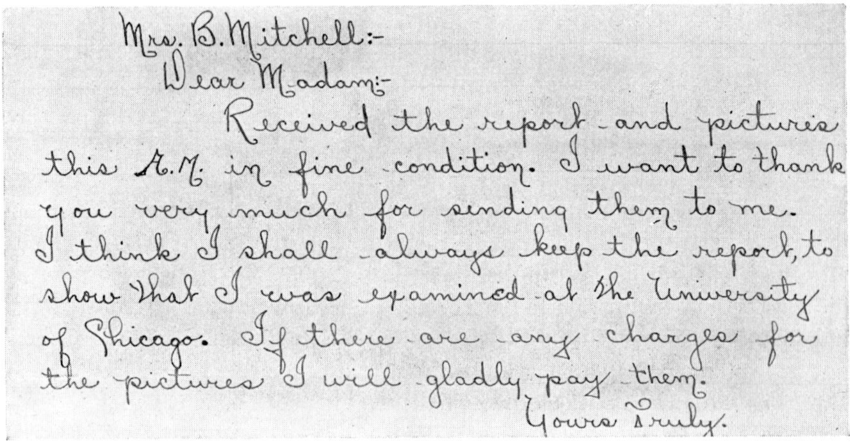
Mrs. B. Mitchell:-
Dear Madam:-
Received the report and pictures
this A.M. in fine condition. I want to thank
you very much for sending them to me.
I think I shall always keep the report, to
show that I was examined at the University
of Chicago. If there are any charges for
the pictures I will gladly pay them.
Yours Truly.

Formal Writing of Paul O.

CASE IV. TWINS MABEL AND MARY

These young women, twenty-nine years old when examined, were separated at five months of age and were adopted by different families of close relatives. They have always lived rather near together in the same part of Ohio and have visited back and forth all their lives. Thus, their separation has been far less complete than in most of our other cases, yet they are now less similar than the majority of the other pairs of separated twins studied. Both girls lived on farms until they were six; but after that time Mary moved to a small town where she has lived ever since, while Mabel stayed on the farm and has lived the typical life of a farm woman.

EDUCATIONAL CAREERS

Mary went through grade school in her home town and attended for three years the small local high school—a school of about forty pupils. Then she took her final year in a large city high school of sixteen hundred pupils. She has always been in the upper 25 per cent of her class. In grade school she preferred English and arithmetic; in high school, English and Latin. She began the study of music at ten years of age and has kept up her music ever since. For some years she has given piano lessons in the evenings. For a good many years she has clerked in her foster-father's store, and her life has been lived largely indoors.

Mabel's education was confined to attendance in country schools. Country schools have a shorter session than others. Mabel completed the eighth grade and had barely started her high-school course when she was badly needed at home to take care of her foster-mother's new baby. Thus, her formal schooling came abruptly to an end. Since that time she has had no time for cultural pursuits. Her reading has been confined to newspapers and popular magazines.

SOCIAL ENVIRONMENTS

The greatest contrast is that of town life versus country life, with all the social corollaries involved. The other children in Mary's family were ten or more years older than she and did not seem much like brothers and sisters, while Mabel was brought up in a family of boys and girls of about her own age. She has always been treated as one of the family. There is no marked difference in economic status between the two families, both being in very good circumstances though not wealthy. Both have been brought up in a religious environment. Neither young woman has traveled to any extent, the trip to Chicago being the longest journey either had taken. A part of the social environment of Mabel was a contact with farm hands and others of that type. She has, like other farm women, some familiarity with

PLATE VIII

CASE IV, MARY (*left*) AND MABEL AT SEVENTEEN YEARS OF AGE
(At this time the differences noted in the text had not developed)

animal breeding and other farm pursuits that would tend to dull certain types of sensitiveness. Mary has been more sheltered from the cruder aspects of life and has been brought up definitely as a lady.

PHYSICAL AND HEALTH ENVIRONMENTS

Both twins had the usual children's diseases. Mary had measles twice, chicken pox, and whooping cough, and she has had what she calls "flu" almost every winter. Mabel had measles twice and whooping cough but is rarely troubled with "flu" or bad colds. At the time of the examination Mabel was in superb health and Mary had a low-grade cold and was feeling under par.

As a factor in the physical environment it seems to us that the active manual labor on the farm, much of it out of doors, has had much to do with Mabel's robust health; while Mary's largely sedentary, indoor life and lack of exercise have had a deleterious effect on her health and bodily vigor. This last contrast is one of considerable proportions.

PHYSICAL RESEMBLANCES AND DIFFERENCES

The twins were extremely similar as babies and were hardly distinguishable at two years of age, as is evidenced by the photograph. Even when they were seventeen (Pl. VIII), they were as similar physically as almost any pair of identical twins. Since that time they have grown progressively more dissimilar, largely as the result of a very marked difference in weight, muscular development, and general health.

When examined, Mary was $65\frac{1}{4}$ inches tall and Mabel $66\frac{3}{4}$ inches. Mary weighed $110\frac{3}{4}$ pounds; Mabel, $138\frac{1}{2}$ pounds—a difference of nearly 28 pounds. This difference is largely one of muscular development, for Mabel is not in the least fat. Mary's head length is 17.2 centimeters; Mabel's, 17.25 centimeters. Mary's head width is 13.4 centimeters; Mabel's, 13.3 centimeters. Mabel's hands and feet are both distinctly larger than Mary's, due probably to manual labor. Both are right-handed and have clockwise crown whorl. The hair color differs slightly, both being medium brown, but Mabel's is a little lighter, doubtless due to exposure to the sun. The hair is now short in both but at one time was unusually long and silky in both. Mabel's complexion now is clearer and a better color than Mary's. The features are still strikingly similar—the nose long and narrow, mouth small, lips rather thin, and chin prominent. The teeth are nearly identical in shape and condition. The ears are almost identical—small and close to the head. Both are farsighted, and their glasses have nearly the same correction, Mary's having a little greater correction. Both use the left eye in sighting. The palm prints and fingerprints, which have been published,

TABLE 54

TEST RECORD AND ENVIRONMENTAL RATING OF PAIR NO. 4
(MABEL AND MARY)

Test	Mabel	Mary	Diff.	Ratio of Diff. to Mean Diff.
Stanford-Binet:				
M.A.	14–2	17–0	34 mo.	2.20
I.Q.	89	106	17	2.07
Otis S.-A.:				
Score	39	53	14	....
I.Q.	97	111	14	1.75
Percentage right	66.7	85.4	18.7	1.30
American Council score	45	115	70	2.59
International score	96	104	8	.52
Stanford Achievement:				
Reading age	15–6	17–2	20 mo.	....
Arithmetic	11–2	17–6	76	....
Nature study and science	15–7	16–3	8	....
History and literature	13–3	15–7	28	....
Language usage	15–4	18–6	38	....
Dictation	15–9	18–4	31	....
Total	14–5	17–3	34	2.09
Downey:				
Total	52	76	24	2.62
Pattern difference	....	....	3.0	1.52
Woodworth-Mathews:				
Number of neurotic traits	3	8	5	1.00
Pressey Emotions:				
Total crossed out	195	231	36	.76
Deviations	53	50	3	.61
Kent-Rosanoff:				
Number of common responses	95	96	1	.10
Average frequency	130	121	9	.23
Number of identical responses	18	18*	....	....
Average of all tests	....	....	....	1.38
Environmental rating:				
Educational			22	1.45
Social			15	.84
Physical			23	1.45

* Ratio to mean, 1.25.

would be sufficient in themselves to give a positive diagnosis of monozygocity. The two rights are nearly identical and so are the two lefts, while there are distinct differences between right and left hands of the two individuals. The total ridge-count values of the finger patterns are 105 for Mary and 99 for Mabel—a moderately close correspondence. Thus, in all the purely hereditary traits, there is an extremely close correspondence, but there is a great difference in body weight, general health, muscular development, and bodily vigor.

TESTS OF ABILITY

The twin with the greater amount of education, as is always the case when the difference is large, is superior in all the tests of ability. With the exception of the International Test, the difference in favor of Mary is about twice the average difference for the nineteen pairs. This amounts to nearly three years in mental age and to seventeen points in I.Q. on the Binet Scale. The International Test score, as we should expect, is less affected by the difference in education. The difference on this test has a lower correlation with difference in education than do the others. In this case the difference is less than we should expect even in the light of this fact. No explanation of this fact is at hand. On the Stanford Achievement Test Mary's superiority is consistent but is least, as we might perhaps expect, on nature study and science. Mabel's experience on the farm may have partly made up for her deficient schooling on this point. On the Otis test Mary is not only more rapid but also more accurate.

TESTS OF PERSONALITY

The difference in the total score on the Downey test is large—about two and one-half times the average difference. The significance of this total score is not very clear, but it will be remembered that the difference in total score is positively correlated with the difference on the ability tests. The superiority in total score on the part of Mary is due to greater speed and freedom of movement, more aggressiveness in reaction to contradiction and opposition, more persistent study of details, and better co-ordination of impulses. Perhaps these manifestations may be due to a greater excitability or responsiveness to the stimulation of the surroundings, particularly of persons. Mabel's responses may be characterized as somewhat more phlegmatic. This might well be the result of living in the quieter environment of the country, requiring as it does less frequent and rapid adjustments.

On the Woodworth-Mathews Personal Data Sheet both sisters deviate from the general run of our twins in the fewness of their unfavorable responses. In this respect they are alike. Mary, however, makes five more than Mabel, the difference being exactly equal to the average. From this it may, perhaps, be inferred that the more stimulating environment of the town has produced slightly more neurotic symptoms.

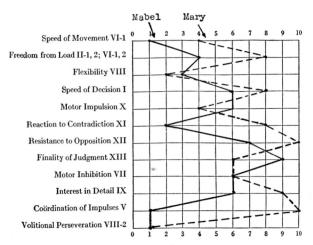

Fig. 18.—Downey Individual Will-Temperament Test profiles

TABLE 55

TOTAL NUMBER OF WORDS CROSSED OUT AND NUMBER OF DEVIATIONS ON THE PRESSEY X–O TEST

TEST	WORDS CROSSED OUT		DEVIATIONS	
	Mabel	Mary	Mabel	Mary
Test I: Unpleasant words...............	43	67	14	12
Test II: Words associated in mind with given word.........................	33	52	8	10
Test III: Things thought wrong.............	80	66	15	7
Test IV: Worries........................	39	46	16	21
Total........................	195	231	53	50

Mary's higher score on the Pressey test agrees with the finding of the Woodworth-Mathews test. As Table 55 indicates, she marked more words on all parts except Part III, "things thought wrong." Mabel's higher score on this part may be due to the greater conservatism of mores of people in the country. On the whole, the test seems to indicate that Mary's feelings are the more easily aroused.

The Kent-Rosanoff Free Association Test indicates marked similarity in the degree of commonness of the associations and a fair number of identical responses, though not so many as are given by some of the other pairs.

HANDWRITING

The handwriting specimens of only two of the pairs are enough alike to enable the one of the authors who undertook it to match them. Mary and Mabel are one of these pairs. It will be seen from the reproductions that their handwriting does have some general similarity. Examine, for instance, the word "lonesome" in the fifth sentence. The slant is nearly vertical, the letters are similarly formed, and letters have a characteristic square appearance due to the alternation of straight vertical downstrokes and diagonal connecting strokes. Nevertheless, there are also marked differences, so that the two specimens would never be mistaken for the writing of the same person. While both writings would probably be judged to be feminine in style, Mary's is considerably the more feminine of the two. More particular differences may be observed. Mary's writing is larger, the lines are closer together and overlap, loops are larger, and the pencil stroke is lighter. It appears to exhibit less restraint and a freer expression of impulses than does Mabel's. This agrees with the result of the Downey test.

SUMMARY

These twins differ markedly in physical appearance, weight, muscular development, and movements. They are very similar in strictly genetic features, and there is no doubt that they are monozygotic. The physical differences, therefore, are attributable to the fact that Mary has lived a sedentary life in town while Mabel has lived an active life on the farm.

The difference in ability is marked and agrees with the difference in educational opportunities. Mary, who was brought up in the town and had four or more years longer schooling than Mabel, made decidedly higher scores on the tests of intelligence and educational achievement. On the other hand, Mabel does not give the impression of being at all dull, and her performance on the International Test nearly equals that of her sister. She takes the lead in planning and seems to be quite competent in practical affairs.

In temperament, as revealed by the tests, the difference is less. There is a good deal of difference in general manner, due in part to a difference in physical vigor. Mabel assumes a more mannish hairdress and walks with long vigorous strides, in contrast to her sister. Mary appears from the test

PLATE IX

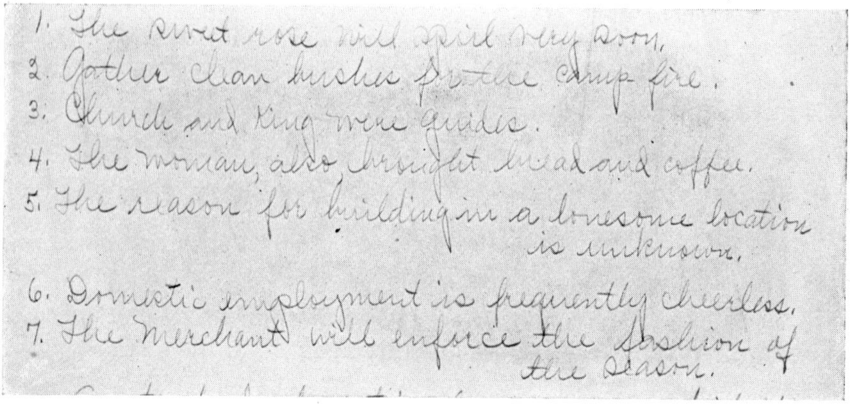
1. The sweet rose will spoil very soon.
2. Gather clean bushes for the camp fire.
3. Church and King were guides.
4. The woman, also, brought bread and coffee.
5. The reason for building in a lonesome location is unknown.
6. Domestic employment is frequently cheerless.
7. The Merchant will enforce the fashion of the season.

HANDWRITING OF MARY, CASE IV

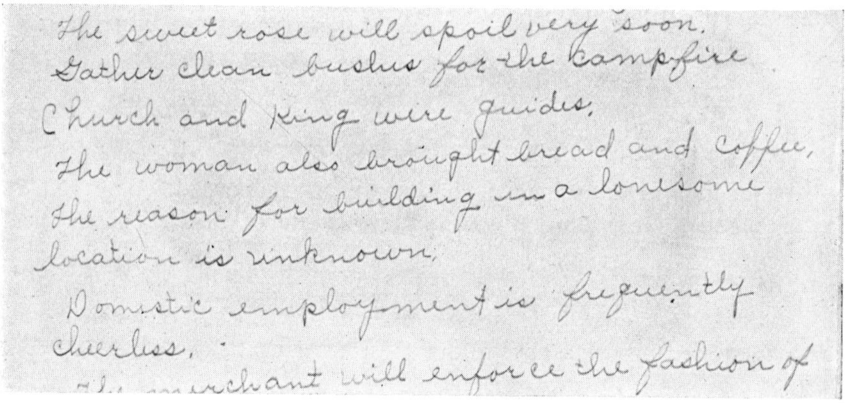
The sweet rose will spoil very soon.
Gather clean bushes for the campfire.
Church and King were guides.
The woman also brought bread and coffee.
The reason for building in a lonesome location is unknown.
Domestic employment is frequently cheerless.
The merchant will enforce the fashion of

HANDWRITING OF MABEL, CASE IV

to have more nervous excitability, and this is consonant with her general behavior. Such differences as do exist are in the direction we should expect from the diverse environments of town and country.

The sisters show greater difference in overt manner, as judged by observation, than in the tests, with the exception of the Downey test. The tests evidently reveal their basic similarity and thus indicate that the differences which strike the observer are acquired and not inherent. The large differences in the Downey test are especially significant in view of the almost complete identity in this test found in a number of the pairs.

CASE V. TWINS EDITH AND FAY

These women, thirty-eight years old when examined, were born in a small town in Iowa of extremely young parents, eighteen and seventeen years old. These young people made an effort to bring up the twins but, after a struggle of fourteen months, were forced to put the babies in a children's home. A wealthy woman wanted to adopt both the twins, but, when the authorities insisted on their separation, she refused to take either. Shortly after this, however, they were adopted by two different families and did not meet or even communicate again until they were sixteen. Their dramatic first meeting is described in chapter ix. Their first visit together was happy but brief. They had become very fond of each other and enjoyed impersonating each other. When they next met at twenty years of age, they lived together for a year. Then Edith married and moved away. In another year or two Fay married also. Since their marriage they have lived almost entirely apart, though they have corresponded rather regularly.

EDUCATIONAL CAREERS

There is not much contrast between these twins so far as formal schooling is concerned. Fay went to school in good-sized towns and went as far as the completion of her third year in high school (eleventh grade), while Edith went to school mostly in the country and completed the second year of high school (tenth grade). If there is a significant difference in schooling, it is probably qualitative rather than quantitative. There was little if any cultural training in the home of either twin, except that Fay for some years past has belonged to women's clubs and has participated in the usual type of cultural effort appropriate to such organizations.

SOCIAL ENVIRONMENTS

There seems to have been no significant difference in the character of the two foster-homes. Both foster-families were in fairly comfortable circumstances, and the two homes were in small towns and definitely similar in social and cultural status. It was only after marriage that their social en-

PLATE X

CASE V, EDITH (*right*) AND FAY AT THIRTY-FOUR YEARS OF AGE

vironments diverged markedly. Fay married a lumber merchant who always made a good income and was able to engage help for his wife whenever she needed it. She has had four children at well-spaced intervals. Fay has always been socially inclined, being interested in women's clubs, musical organization, and amateur dramatics. She has always had "heaps of friends." On the whole, her life has been relatively pleasant and easy.

Edith's husband was at first a farmer in North Dakota and then a railroad brakeman. The family has always lived either in the country or in rural communities. During the World War, while the husband was in the army, Edith had to remain on the new farm in North Dakota in order to establish their claim on the land. During the hard years on the new farm she had two children very close together. Food was hard to get and of poor quality and variety, especially for a pregnant mother. She has had six children and has had no help in caring for them. Her social environment has been extremely meager, especially in the early years of her married life. They are still living on a very small income, but Edith has brought up all her children to a state where she is proud of their attainments. She has put up an unusually strong fight against adverse circumstances and now seems to be reaping the reward of her efforts, for the family seems to be past the crisis. The very marked difference in social environments since marriage is the only noteworthy one in the whole environmental complex.

PHYSICAL AND HEALTH ENVIRONMENTS

There were no contrasts in physical or health factors until after marriage. The one striking item of physical environment has already been mentioned, namely, the inadequate food of Edith during her early childbearing years. Edith also had a very serious attack of true influenza in 1918, when the very severe epidemic prevailed in the United States. It seems to have taken her three years to accomplish a complete recovery from this attack. She thinks that she has never fully regained her normal health since that illness. There is some difference in the childbearing experiences that may be significant, for Edith has had six children and Fay four. Edith's children came closer together, at least the earlier ones. Fay has never had any serious illnesses and has always had the best of food.

PHYSICAL RESEMBLANCES AND DIFFERENCES

The most obvious differences in these twins at present have to do with general physical condition. Fay is much better preserved in every way. Both are rather small, delicately formed women, and rather slender. Fay weighed 110.5 pounds; Edith, 102.1 pounds—a difference of over 8 pounds, which means that Edith is that much underweight. All circumference measures of Fay exceed those of Edith. Fay has the appearance of a woman in the early thirties, while Edith looks fully her age or over it. Fay's hair is thicker and in better condition. Fay has an absolutely perfect set of teeth without a spot of decay. This is unusual for a woman of her age. In contrast, Edith's teeth are in extremely bad condition, the upper incisors being discolored and worn down to about half their original length, and fully half of her other teeth are decayed or have been extracted. The poor diet during pregnancies probably accounts for the destruction of what were originally very fine teeth.

In purely genetic characters there is almost complete correspondence. Fay's height is 61.7 inches; that of Edith, 61.6 inches. The head length of both is 17.2 centimeters, and the head width of both is 12.3 centimeters. The hair color of both is light golden brown, long, soft, and wavy. Both have clockwise hair whorl, and both are fully right-handed. Both have the same eye color—a greenish gray. Ears are extremely similar—small and shapely. Complexion is very fair and smooth in both. Both are slightly pigeon-toed in walking. The features are much less similar today than they once were, for Edith's cheeks are more hollow and her worn teeth change the set of her mouth, yet even now one would hardly doubt that they are monozygotic twins. The earlier photographs indicate their very striking similarity, and the facts, first, that they rediscovered each other through one's being mistaken by a stranger for the other, and, second, that they were able to impersonate each other with complete success demonstrate that they are monozygotic.

The palm patterns themselves would force a monozygotic diagnosis. The right palm of Fay is almost identical with the left of Edith, and the left of Fay with the right of Edith—an instance of complete mirror-imaging but without reversal of handedness. The finger patterns show a stronger correspondence between the two right hands than between the two hands of either individual. The total ridge-count value of the finger patterns of Fay is 115, that of Edith, 114—an exceptionally close correspondence.

TESTS OF ABILITY

It will be remembered that Fay and Edith had about the same amount of schooling but that Fay remained in high school to the end of the Junior year and Edith only to the end of the Sophomore year. Thus, Fay had somewhat the advantage. On all the tests of ability Fay makes a higher score, but the difference is small, being in each case less than half the average difference. On two of the parts of the Stanford Achievement Test, Fay equals Edith, and on the rest she excels. Fay is slightly less accurate on the

TABLE 56

TEST RECORD AND ENVIRONMENTAL RATING OF PAIR NO. 5
(EDITH AND FAY)

Test	Edith	Fay	Diff.	Ratio of Diff. to Mean Diff.
Stanford-Binet:				
M.A..........................	14–3	14–10	7 mo.	.45
I.Q...........................	89	93	4	.49
Otis S.-A.:				
Score........................	28	31	3	....
I.Q..........................	86	89	3	.38
Percentage right...............	70.0	63.3	6.7	.47
American Council score.............	20	30	10	.37
International score................	59	60	1	.06
Stanford Achievement:				
Reading age....................	15–4	16–0	8 mo.	....
Arithmetic....................	13–0	13–3	3	....
Nature study and science.........	15–10	15–10	0	....
History and literature............	12–7	12–7	0	....
Language usage.................	14–6	15–2	8	....
Dictation.....................	16–5	17–4	11	....
Total......................	14–8	15–2	6	.37
Downey:				
Total.......................	55	56	1	.11
Pattern difference................	....	....	2.9	1.46
Woodworth-Mathews:				
Number of neurotic traits..........	18	15	3	.60
Pressey Emotions:				
Total crossed out...............	184	167	17	.36
Deviations.....................	44	41	3	.61
Kent-Rosanoff:				
Number of common responses......	92	86	6	.62
Average frequency...............	133	81	52	1.32
Number of identical responses......	6	6*	....	....
Average of all tests.............	....	....	....	.55
Environmental rating:				
Educational......................	....	....	11	.73
Social..........................	....	....	26	1.45
Physical........................	....	....	23	1.45

* Ratio to mean, .42.

Otis Self-administering Test, but she achieves a higher score by greater speed. Fay's superiority may be due to her longer schooling, and it may also be due partly to her better physical and social environment.

TESTS OF PERSONALITY

The total scores on the Downey Will-Temperament Test are nearly identical. This identity may not be very significant in view of the rather marked divergence in pattern. If we follow Dr. Downey's interpretation of the scores, we infer that Edith is generally less inhibited in her movements, slower in making decisions, reacts more strongly against contradiction, and has less ability to co-ordinate her impulses. In half or more of the indi-

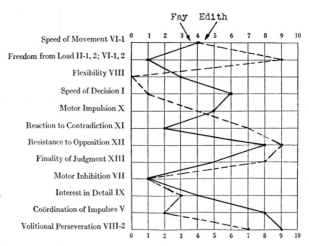

Fig. 19.—Downey Individual Will-Temperament Test profiles

vidual parts of the test, on the other hand, the responses are very similar. Perhaps all that can be said with assurance is that the two profiles show a considerable degree of difference as compared with those of the other pairs.

On the Woodworth-Matthews Personal Data Sheet the responses are remarkably similar. Although Edith gave 3 more unfavorable responses than Fay, she gave all 15 of the unfavorable responses given by Edith. This degree of similarity is unusual.

On the Pressey X–O test the resemblance is not quite so close. The total number crossed out and the number of deviations from common responses are rather closely similar, but the similar totals are made up of greater differences on the parts of the test. Edith, who has lived in the less favorable physical and social environment, gave a few more unfavorable responses on the Woodworth-Mathews test and marked more items and gave more individual responses on the Pressey test.

On the Kent-Rosanoff Free Association Test, Edith's responses are somewhat more like those of people in general, but the difference is not great. On the other hand, these twins give only about as many identical responses as should probably be expected from a pair of persons picked at random.

TABLE 57

TOTAL NUMBER OF WORDS CROSSED OUT AND NUMBER OF
DEVIATIONS ON THE PRESSEY X–O TEST

TEST	WORDS CROSSED OUT		DEVIATIONS	
	Edith	Fay	Edith	Fay
Test I: Unpleasant words...............	51	33	11	6
Test II: Words associated in mind with given word........................	39	48	8	9
Test III: Things thought wrong............	62	56	10	11
Test IV: Worries.......................	32	30	15	15
Total........................	184	167	44	41

HANDWRITING

The handwriting of these twins is strikingly different. If handwriting reveals the personality, Fay and Edith must be very unlike in this respect. Since we do not pretend to say how far handwriting does express personality or what characteristics are represented by particular features of handwriting, we shall content ourselves mainly with pointing out the marked objective differences. Edith completes the form of each individual letter with care, so that it would be possible to read it if it were isolated from the word. Fay, on the other hand, slurs over the letters so much that some of the words have almost the appearance of a wavy line. Fay's writing is also much more spread out laterally but much less vertically. That is, the letters are shorter but wider and with more space between them. Fay also writes with much less pressure and emphasis. These characteristics suggest that Fay is more facile and careless and acts with less force and energy. These

PLATE XI

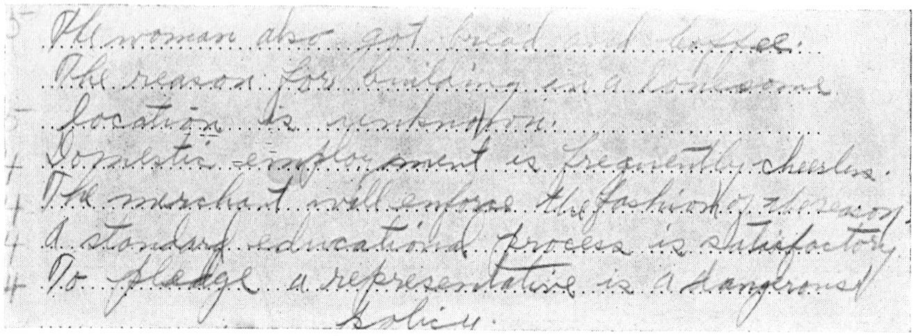

HANDWRITING OF EDITH, CASE V

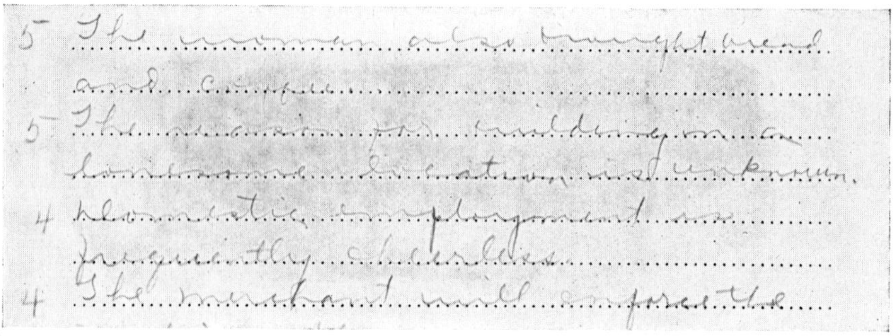

HANDWRITING OF FAY, CASE V

suggestions are quite tentative, and it must be confessed that supporting evidence for them cannot be found in the Downey profiles. Nevertheless, differences as great as these would appear to have some significance.

SUMMARY

These twin sisters have had about the same education and similar physical and social environments until their marriage at about twenty years of age. Since then Fay has had a much easier life. This is reflected in a marked difference in certain physical characteristics. In mental ability the twins differ by a small amount, but the difference is consistently in favor of Fay, who had the better education and social environment.

The tests of personality do not give a very clear or consistent picture. In some respects the responses are very similar, and in others the difference is fairly marked. The greatest difference is in the pattern of the Downey test and in handwriting. On the whole, more marked differences might, perhaps, have been expected from the difference in environment, unless the similarity up to twenty years of age may be regarded as the dominant factor and the divergence as coming too late to have much effect. One might have expected to find more differences in personality than are revealed by the tests. Differences in social behavior do appear. "Fay's behavior is much more confident and self-reliant than Edith's. She takes the lead in all social relations." There is also a marked difference in handwriting. But in emotional reactions the sisters are very similar, and in will-temperament the differences are not great.

CASE VI. TWINS ADA AND IDA

These twins are of some special interest because they are much the oldest of our separated twins, being fifty-nine years old when examined. They were born in a small Canadian town and were separated at three years of age, remaining entirely apart until they were sixteen. Since then they have seen a good deal of each other, sometimes living together for months at a time. The father of the twins became hopelessly diseased and nearly blind when the twins were three, and, somewhat against their desires, relatives had to take care of the twins. Both led miserable lives with their respective foster-families. Ada married at seventeen, while Ida did not marry until thirty-four. Ada had rather a stormy married life and was separated from her husband after ten years of effort to reform him. Ida has had a placid and satisfactory married life and still has her husband, who seems to be morally and temperamentally suited to her. Ada has reared five children, Ida four.

EDUCATIONAL CAREERS

It might be said that neither twin has had any significant amount of schooling. Each had about the equivalent of third-grade training, though even this meager amount of schooling was badly interrupted. Both have educated themselves to the point of making a score equivalent to nearly seventh-grade level on the Stanford Achievement Test.

SOCIAL ENVIRONMENTS

The early life of both twins was similar—extremely hard and cruel in both cases. Neither foster-family wanted the children, and the result was that both of them were neglected and badly mistreated. Both women tell a tragic story of hardship and abuse, the details of which it seems inadvisable to divulge. Suffice it to say that the atmosphere of their homes was decidedly on the immoral side, according to their standards. The most significant fact in this connection is that both women have reacted toward their early bad environments in almost identical fashion, for both are now militantly moral and almost fanatically religious, Ada being a Seventh Day Adventist and Ida a Holiness Methodist. Both are militant opponents of the use of alcohol and tobacco. The early marriage and unhappy married life of Ada contrasts with the late but happy married life of Ida. Both women are devoted mothers. They both say: "Our children love us anyway, so there is much to be thankful for."

PHYSICAL AND HEALTH ENVIRONMENTS

Ada has lived largely in cities, having spent a large part of her life in Chicago, though she has moved about a great deal. Ida has spent nearly all her life on a farm in northern Michigan. The mother of the twins had a pronounced goiter. Both twins seem to have inherited a tendency to goiter; but Ada has used iodized salt and a variety of sea foods for many years, thus, apparently, preventing the onset of goiter, though she had an incipient goiter over ten years ago. Ida at present has an advanced goiter and all the usual associated symptoms. She has always lived in a region of the country where goiter is prevalent and has used largely the food and water of her immediate neighborhood. This seems to be the only significant contrast in the physical environment. As children both were strong and robust and never seriously ill.

PHYSICAL RESEMBLANCES AND DIFFERENCES

In spite of the great difference in health at the present time, these women make a strong impression of physical similarity. The only real difference between them now is that Ida has a large disfiguring goiter and is myxedematous to a marked degree. Her condition is reflected in a general puffiness

PLATE XII

CASE VI, ADA (*left*) AND IDA AT FORTY-FIVE YEARS OF AGE

of face, hands, and doubtless other parts of the body. She weighed 227.2 pounds as compared with 208.1 pounds for Ada. Both are very heavy women; but Ada seems normal and active in spite of her weight, while Ida is very slow and heavy in her movements and becomes exhausted from walking up one flight of stairs.

Ada's height is 66.0 inches; Ida's, 65.7 inches. The head length of both is 19.5 centimeters, and the head width of both is 13.5 centimeters. The eyes of both are deep-bluish gray. The hair is iron gray in both, straight and rather coarse, the hair line having three peaks on the forehead. Both are right-handed, and both have clockwise hair whorl. The ears are nearly identical—unusually long and well set. Ada has a complete set of false teeth, while Ida has most of her original teeth, though they are in poor condition. The features are regular, individual, and strikingly similar.

The palm patterns are remarkable in that three of the four palms (Ada's right and left and Ida's left) are unusually similar, while Ida's right is the odd member. This is a condition often found in identical twins. A remarkable correspondence is the thenar pattern on both right hands, though this pattern is more characteristic of left hands. The two left hands are more similar than is either left to own right hand. In finger patterns Ada's right and Ida's left hand are more similar than any other two hands. The total ridge-count values are for Ada, 76; for Ida, 70—a correspondence well within the expected range for monozygotic twins.

TESTS OF ABILITY

The tests of ability present a picture of close similarity. On the Stanford-Binet test Ada is superior by an amount equal to the average difference of the nineteen pairs and by about one-third of the average on the International Test. Ida, on the other hand, is superior by one-quarter of the average age on the Otis Self-administering Test and the Stanford Achievement Test. An interesting difference in behavior appeared in the reactions to the Binet and Otis tests. In both Ada worked more rapidly. On the Otis test she attempted forty-four items to Ida's thirty-three, but her 25 per cent lower accuracy gave her a lower score. Thus, while the sisters are very similar in ability, as in education, they are somewhat different in manner of working.

TESTS OF PERSONALITY

Both the total scores and the patterns on the Downey Will-Temperament Test are strikingly similar. Both, according to Dr. Downey's interpretation, are very slow and deliberate. They also lack the ability to inhibit movements and to co-ordinate their motor impulses. On the other hand, they both exhibit marked tendencies to aggressive behavior and

TABLE 58

TEST RECORD AND ENVIRONMENTAL RATING OF PAIR NO. 6
(ADA AND IDA)

Test	Ada	Ida	Diff.	Ratio of Diff. to Mean Diff.
Stanford-Binet:				
M.A....................................	16–3	15–0	15 mo.	.97
I.Q.....................................	102	94	8	.97
Otis S.-A.:				
Score...................................	26	28	2	....
I.Q.....................................	68	70	2	.25
Percentage right...................	59.1	84.8	25.7	1.79
American Council score*...............	....	....	....	....
International score...................	75	70	5	.32
Stanford Achievement:				
Reading age......................	17–11	15–9	26 mo.	....
Spelling...........................	10–9	10–6	3	....
Language..........................	17–8	16–2	18	....
Literature.........................	12–3	14–1	22	....
History and civics.................	13–1	13–7	6	....
Geography.........................	12–0	13–3	15	....
Physiology and hygiene............	16–7	16–5	2	....
Arithmetic........................	9–11	10–0	1	....
Total.........................	12–7	12–11	4	.25
Downey:				
Total.............................	45	41	4	.44
Pattern difference................	....	....	1.3	.66
Woodworth-Mathews:				
Number of neurotic traits..........	17	17	0	0
Pressey Emotions:				
Total crossed out.................	210	179	31	.66
Deviations........................	48	46	2	.41
Kent-Rosanoff:				
Number of common responses......	99	81	18	1.87
Average frequency.................	134	101	33	.84
Number of identical responses......	12	12†	....	....
Average of all tests.............	....	....	....	.73
Environmental rating:				
Educational.......................			7	.46
Social............................			10	.56
Physical..........................			22	1.38

* Omitted.
† Ratio to mean, .84.

strong disposition to persist in an activity once it has been started. The aggressiveness and perseveration seem evident also from the observation of the social behavior of the sisters, and in this respect the verdict of the test seems confirmed. The slowness and inadequacy of movement, on the other hand, may be due partly to their age. Even making allowance for this factor, however, it appears that the test indicates that the genetic similarity has persisted.

The number of unfavorable answers on the Woodworth-Mathews Personal Data Sheet is the same and is a little above the average. Ten of the 17 unfavorable responses are identical, which indicates rather close agree-

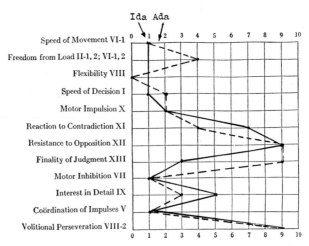

FIG. 20.—Downey Individual Will-Temperament Test profiles

ment on the particular items as well as on the total number. This test also indicates close similarity in personality.

The Pressey test seems to indicate a greater difference, and, curiously enough, the difference is greatest in Part IV, which is most like the Woodworth-Mathews test. The detailed scores are as shown in Table 59. Ada marked more items of each type in Test IV, as shown in Table 60. No very plausible interpretation of this discrepancy occurs to the writers. Even as it is, the differences on the test are small in comparison with the average.

The Kent-Rosanoff test is an exception in that it yields a moderately large difference in the degree of commonness of the responses. It yields almost the average number of identical responses. The burden of evidence of the tests as a whole is that the sisters are closely similar both in ability and in personality.

The handwriting of these sisters was not obtained when they were examined and had to be sent for later. In the meantime, Ida had been very ill, and her writing is possibly somewhat affected by this circumstance. Her writing gives the appearance of somewhat less motor control. It is larger

TABLE 59

TOTAL NUMBER OF WORDS CROSSED OUT AND NUMBER OF
DEVIATIONS ON THE PRESSEY X–O TEST

Test	Words Crossed Out		Deviations	
	Ada	Ida	Ada	Ida
Test I: Unpleasant words...............	36	44	9	8
Test II: Words associated in mind with given word........................	37	24	5	6
Test III: Things thought wrong............	76	82	18	11
Test IV: Worries........................	61	29	16	21
Total........................	210	179	48	46

TABLE 60

NUMBER OF ITEMS OF EACH TYPE IN TEST IV
MARKED BY ADA AND IDA

Type of Personality Indicated	Ada	Ida
Suspicious (paranoid).................	9	2
Jumpy (neurotic).....................	11	4
Self-conscious (shut-in personality)......	13	6
Melancholic........................	12	9
Hypochondriacal.....................	16	8
Total........................	61	29

and also differs somewhat in general appearance, so that it would not be mistaken for that of Ada. Some similarity grows out of the fact that neither has had much education or practice in writing. Underlying these differences there is a general similarity between the two specimens. On the whole, there is probably more difference in the writing than in the reactions to the tests.

PLATE XIII

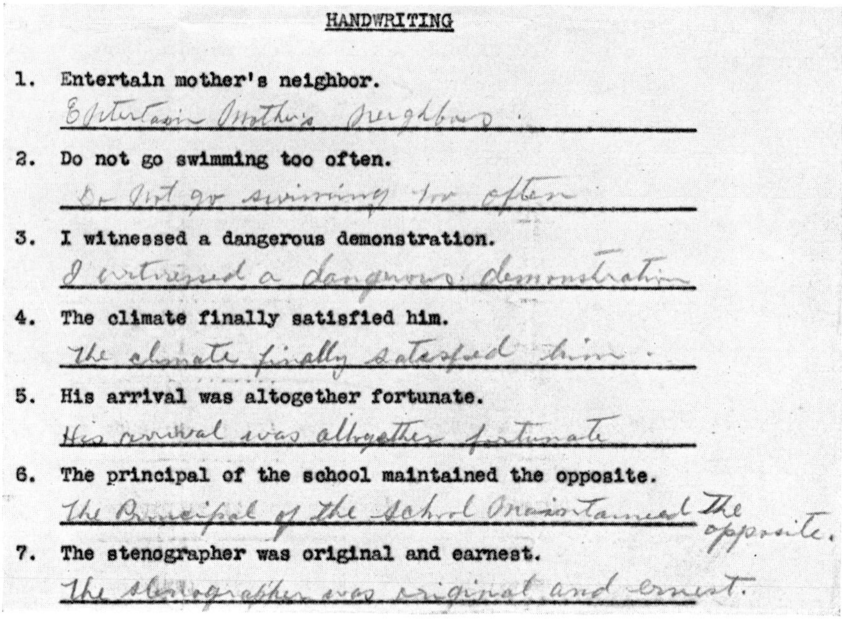

HANDWRITING

1. Entertain mother's neighbor.

2. Do not go swimming too often.

3. I witnessed a dangerous demonstration.

4. The climate finally satisfied him.

5. His arrival was altogether fortunate.

6. The principal of the school maintained the opposite.

7. The stenographer was original and earnest.

HANDWRITING OF ADA, CASE VI

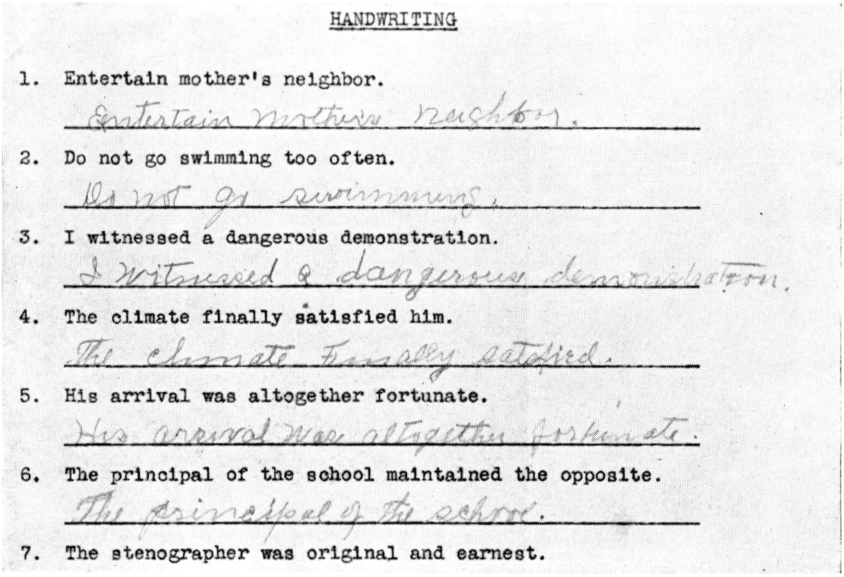

HANDWRITING

1. Entertain mother's neighbor.

2. Do not go swimming too often.

3. I witnessed a dangerous demonstration.

4. The climate finally satisfied him.

5. His arrival was altogether fortunate.

6. The principal of the school maintained the opposite.

7. The stenographer was original and earnest.

HANDWRITING OF IDA, CASE VI

SUMMARY

In general summary we may adjudge these twins equal in mental rating, very similar in temperament, and differing physically to a marked extent only in those features associated with the presence or absence of goiter. This one difference is an important one and definitely referable to an environmental cause. Some differences in general behavior were observed. Ada is quicker and more aggressive in her social reactions. She took the lead in all the arrangements for the examination. This may be due in part to her superior physical condition and in part to her residence in a large city.

On the whole, the physical characteristics (aside from the goiter), the mental ability and educational attainment, and the personality are closely alike, corresponding to very similar environments. Such detailed differences as appear may be correlated with the few differences in the environment.

CASE VII. TWINS RAYMOND AND RICHARD

These twin boys, thirteen and one-half years old when examined, were separated at one month of age. They were born in a medium-sized Indiana city. Their parents are of Middle European extraction, hard-working, honest, and respectable. They had already a large family of children to support, and, when two more were added at once, it was necessary to offer them for adoption. Richard was adopted at one month and Raymond at fourteen months of age.

Raymond was adopted by the family of a well-to-do physician in the city where he was born and has had many advantages incident to such a home. Richard's foster-father is at present a truck farmer in southern Illinois. He has not lived long in any one place or continued long in any one occupation. One judges that he is an opportunist, waiting for something to turn up. He has had many ups and downs, more of the latter than of the former. Nevertheless, Richard has had the advantage of one important home influence— an excellent foster-mother greatly interested in his welfare. The boys have had almost annual visits, chiefly in Raymond's home.

EDUCATIONAL CAREERS

The boys have had the same amount of formal schooling, and both were in the eighth grade when examined. The school attended by Raymond would appear to be superior to the various schools attended by Richard. Also, Raymond's schooling has been little if any interrupted, while Richard has had several changes of schools. The cultural environments of the home would seem to be all in favor of Raymond, for he has lived with and been

PLATE XIV

CASE VII, RICHARD (*left*) AND RAYMOND AT TEN YEARS OF AGE
(They were physically as nearly identical as are the most similar types of twins reared together)

under the influence of cultured people from infancy; while the foster-parents of Richard have had very little education, and there is no cultural stimulus in their home.

SOCIAL ENVIRONMENTS

Raymond was brought up in the family of a middle-aged physician, his wife, and two daughters much older than Raymond, one of them a college graduate and a charming person. He has had every advantage, and much has been done for him. There are some indications that he has had things too easy and has not been put on his own resources sufficiently. He has always lived in the same community and has seen little of the seamy side of life.

Richard, on the other hand, has had a much wider range of experience, some of which might seem to have been deleterious, but he has a good foster-mother, who has been very ambitious for him and has shielded him from the possible harmful effects of his environment. There have been no other children in his family, but he has not been pampered as is frequently the case with only children. He has had to do a great deal for himself and has developed a good deal of self-reliance.

PHYSICAL AND HEALTH ENVIRONMENTS

Apart from having the usual children's diseases, both boys have been very healthy. Raymond had a rather severe cartilage infection in one knee, which has caused one leg to be a little shorter than the other. One might suppose that the dietary regime in a physician's family would be superior to that in the home of a relatively poor family, but there are no evidences that, if such existed, it was at all effective. So far as we can see, then, there has been only a slight difference in physical environments.

PHYSICAL RESEMBLANCES AND DIFFERENCES

Physically these twins are among the most similar that we have ever seen. They are about as much alike as the proverbial two peas, as may be judged from their photograph. Richard is a little taller, 56.9 inches, than Raymond, 55.7 inches. Raymond is $\frac{1}{2}$ pound lighter. The head length of both is 17.3 centimeters, and the head width of both is 14.4 centimeters. Both are right-handed and have clockwise hair whorl. The hair color and texture is the same—medium brown, soft, and straight. The eye color is the same—slate gray. Raymond's two ears and Richard's right ear are extremely similar, but Richard's left is slightly different in shape. The teeth are rather small and regular, of the same shape and arrangement, and both have the lower-right first and second molars beginning to decay. Needless to say, the features are all strikingly similar.

TABLE 61

TEST RECORD AND ENVIRONMENTAL RATING OF PAIR NO. 7
(RAYMOND AND RICHARD)

Test	Raymond	Richard	Diff.	Ratio of Diff. to Mean Diff.
Stanford-Binet:				
M.A..........................	14–2	14–4	2 mo.	.13
I.Q...........................	105	106	1	.12
Otis S.-A.:				
Score........................	36	31	5	....
I.Q..........................	105	101	4	.50
Percentage right..............	63.2	50.0	13.2	.92
American Council score...........	43	58	15	.55
International score...............	101	107	6	.39
Stanford Achievement:				
Reading age...................	15–9	15–0	9 mo.	....
Spelling......................	14–6	15–4	10	....
Language.....................	16–10	15–6	16	....
Literature....................	15–2	15–6	4	....
History and civics.............	17–11	16–5	18	....
Geography....................	17–0	17–0	0	....
Physiology and hygiene.........	16–6	15–6	12	....
Arithmetic....................	14–8	16–3	19	....
Total.....................	15–11	15–9	2	.12
Downey:				
Total........................	52	69	17	1.86
Pattern difference.............	....	....	2.3	1.16
Woodworth-Mathews:				
Number of neurotic traits.........	14	12	2	.40
Pressey Emotions:				
Total crossed out...............	200	186	14	.30
Deviations....................	59	56	3	.61
Kent-Rosanoff:				
Number of common responses......	33	87	54	5.61
Average frequency..............	61	116	55	1.40
Number of identical responses......	1	1*	....	....
Average of all tests...........	....	....	....	1.01
Environmental rating:				
Educational...................	....	....	9	.60
Social.......................	....	....	27	1.51
Physical.....................	....	....	9	.57

* Ratio to mean, .07.

The palm and finger patterns show considerable difference. However, Raymond's right and Richard's left palm have identical formulas and are much more similar than any other two palms. In the finger patterns there is again mirror-imaging, for Richard's right and Raymond's left hand are more similar than are the two hands of either individual. The total ridge-count values for the finger patterns for Richard are 111; for Raymond, 113—a striking correspondence.

TESTS OF ABILITY

The tests indicate that these twins have equal mental ability. Richard scored a little higher on three tests; Raymond higher on two tests. If there is any difference between them, and there seems to be none of any sig-

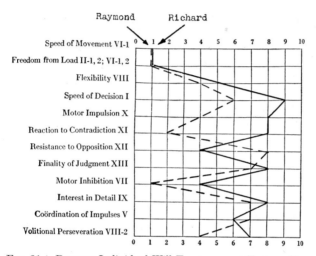

FIG. 21.—Downey Individual Will-Temperament Test profiles

nificance, Richard, the one with apparently the less favorable educational environment, is a little more alert mentally. Both boys have excellent reputations as students. They work well in school and are considered unusually bright. There is a look of alertness and intelligence in their faces. Both make a score on the Stanford Achievement Test over two years in advance of their ages.

TESTS OF PERSONALITY

On the Downey Will-Temperament Test (Fig. 21) Richard had a total score of 69; Raymond, 52. This is a difference of some consequence and is probably not accidental. The greatest differences are in motor impulsion and reaction to contradiction, where Richard is distinctly superior, and in resistance to opposition, where Raymond is superior. The latter two are somewhat contradictory. It appears that Richard is the more positive, more aggressive of the twins. It seems natural to attribute this difference to his more intimate contact with the difficulties of life and to the fact that he has had to rely on his own resources to a greater extent than Raymond. Notwithstanding these differences, there is a good deal of similarity in the two patterns of response.

On the Woodworth-Mathews Personal Data Sheet Raymond gave 14 unfavorable answers; Richard, 12. Four of these were the same for both.

TABLE 62

TOTAL NUMBER OF WORDS CROSSED OUT AND NUMBER OF DEVIATIONS ON THE PRESSEY X–O TEST

TEST	WORDS CROSSED OUT		DEVIATIONS	
	Raymond	Richard	Raymond	Richard
Test I: Unpleasant words..............	46	33	13	17
Test II: Words associated in mind with given word.......................	31	30	7	12
Test III: Things thought wrong...........	96	100	20	10
Test IV: Worries......................	27	23	19	17
Total......................	200	186	59	56

This seems to indicate that their nervous balance is about the same and at least equal to the average.

On the Pressey X–O test Raymond showed himself slightly more emotionally reactive than Richard. The main difference between them appeared in Part I of the test, which has to do with reactions to unpleasant words. Raymond marked 46 and Richard 33 words. Richard has probably seen more of the unpleasant features of life and is inured to them. Raymond reacted to 9 words with sex implications and Richard to only 2. Raymond's fear reactions were 9 and Richard's 5. The two tests agree in showing very little difference in emotion and nervous stability.

The record of Raymond on the Kent-Rosanoff test is most bizarre. Whereas Richard gave only 13 individual reactions, Raymond gave 67—a most unusual number. Not only are many of these responses absent from the table of common reactions, but they appear to have no connection whatever with the stimulus words. Consider, for example, the associations sickness—shoe, soft—building, eating—paper, mutton—bulb, butterfly— milk, and river—rubber. A few such responses might be explained as due to accidental associations of experience or thought, but such a large number seems to call for some other explanation. The examiners suspected that the boy might be trying to be funny at their expense, but when this suggestion was made to Miss D., his foster-sister, she reported that the boy was not accustomed to playing such pranks. We can only say that Raymond's response on this test appears to be a freak of behavior in an otherwise normal performance. The result is that the boys give only one identical response.

There was very little indication of marked personality differences in the boys' overt behavior. Richard was throughout somewhat more aggressive and positive in his actions, but the difference was not marked.

HANDWRITING

The writing of these twins shows marked similarity. This similarity is not such as might be ascribed to identity of age or to similarity in instruction. It is much more than an expression of the same stage of maturity or the same general style of penmanship. One might think that the two specimens were written by the same person in somewhat different mood. The chief difference is that Raymond's writing is somewhat larger. Consider the similarities. Both are very messy. The letters are formed so as to be legible, but they are irregular in shape, size, and slant. The movement by which they are produced is loose and unco-ordinated, suggesting either poor motor control or poor sense of form or both. The writing gives the impression of haste and carelessness. The crosses of the small *t*'s and the cap strokes of the large *T*'s, for example, are put on with a fling of the pencil instead of being placed with care and precision.

SUMMARY

Physically these boys resemble each other as much as though they had been reared together. If we disregard the free-association test, as perhaps we should, our verdict is that these twins are very similar indeed, both in ability and in behavior. We might expect close similarity in ability from the similarity in schooling, but the considerable difference in social and physical environment might have been expected to produce greater differences in personality. Even the handwriting, however, shows unusually close similarity. This case, then, suggests a decided predominance of genetic factors in the development of a pair of twins.

PLATE XV

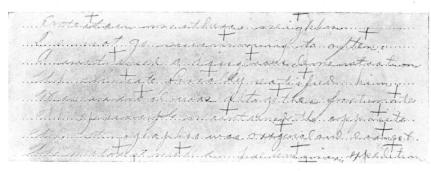

HANDWRITING OF RICHARD, CASE VII

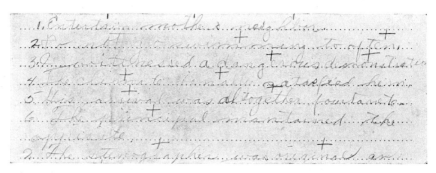

HANDWRITING OF RAYMOND, CASE VII

CASE VIII. TWINS MILDRED AND RUTH

These young girls were examined when they were fifteen years old. Their mother died when they were three months old, and they were at once adopted by two different families of relatives. Mildred was reared in the home of a maternal uncle, a man of prominence in his town of five thousand inhabitants. He is a bank president and former mayor. Ruth was taken by the brother of Mildred's foster-mother, but she was legally adopted only a year ago. Ruth has lived in a rather large city about one hundred miles from Mildred's home. They have always been acquainted but have spent very little time together.

EDUCATIONAL CAREERS

There is very little difference between them as to the amount of formal schooling. At the time they were examined Mildred was in Grade X A, half a grade ahead of Ruth. Both have attended grade schools of about the same rating. Mildred has lived in a highly intellectual family. The home of her foster-parents is a center of culture in their town. She has studied music with an older sister who was taken into the foster-home with her. Her mother's sister, a next-door neighbor, who is an honor graduate of the University of Chicago and is a teacher in Mildred's high school, has had a good deal to do with her bringing up. Mildred has always been an inveterate reader and has had the advantage of a well-chosen library. At the present time she plays the violin in the high-school orchestra. It is obvious, then, that the cultural influence of her home has supplemented her formal schooling.

Ruth, while having had nearly as much formal schooling as Mildred, has not had the advantage of a stimulating cultural home environment; quite the contrary. Her foster-mother and father are persons of relatively little education and have no cultural background. Ruth has been closely confined to her home, where there are few books, no good music, and no intellectual activities. For a short time she had music lessons but did not become proficient in that field. Her foster-mother, who had only a grade-school education, has been her almost constant companion and has been "jealously fond" of her. The home has had an inhibiting rather than a stimulating cultural influence. It is, we believe, the great difference in the informal educational influence of the two homes that constitutes the important differences between their educational environments.

SOCIAL ENVIRONMENTS

There is a great difference in the social status of the two homes. Mildred's family is well to do, and Ruth's quite the opposite. Ruth's foster-father

PLATE XVI

CASE VIII, MILDRED (*right*) AND RUTH AT EIGHT YEARS OF AGE

(Even at this early age the differences in expression are prophetic of marked
differences in the personalities so evident in later years)

was, until his death a few years ago, a foreman of day laborers in a rather large city. Her home is very plain in contrast to the attractiveness of Mildred's home.

Mildred has been a member of a considerable family group, including her own older sister and the numerous relatives who are near-neighbors. She has always been encouraged to make friends and has constantly played with other children in groups. Ruth, on the contrary, has been reared as an only child, and the foster-mother has apparently been reluctant to have her grow up, for she has discouraged any desire in Ruth for companions of her own age and has kept her at home playing with dolls as her only playmates. The family of Ruth has not been socially inclined, so that Ruth has led a lonely, rather friendless life. Mildred's social environment has been stimulating; Ruth's depressing.

PHYSICAL AND HEALTH ENVIRONMENTS

There has been little difference in the health records of the sisters. Mildred weighed 6 pounds at birth, and Ruth only $3\frac{1}{2}$ pounds. It is possible that Ruth suffered a disadvantage prenatally that might account for her present relative lack of vitality. Both girls had the same children's diseases early in life. Mildred had, in addition, a mild attack of infantile paralysis that has left one leg a half-inch shorter than the other. Both are troubled with rather poor eyesight. Life in a rather large city as compared with that in a small town might be considered as offering some environmental contrast, but both homes are in the same part of Indiana with almost identical climates. On the whole, the postnatal physical environments offered no marked contrasts. Whether the obvious difference in prenatal environment has had a lasting effect is uncertain, but the possibility cannot be cast aside.

PHYSICAL RESEMBLANCES AND DIFFERENCES

Apart from the fact that Mildred has a bright and happy expression and a light in her eyes, as contrasted with the rather dull eyes and unhappy expression of Ruth, there are no marked contrasts in physical characters. Mildred is 66.1 inches in height; Ruth, 65 inches. Mildred weighs $120\frac{3}{4}$ pounds; Ruth, $120\frac{1}{2}$ pounds. The head length of both is 18.4 centimeters. Mildred's head width is 14.4 centimeters; that of Ruth, 13.4 centimeters. The eye color is the same—best described as "hazel." Mildred's right eye is badly crossed, and the same condition is present in Ruth's left eye—a clear case of mirror-imaging. The hair of both is light brown, straight, and fine. Both have clockwise hair whorl, though that of Ruth is indistinct (probably partially reversed). The ears of both are unusually similar— large and protruding. The mouth is unusually wide in both. Their teeth show the same peculiarities. The front teeth are too small and widely spaced, and the dentition as a whole is in poor condition, that of Ruth not so bad as that of Mildred. Mildred is left-handed; Ruth, right-handed.

The palm patterns show marked mirror-image resemblance—the right hand of Ruth being like the left of Mildred and the left of Ruth like the right of Mildred. There is much less resemblance between the two hands of either individual. The finger patterns show no mirror-imaging, but the two right hands are extremely similar, and the two left hands are more alike than either is to own right hand. The total ridge-count values of the finger patterns is 83 for Mildred and 82 for Ruth—practical identity.

TESTS OF ABILITY

Mildred is consistently higher than Ruth on the tests of ability. On the four intelligence tests her superiority is from one and a half to twice the average difference of the nineteen pairs. In accuracy she is superior by twice the average difference. While she was somewhat more rapid than Ruth, then, her superiority cannot be attributed to her speed. The speed is probably but one expression of her superior ability.

It may be significant that Mildred's superiority in the educational test is, relative to the entire group of twins, less than that in the general tests. The difference is thirteen months, whereas the difference on the Stanford-Binet test is twenty-eight months.

It is possible, of course, that part of the superiority of Mildred is inherent, though it cannot be genetic. The large physical difference at birth suggests this hypothesis. Against this supposition, however, is the fact that Ruth made up all the physical handicap, and it may be reasonably inferred that the physical difference did not, therefore, seriously affect mental growth. The greater superiority of Mildred on the tests of general ability than on the tests of educational achievement may be due to the fact that this formal schooling was nearly identical, whereas the informal stimuli to general intellectual development were very different. It seems reasonable to attribute at least a large share of Mildred's superior ability to her more stimulating environment.

TESTS OF PERSONALITY

Mildred's larger total score on the Downey test may be significant. The patterns exhibit a general similarity, in some respects a close similarity. On seven parts the scores are within one point of each other. On "freedom from load" Ruth's score is higher than Mildred's, which would appear on the surface to mean that Mildred is the more inhibited of the two. It seems possible, however, that a somewhat different interpretation should be given to the record of this part of the test than that given in the directions. Ac-

TABLE 63

TEST RECORD AND ENVIRONMENTAL RATING OF PAIR No. 8
(MILDRED AND RUTH)

Test	Mildred	Ruth	Diff.	Ratio of Diff. to Mean Diff.
Stanford-Binet:				
M.A..........................	14–2	11–10	28 mo.	1.82
I.Q..........................	92	77	15	1.83
Otis S.-A.:				
Score.........................	38	23	15	....
I.Q..........................	101	86	15	1.88
Percentage right................	73.1	44.2	28.9	2.01
American Council score............	74	35	39	1.44
International score.................	144	114	30	1.93
Stanford Achievement:				
Reading age.....................	16–7	15–11	8 mo.	....
Spelling........................	9–11	10–1	2	....
Language.......................	17–4	16–3	13	....
Literature......................	15–8	13–9	23	....
History and civics................	15–8	15–4	4	....
Geography......................	12–10	12–6	4	....
Physiology and hygiene............	17–6	13–7	47	....
Arithmetic......................	12–10	12–8	2	....
Total......................	14–7	13–6	13	.80
Downey:				
Total......................	72	57	15	1.64
Pattern difference..................	....	....	2.1	1.06
Woodworth-Mathews:				
Number of neurotic traits..........	11	19	8	1.60
Pressey Emotions:				
Total crossed out................	221	185	36	.76
Deviations......................	43	67	24	4.91
Kent-Rosanoff:				
Number of common responses......	93	85	8	.83
Average frequency................	170	96	74	1.88
Number of identical responses......	8	8*	....	....
Average of all tests.............	....	....	....	1.74
Environmental rating:				
Educational......................	....	....	14	.93
Social..........................	....	....	32	1.79
Physical........................	....	....	13	.82

* Ratio to mean, .56.

cording to Dr. Downey's interpretation, the person is inhibited if his speeded writing is much faster than his ordinary writing and vice versa. No account is taken of the absolute speed of either the normal or the speeded writing. In the present case Mildred wrote the phrase "United States of America" slightly faster than Ruth when they were told to write at ordinary speed—the two times being $10\frac{1}{4}$ and 11 seconds, respectively. The style of writing was quite different. Mildred's writing is larger and more fluent. Her phrase covers 4 inches and Ruth's but $2\frac{1}{2}$. This seems to indicate that Ruth is the more inhibited. When they were asked to write

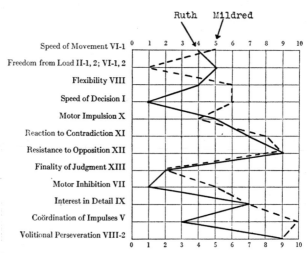

FIG. 22.—Downey Individual Will-Temperament Test profiles

rapidly, Mildred decreased the time to $6\frac{3}{4}$ seconds and Ruth to only 8 seconds. This seems to indicate not that Mildred is more inhibited but that she is more flexible. This is shown further by the fact that her speeded writing showed less marks of disorganization than did Ruth's, in spite of the fact that it was faster.

A clue to the suggested conclusion that Ruth is more inhibited is found in the self-rating which she made in Test I. The purpose of this test is merely to see how fast the person will make the decisions required. The ratings themselves, however, sometimes give important revelations. For example, Ruth rates herself as having inferior intelligence, inferior character, being slow, and having at least seven other undesirable traits. Mildred, on the other hand, rates her intelligence and her quickness as 50–50 and her character as 80–20, that is, above average. She does not indicate unqualifiedly that she possesses any other undesirable traits. It seems quite reasonable to conclude that Ruth's training has developed a decided feeling of inferiority and an accompanying habit of cautious, inhibited behavior, whereas Mildred's freer and happier life has produced in her a feeling of confidence and a more or less expansive and spontaneous habit of behavior.

Observation of the sisters revealed a marked difference in their overt behavior. Mildred was sociable and relatively easy in her manner and conversed freely. While not at all bold, she seemed to show no signs of timidity or embarrassment. Her diction was good and her enunciation clear. Ruth, on the contrary, was excessively timid, would not converse, never spoke except when questioned, and then spoke with a pronounced lisp. Both girls were somewhat awkward in their movements. Because of this, they are said to be the despair of their respective teachers of physical culture. This accords with the findings of the Downey test, as a whole, and the apparent contradiction of Part II turns out to be a confirmation rather than a contradiction.

The Woodworth-Mathews test indicates that Ruth reports 8 more neurotic symptoms than does Mildred—a difference one and one-half times the average difference. This is what we should expect from the foregoing interpretation of their overt behavior. Five of the unfavorable responses are given by both sisters, and 20 are given by one but not by the other. In addition to making her responses to the items of the test, Ruth added the following spontaneous written comment, "I feel that people don't want me," probably referring to people outside the family. She thus manifests a shy and seclusive disposition, which points in the direction of neurotic character.

The Pressey test appears to offer a contradiction to the other evidence in the contrast in the total number crossed out. An analysis shows, however, that Mildred's larger score is made on Tests I and III, chiefly the latter, and that the number of worries, Test IV, is practically the same. The large number crossed out by Mildred on Test III may merely mean that she has been taught to recognize a great many acts as socially unacceptable. The greater number of deviations among Ruth's responses, giving nearly five times the ordinary difference between separated twins, may be very significant. It probably reflects the somewhat secluded way she has been brought up. On the whole, then, the Pressey test falls in line with the others.

The Kent-Rosanoff Free Association Test indicates also that Mildred gives responses more like those of people in general than does Ruth. The number of identical responses is unusually small, again, perhaps, revealing the effect of a marked difference in the environment.

The difference in handwriting, mentioned in connection with the Downey test, is clearly shown in the reproduced specimens. Mildred's writing is larger and more spread out. It is also much freer and more fluent. It has a rather dashing style, while Ruth's is very quiet and modest. Besides the difference in size, the difference in pressure, in smoothness and boldness of the pencil strokes, and the flourishes at the end of many of Mildred's words in contrast to the abrupt endings of the words in Ruth's writing may be

TABLE 64

TOTAL NUMBER OF WORDS CROSSED OUT AND NUMBER OF
DEVIATIONS ON THE PRESSEY X–O TEST

TEST	WORDS CROSSED OUT		DEVIATIONS	
	Mildred	Ruth	Mildred	Ruth
Test I: Unpleasant words.................	67	51	7	6
Test II: Words associated in mind with given word..........................	32	45	9	16
Test III: Things thought wrong.............	80	48	13	24
Test IV: Worries.........................	42	41	14	21
Total.........................	221	185	43	67

noted. Ruth's writing is evidently produced by a cramped movement, whereas Mildred's movement is relaxed and free. The difference fits into the picture of the two personalities perfectly.

SUMMARY

Physically these sisters are very closely similar, in spite of a rather large difference at birth. Their physical characteristics are evidently determined chiefly by genetic factors.

We have here a case in which the intellectual and emotional or active characteristics are closely interrelated. The difference in schooling is slight. The marked differences in home and general social environment have, however, had a marked direct influence on feelings and actions and also a marked direct and indirect influence on intellect and activity. The detailed

PLATE XVII

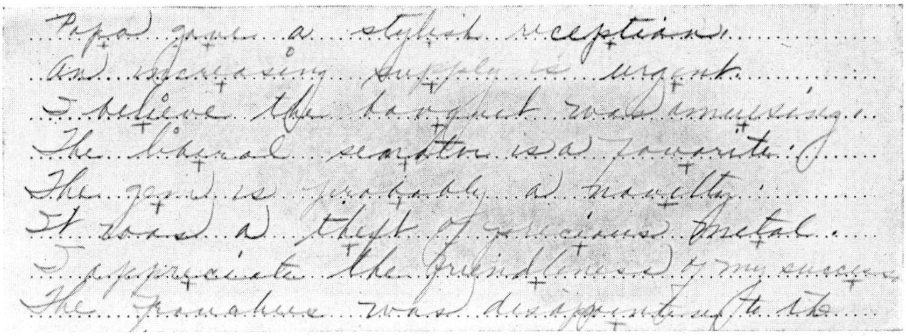

HANDWRITING OF MILDRED, CASE VIII

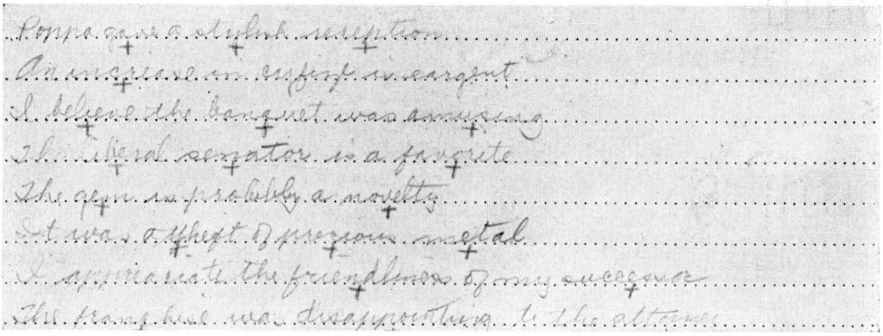

HANDWRITING OF RUTH, CASE VIII

agreement between the behavior of the two girls and the behavior we should expect from the nature of their environment is convincing evidence that the difference in behavior is chiefly environmental in origin. The superiority of Mildred in intellectual ability and educational achievement is probably due both to the richer intellectual stimulation of her environment and to the favorable influence of her happier and more self-confident attitude on her learning. The discrepancy between great physical similarity and marked difference in ability and personality indicates that behavior is not closely correlated with obvious or gross physical features and that physical resemblance cannot be taken as an indication of close similarity in ability and personality.

CASE IX.   TWINS HAROLD AND HOLDEN

These twin boys were nineteen years old when examined. Their mother died when they were born, and they were adopted very soon afterward by two different families of relatives living in the same neighborhood. While living largely separate, their homes have been only three miles apart, and they have seen a good deal of each other.

Harold was adopted by a maternal uncle and has lived in a village of six hundred inhabitants near Madison, Wisconsin. His foster-father was, until his death a few years ago, a mason by trade. Holden has always lived with an aunt on an eighty-acre farm three miles from the village where Harold lived. Ever since he was old enough to work, Holden has helped regularly on the farm after school hours and all summer.

EDUCATIONAL CAREERS

Harold attended a rather good village school with several rooms and a teacher for each two grades. Holden attended a country school with only one room, one teacher, and thirty pupils. They both attended the same township high school and were together in this school for three years. Holden was graduated from high school one year ahead of Harold not because he was brighter but because his grade-school progress was more accelerated. As a result, Harold's school work was one year fresher in mind than Holden's when the tests were given. There was no contrast in the cultural environments of the two homes. Their educational environments may be considered as essentially equal.

SOCIAL ENVIRONMENTS

Harold, living in a village and not having to work while at school, had more opportunity for social contacts than Holden. There were four other children in his home, one of his foster-sisters being a grade-school teacher in

PLATE XVIII

CASE IX, HOLDEN (*left*) AND HAROLD AT NINETEEN YEARS OF AGE

the village school. He has always participated in group activities, having been captain of the high-school basketball team and a drummer in the school band.

Holden, because of the ill health of his foster-mother, was obliged at an early age to assume some responsibility for the farm and had little time for play and social contacts out of school hours. When he has leisure, he prefers solitary recreations, such as hunting and fishing. On Sundays he occasionally joins a rural group in a baseball game. On the whole, Holden has been much less sociable than Harold.

PHYSICAL AND HEALTH ENVIRONMENTS

Both boys have always been strong and healthy, but Holden is a little more robust and muscular, doubtless as the result of manual labor on the farm. Harold, however, has engaged more in athletics, which should be a good substitute for manual labor. There seem to be no marked contrasts in the physical environments.

PHYSICAL RESEMBLANCES AND DIFFERENCES

These boys are at present extremely similar. Harold's height was 69.4 inches; Holden's, 70.2 inches. Harold weighed 135.5 pounds; Holden, 132.25 pounds. Harold's head length was 18.2 centimeters; Holden's, 18.6 centimeters. Harold's head width was 14.6 centimeters; Holden's, 14.3 centimeters. The other anthropometric measurements were very similar. Holden is somewhat stronger, as indicated in the hand-grip test. Holden appears more muscular and somewhat more robust, but he weighs a little less than Harold. Both have blue-gray eyes of the same shade and medium-brown straight hair of the same color and texture. The ears are very similar in all respects except that Harold's left ear is a little larger than the other three ears. The teeth are unusually similar in all particulars. The features correspond in every way except that Holden's are a little less clean cut. Both have clockwise hair whorl. Harold is left-handed; Holden, right-handed.

The palm patterns of all four hands are extremely similar, but there is a slightly closer correspondence between the two rights and between the two lefts than between left and right of either individual. The finger patterns are not particularly favorable to a monozygotic diagnosis, for Holden's two hands are almost identical, more similar than either of his hands is to either of Harold's hands. The resemblances between the finger patterns of the two individuals is up to the standard for monozygotic twins. The total ridge-count value of the finger patterns is, for Harold, 118; for Holden, 122.

TABLE 65

Test Record and Environmental Rating of Pair No. 9
(Harold and Holden)

Test	Harold	Holden	Diff.	Ratio of Diff. to Mean Diff.
Stanford-Binet:				
M.A....................	16–3	15–5	10 mo.	.65
I.Q.....................	102	96	6	.73
Otis S.-A.:				
Score...................	46	41	5	....
I.Q.....................	104	99	5	.62
Percentage right........	83.6	93.2	9.6	.67
American Council score*........	139	105	34	1.26
International score............	154	146	8	.52
Stanford Achievement:				
Reading age.............	17–11	16–6	17 mo.	....
Spelling................	15–11	16–5	6	....
Language...............	18–5	17–4	13	....
Literature..............	17–6	15–11	19	....
History and civics.......	16–6	16–8	2	....
Geography..............	18–2	18–2	0	....
Physiology and hygiene....	19+	19+	0	....
Arithmetic..............	16–8	15–8	12	....
Total..............	17–6	16–10	8	.49
Downey:				
Total..................	51	50	1	.11
Pattern difference...........			1.3	.66
Woodworth-Mathews:				
Number of neurotic traits.....	12	8	4	.80
Pressey Emotions:				
Total crossed out...........	154	221	67	1.42
Deviations..............	42	42	0	0
Kent-Rosanoff:				
Number of common responses.....	99	87	12	1.25
Average frequency...........	154	156	2	.05
Number of identical responses.....	19	19†	....	
Average of all tests...........	....	....	....	.66
Environmental rating:				
Educational..............	....	....	7	.46
Social.................	....	....	14	.78
Physical................	....	....	10	.62

* The scores on this test were furnished by Dr. J. S. Park, of the University of Wisconsin.
† Ratio to mean, 1.32.

On all the tests Harold was slightly superior to Holden. This superiority was most marked on the American Council Test but was small on the other tests, being from one-half to three-quarters of the average of all differences. Undoubtedly, Harold was slightly superior when the tests were given, but he had just finished high school and was in good training for tests, while Holden had done no school work for a year. Possibly, also, Harold's grade-school education was a little better than Holden's. Harold's superiority was greatest in the tests involving language—namely, the first three intelligence tests—and reading, language, and literature of the Stanford Achievement Test, which is consistent with this supposition. In any case, the differences in their scores were scarcely any greater than the mean difference of identical twins reared together.

TESTS OF PERSONALITY

The Downey Will-Temperament Test profiles are remarkably similar—one of the most similar of our collection. The difference in the second part,

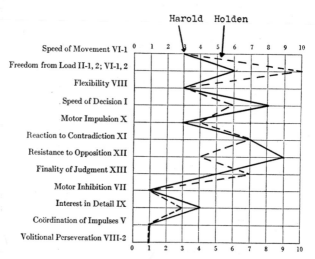

Fig. 23.—Downey Individual Will-Temperament Test profiles

"freedom from load," is due almost wholly to the fact that, in the first of the two comparisons on which the score is based, Harold, when asked to write his name in his usual style and speed, wrote it more slowly than did Holden. In writing the phrase "United States of America," however, they reacted in an almost identical manner. The only other noticeable difference is in resistance to opposition. Holden opened his eyes in surprise when an obstacle was placed in front of his pencil, while Harold pushed on steadily against it. On the whole, the similarities are remarkable, indicating that the test measures fairly stable features of behavior, that these boys react alike by nature, and that the environment has not differed sufficiently to change their reactions.

On these twins we have the results of an additional test of personality, The Personality Inventory of Robert G. Bernreuter, kindly furnished us by Dr. J. S. Park, of the University of Wisconsin. The percentiles on this test are as follows:

	Harold	Holden
1. Neurotic	65	57
2. Self-sufficiency	25	26
3. Introversion	67	41
4. Dominance	30	30

The first and third parts are similar in nature to the Woodworth-Mathews test. They all agree in making Harold somewhat more neurotic than Holden. In self-sufficiency and dominance there is no difference. The Pressey test does not agree with this. Perhaps this is due to the fact that a test, like the Pressey, which bases its score on the number of items to which the individual responds, is not so reliable as one that requires one to make some response to all the items. For sake of completeness the table of scores on the four parts of the Pressey test is given (Table 66). A peculiar thing about the Woodworth-Mathews test is that only one of the unfavorable responses was the same. A number of Harold's unfavorable responses related to his home life. The tests indicate that both boys are relatively stable emotionally, but Holden seems to be somewhat the more stable of the two. On the whole, the difference is less than the average.

The Kent-Rosanoff Free Association Test indicates rather close similarity in associations. While Harold gives somewhat more common responses than does Holden, the average frequency is practically the same, and the number of identical responses fairly high.

In overt behavior Harold gave an impression of having a livelier, more sociable disposition, while Holden seemed comparatively stolid. The differences, however, were not particularly marked.

HANDWRITING

The handwriting is very similar. Holden writes with a little more slant, and he is a little more careless in forming the letters. Both exhibit a rather jerky unrhythmical movement and a lack of a sense of form. They complete each letter in most cases but do not arrange the letters in an orderly pattern. The difference between them is a matter of degree. Holden's writing might have been written by Harold when very tired or in great haste. The difference may be due to the fact that Holden's heavy work has impaired the accuracy of his fine co-ordinations, or it may be due to a more fundamental difference. In any case, the similarity is the striking fact in comparison with identical twins in general.

TABLE 66

TOTAL NUMBER OF WORDS CROSSED OUT AND NUMBER OF
DEVIATIONS ON THE PRESSEY X–O TEST

TEST	WORDS CROSSED OUT		DEVIATIONS	
	Harold	Holden	Harold	Holden
Test I: Unpleasant words..............	35	56	8	11
Test II: Words associated in mind with given word......................	33	55	10	6
Test III: Things thought wrong...........	58	76	11	15
Test IV: Worries.....................	28	34	13	10
Total......................	154	221	42	42

SUMMARY

The striking fact about these twins is their close similarity in ability, personality, and physique. This corresponds to their very similar educational, social, and physical environment. The slight difference in ability is, perhaps, due to Harold's more recent school experience, though it is only slightly greater than the average difference in twins reared together who have had simultaneous and equal schooling, the mean differences of this group being: Stanford-Binet I.Q., 5.9; Otis I.Q., 4.5; and Stanford Achievement, 6.4 months. The slight difference in emotional stability may be due to unknown circumstances of their lives. The close similarity of these twins, brought up under such similar circumstances, suggests that such similarity may be expected when genetic factors alone operate. Conversely, when differences appear, we must look for nongenetic factors. These may be either prenatal or postnatal. The similarity of these twins indicates that, in some cases at least, prenatal factors may not produce any important differences.

PLATE XIX

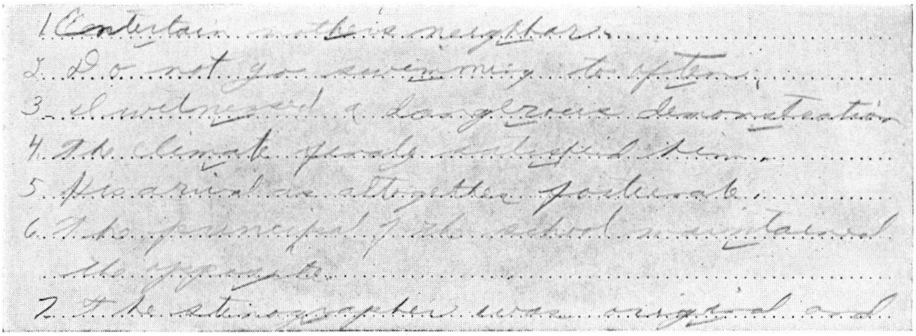

HANDWRITING OF HOLDEN, CASE IX

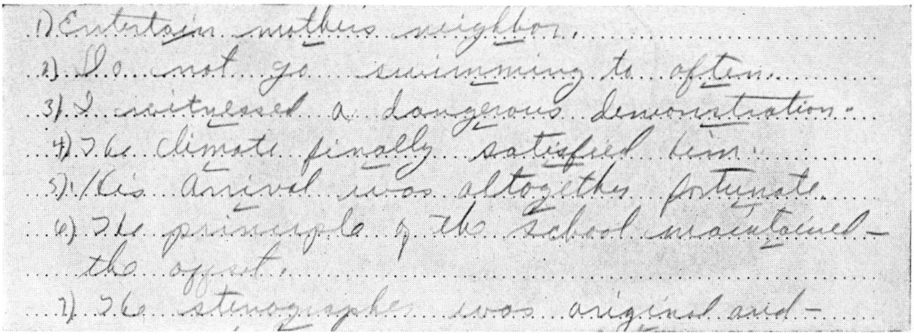

HANDWRITING OF HAROLD, CASE IX

CASE X.   TWINS BETTY AND RUTH

These young girls, twelve and one-half years old when examined, were born in Chicago and, for reasons not revealed, sent to an orphanage in Evanston when a few months old. When they were less than a year old, they were adopted by two different families, both of whom for a time continued to live in Chicago. The first meeting after separation occurred when they were five years old. Betty has lived all her life in a suburb of Chicago, while Ruth at the age of seven moved with her foster-parents to a rather small town in Iowa, where they still live.

EDUCATIONAL CAREERS

Ruth started school when she was five years old and is now in the eighth grade. Betty started a year later than Ruth and is now in the seventh grade. Both have progressed at the normal rate, but the fact remains that Ruth has had one year more schooling and is now in a more advanced grade than her sister. On the other hand, Betty has had somewhat superior home cultural advantages. She has been brought up in a home of wealth and has had more encouragement to read good books, hear good music, and see good drama than has Ruth. Quantitatively considered, the advantages of one seem to be about balanced by those of the other. As we shall see, however, qualitative differences must also be taken into account.

SOCIAL ENVIRONMENTS

Betty's foster-father is a manufacturer who has always had a large income. Her home has been relatively large and commodious. She has been the only child in the family and has evidently been pampered by her foster-mother. For example, she is in the habit of having her breakfast served in her room whenever she feels disinclined to come downstairs. Her foster-mother has shielded her from all social contacts outside her social milieu. On the other hand, she has attended many parties of a somewhat exclusive sort. Her manners have been carefully cultivated, and she has been trained to be reserved and not boisterous. Betty claims that her foster-mother is a highly nervous person who has had a nervous breakdown. She thinks that she herself has acquired something of her alleged nervous temperament from association with her mother. It is a question whether she actually has a nervous temperament. The tests should be of value on this point.

Ruth's foster-father has until recently been foreman in a railroad shop. He is now retired on a pension. Ruth has had two foster-mothers. The first one died when she was six years old, and she does not remember her very clearly. The present foster-mother is described as good-natured, efficient, and always kind. Our impression of the latter is that she is a plain, com-

PLATE XX

CASE X, BETTY (*left*) AND RUTH AT TWELVE YEARS OF AGE, SHORTLY BEFORE THEY
WERE EXAMINED

mon-sense woman, without any affectation, and without much educational or cultural background. According to her statement, the home has always been provided with good books, but Ruth has not cared much for reading. She has been less restrained in her activities and associations than her sister. She has certainly less social polish than her sister. Ruth has been reared in a family with two other children and has not been spoiled or pampered.

Both girls have been affiliated with the Baptist church, but of recent years Ruth has joined her mother in attending the Christian Science church.

PHYSICAL ENVIRONMENTS

The differences in physical and health environments have not been very marked. Both girls have had two serious illnesses—typhoid fever and mastoid trouble. They have had the usual series of infantile infectious diseases. Evidently Betty has been more fortunate than her sister in the matter of food since she has lived in a rather wealthy home. Association with a highly nervous mother seems to have brought on a nervous condition in Betty, though the condition is not marked and is possibly imaginary.

PHYSICAL RESEMBLANCES AND DIFFERENCES

These girls at the time of examination were less strikingly similar than average identical twins but still highly similar. Betty is fully right-handed, Ruth distinctly ambidextrous. Betty has clockwise hair whorl, while Ruth has an indefinite, partially reversed crown whorl. Ruth's ears are both a little smaller than those of Betty. The two left ears are almost identical in shape, but Betty's right ear differs rather markedly in shape from the other three ears, having a more extended upper margin and standing out from the head considerably more than the other ears. The teeth are very similar, being rather large and in fairly good condition. Betty has had the right lower second molar filled, while Ruth has had both right and left lower second molars filled. The other teeth are sound. Ruth's lower incisors are somewhat irregular in position, while Betty's are almost regular. Both have the same iris color—greenish hazel. Both have light-brown, soft, wavy hair, with the same hair line on forehead and neck. The shape of nose in both is distinctly Roman, and the other facial features strikingly similar. The hands are the same in shape, size, and shape of fingernails. The feet are equally similar. The anthropometric measurements show that Betty is a little larger in almost all respects. She is $\frac{1}{4}$ inch taller and 4 pounds heavier. The head measurements are identical. All palm-print and fingerprint data show very marked similarities, the two right hands being almost identical in every item. The most striking physical difference at present is that Betty is postpubescent and Ruth prepubescent. There seems to be about a year's difference between them in physiological age.

The general impression derived from observations of overt behavior is that these twins differ to a considerable extent in their personality traits but have in common some rather unusual traits. Ruth was much less reserved and was inclined to be bold, though not offensively so, while Betty, probably as the result of her more formal home and outside associations, was far more restrained and, in a sense, more lady-like. Both girls were naturally high spirited and somewhat mischievous. In intervals of leisure they enjoyed themselves running the automatic elevator up and down and made themselves very obvious around the building. On one occasion they were interrupted while dancing on a table top in one of the examination rooms. It was difficult to get them posed for a photograph because of a tendency to giggle at the critical moment. Their sense of humor seemed to be very keen and very little stimulus was required to excite laughter. In all these high-spirited performances Ruth seemed to be the leader, but Betty was entirely co-operative. Betty seemed to consider Ruth very smart and showed admiration and approval of the latter's joking remarks and unconventional acts. The influences of Ruth's less formal home environment and Betty's more careful training in manners were obvious from the first interview, but the lack of inhibition of the former and the restraint of the latter did not seem to us to be very deep-seated, for, when together, they behaved in a very similar fashion. In other words, Betty's training had not very materially altered her true temperament, which was actually high-spirited and mischievous, though not to an objectionable degree. The tests, however, indicate some rather definite differences.

TESTS OF ABILITY

On four of the tests of ability Ruth makes a higher score, and on one, the International Test, the scores are equal. Both girls are high in intelligence, as is indicated by their I.Q.'s. This accounts for their ability to score on such advanced tests as the American Council Test and the International Test. The fact that the sisters are equal on the International Test and differ most on the educational test suggests strongly that they are natively equal and that the differences in ability which appear are due to Ruth's extra year of schooling. The small difference on the American Council Test may be due to the fact that neither could do much on any part except the analogies test. The greater difference on the Otis than on the Stanford-Binet is doubtless due to the fact that the former is more affected by schooling.

In the Stanford Achievement Test it is interesting to note that Betty, who has been encouraged to read widely at home, does about as well as her

TABLE 67

Test Record and Environmental Rating of Pair No. 10
(Betty and Ruth)

Test	Betty	Ruth	Diff.	Ratio of Diff. to Mean Diff.
Stanford-Binet:				
M.A.	15–7	16–3	8 mo.	.52
I.Q.	122	127	5	.61
Otis S.-A.:				
Score	40	48	8	....
I.Q.	113	121	8	1.00
Percentage right	63.5	72.7	9.2	.64
American Council score	62	67	5	.18
International score	144	144	0	0
Stanford Achievement:				
Reading age	16–11	16–6	5 mo.	....
Spelling	14–6	15–9	15	....
Language	17–0	15–9	15	....
Literature	15–8	16–5	9	....
History and civics	14–8	16–6	22	....
Geography	16–2	18–2	24	....
Physiology and hygiene	13–3	17–7	52	....
Arithmetic	12–6	17–4	58	....
Total	15–1	16–8	19	1.17
Downey:				
Total	52	62	10	1.09
Pattern difference	....	....	2.5	1.26
Woodworth-Mathews:				
Number of neurotic traits	14	11	3	.60
Pressey Emotions:				
Total crossed out	221	188	33	.70
Deviations	54	49	5	1.02
Kent-Rosanoff:				
Number of common responses	87	93	6	.62
Average frequency	148	133	15	.38
Number of identical responses	11	11*	....	....
Average of all tests	....	....	....	.70
Environmental rating:				
Educational	....	....	10	.66
Social	....	....	15	.84
Physical	....	....	16	1.01

* Ratio to mean, .77.

sister in "reading and literature" but that Ruth does much better in the "content" subjects—history, geography, physiology, and arithmetic. These, doubtless, depend more on schooling.

The will-temperament profiles are very interesting. Ruth, the sister who was brought up in the economically poorer home, has the larger total score. The profiles are very similar, however, except on three parts, namely, speed of decision, reaction to contradiction, and resistance to opposition. The difference in each of these can, we believe, plausibly be referred to the different social training received by the twins. The test of speed of decision

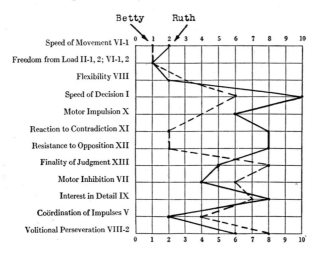

FIG. 24.—Downey Individual Will-Temperament Test profiles

calls for self-rating on twenty-two pairs of personal traits. A person who had been carefully trained in social manners would be more self-conscious and hence more hesitant in rating himself. Again, one so trained according to the canons of polite society would be less likely to contradict or to persist against opposition in a matter which might appear of no consequence. So Betty, upon being shown the wrong envelope the second time, acquiesced with the polite "Was it? I thought it was *M* but guess it wasn't." Ruth, on the contrary, said on the third presentation, "Yes, you did make a mistake." It appears, then, that the twins are, by nature, remarkably similar in overt behavior but that their behavior has been decidedly modified in certain definite respects by their training.

The twins give nearly the same number of unfavorable responses on the Woodworth-Mathews test, but Betty gives the larger number. This accords with the fact that her foster-mother is reported to have had a nervous breakdown and that the girl thinks that she has been made nervous by association with her foster-mother. This small difference alone would not be worthy of much credence if the score on the Pressey did not agree with it. As will be seen from Table 68, Betty crossed out 33 more words than did Ruth; and 23 of these were in Test IV, "things you have worried about." On this test Betty marked 51 to Ruth's 28. The difference is the more significant since the number marked on the other tests is about the same. The slightly larger number of deviations in Betty's responses is confirmatory, so

TABLE 68

TOTAL NUMBER OF WORDS CROSSED OUT AND NUMBER OF
DEVIATIONS ON THE PRESSEY X–O TEST

TEST	WORDS CROSSED OUT		DEVIATIONS	
	Betty	Ruth	Betty	Ruth
Test I: Unpleasant words..................	54	53	14	10
Test II: Words associated in mind with given word...........................	25	26	7	7
Test III: Things thought wrong.............	91	81	13	15
Test IV: Worries..........................	51	28	20	17
Total..........................	221	188	54	49

far as it goes. The evidence seems fairly clear that something about Betty's life has made her disposed to neurotic feelings. Whether her foster-mother's behavior is the chief cause or other features are equally or more influential, we cannot say.

The responses on the Kent-Rosanoff Free Association Test indicate that the girls have associations of about equal commonness. Ruth gives more common responses, but Betty gives responses of higher average frequency. The number of identical responses is rather small. Not much is to be learned from this test.

HANDWRITING

The handwriting shows a good deal of similarity for sisters brought up apart since we cannot attribute the similarity to imitation or instruction by the same teachers. In addition to an underlying similarity, however, there

PLATE XXI

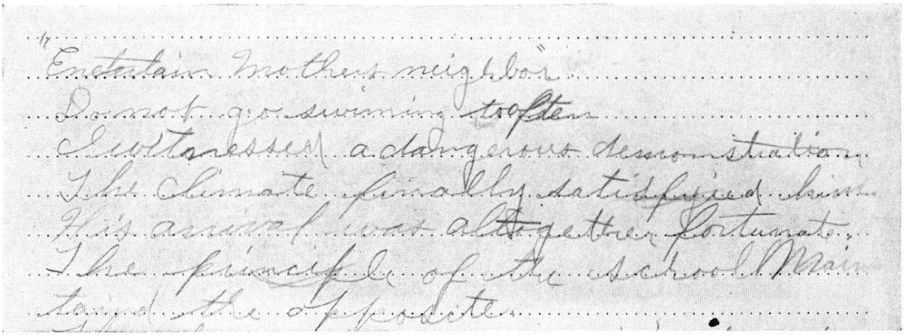

Entertain Mother's neighbor.
Do not go swimming too often.
I witnessed a dangerous demonstration.
The climate finally satisfied him.
His arrival was altogether fortunate.
The principle of the school Main
tained the opposite.

HANDWRITING OF BETTY, CASE X

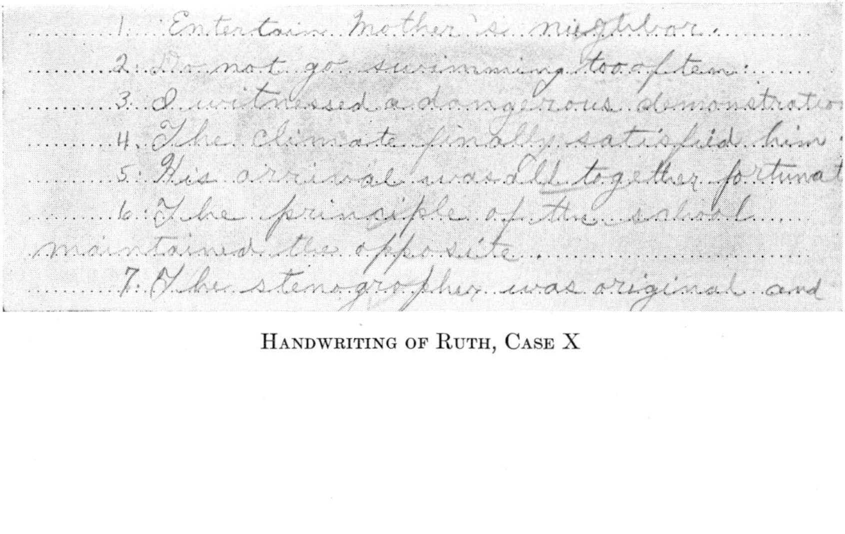

1. Entertain Mother's neighbor.
2. Do not go swimming too often.
3. I witnessed a dangerous demonstration
4. The climate finally satisfied him.
5. His arrival was all together fortunat
6. The principle of the school
maintained the opposite.
7. The stenographer was original and

HANDWRITING OF RUTH, CASE X

is also a marked difference—a difference which is in accord with the result of some of the tests. The similarity is greatest at the beginning, and the difference becomes more manifest as the writing proceeds. The first sentence on the two pages might well have been written by the same person. The chief difference is that Ruth's writing is somewhat less slanting and more rounded. Notice, however, the similarity in the capital E and M, in the gh in "neighbor," and in the way in which the last stroke of the word is made. Other similarities of the same kind can easily be found in the second sentence.

When we come to the third and following sentences, greater differences in general appearance are to be seen. Ruth's writing continues much as before, but Betty's undergoes a marked change. It appears first in the retracing of the word "often." Further marks are an increase in size and a very considerable increase in irregularity, both in the slant and in size of the letters. Ruth's writing also shows some increase in size, but not the marked decrease in regularity. In other words, the writing impulse gathers strength in both as they proceed; but Ruth is able to maintain control of the expression of this impulse, while Betty's control deteriorates to a marked degree. This appears to confirm the findings of the tests and the observations to the effect that Ruth is superior to Betty in nervous stability and control. The difference is doubtless of environmental origin.

SUMMARY

In physical development the twins differ moderately, largely as the consequence of Betty's being physiologically about a year ahead of Ruth. We are inclined to attribute the physiological advantage of Betty to a somewhat richer diet, greater home comfort, and more rest. This suggestion received support from the very similar situation found in twins Virginia and Maxine (Case XVI), where the physiological differences were more marked and more definitely associated with differences in food and rest.

In ability the sisters appear to be basically very similar but to differ both in general ability and in educational attainment in ways that may be attributed to moderate differences in their schooling. Only in the Stanford Achievement Test, however, is the difference much larger than the average of identical twins reared together.

In personality, also, there is evidence of rather remarkable native similarity in temperament and behavior, together with quite evident deviations of a specific nature ascribable to differences in their social environment. Owing either to the overstimulating character of Betty's environment or to the disturbing effect of her foster-mother's illness, she shows distinctly more neurotic symptoms and less general nervous control than does her sister. A special problem of interpretation arises from the difference between these twins in physiological maturation. We have attributed this difference to environmental factors, probably food and social stimulation. The question is, To what extent may this difference be responsible for the difference in ability and personality? Statistical studies[4] have shown a small but positive correlation between precocity of maturing and mental ability during adolescence. We do not have such objective evidence concerning the relation of personality to puberty. We believe such a relation exists, though the trend of psychological opinion is toward an explanation of such a relation as a result of changes in the way the youth is treated rather than in terms of direct physiological effect. The problem is involved, and we can do little more than define the question.

CASE XI. TWINS GLADYS AND HELEN

These twins are both married women, thirty-five years old when examined. They were born in a small Ohio town, were separated at about eighteen months of age, and did not meet again until they were twenty-eight years old. Their meeting was somewhat dramatic and was described in chapter ix.

Helen was twice adopted. The first adoption was an unfortunate one, for the foster-father was a man of unstable character and the foster-mother became insane two years after Helen was taken into her home. Helen was, therefore, taken back to the same orphanage from which she had been originally adopted and, after several months, was adopted for the second time, the foster-parents being a farmer and his wife. The farm of this couple in southeastern Michigan was her home until she was twenty-five years of age, although she was away for four years of college work. Helen's second foster-mother, though having had few educational advantages herself, was determined that the foster-daughter should have every educational opportunity, and stood out for her convictions against the opposition of the foster-father, who considered higher education for women as nonsense. Helen never was required really to work on the farm, though when at home she assisted with the housework.

Gladys was adopted by a Canadian family, the foster-father being a railroad conductor whose home was in a medium-sized city in Ontario. On account of ill health the foster-father was sent by the railroad company to the Canadian Rockies. When, after two years, his health had improved sufficiently, he returned to Ontario and was reinstated in his railroad position.

[4] Ethel M. Abernethy, "Relationships between Mental and Physical Growth." Unpublished Doctor's thesis, Department of Education, University of Chicago, 1933. Pp. 128.

PLATE XXII

CASE XI, GLADYS (*left*) AND HELEN AT THIRTY-SEVEN YEARS OF AGE
The photograph was especially posed for this book

This moving came at a bad time for Gladys' schooling and resulted in her receiving hardly any formal education. She was needed at home for housework and had no other occupation until she was seventeen, when she went to work in a knitting mill. When she was nineteen, she went to Detroit and worked as a saleswoman in stores and also did some clerical work. For the last nine years she has been an assistant to the proprietor of a small publishing concern. She has done almost everything around a printing office, including setting type, copy-writing, and proofreading. These duties must be regarded as having some educational value.

EDUCATIONAL CAREERS

Helen took a Bachelor's degree from a good Michigan college and soon afterward became a schoolteacher, first in a small town and for the last eight years in a large school in Detroit. She has taught principally English and history but has had to fill in her time with a variety of other subjects, including dancing. Her work has been confined to the middle grades. On the whole, her educational experience as student and teacher has been extensive.

Gladys was much less fortunate in her educational opportunities. She went to the Rocky Mountains when she was about ready to go into third grade. During the next two years no school was available, and after her return to Ontario she was probably too old to associate comfortably with third-graders, for she was twelve years old at that time. The result was that she never went back to school. Thus, there was a very marked contrast—the greatest found in any of our cases—between the extensive education of Helen and the nearly total lack of formal education for Gladys.

SOCIAL ENVIRONMENTS

Helen was reared on a farm in Michigan and Gladys in medium-sized towns in Ontario and in the Rocky Mountains. Culturally there is no great difference between Michigan and Ontario, though they are in different countries. On the whole, Ontario is somewhat more conservative than Michigan, and the population of Ontario is somewhat more homogenous than that of Michigan; but it does not seem to us that the contrast is very great. Farm life as opposed to city life offers a greater environmental contrast, but Helen had the advantage of attending high school and college in a fairly large city and has lived for eight years or more in Detroit, where Gladys has lived for over ten years. Hence, the lives of both have been led in urban surroundings for a rather long time.

Helen married when about twenty-six years of age, her husband being a cabinet-maker with a high-school education. Her marriage did not interfere with her career as a teacher except for a short period when her child was born. The child was two and one-half years old in the spring of 1933. Helen, because of her profession, has had rather extensive social opportunities and has been comparatively well off financially. The home life on the farm was none too harmonious, the father being a quiet, easy-going Englishman, who was dominated by his wife, a woman of rather violent temper and exacting in her demands. Helen was fond of her easy-going foster-father, but had many disagreements with her foster-mother. There was little, if any difference between the two foster-families as to social status.

Gladys married when she was twenty-one, her husband being a mechanic with a partial high-school education. She has two children, ten and twelve years old. Her home experiences have been rather similar to those of her sister, for there was much discord between the foster-parents, the mother being high-tempered and exacting but without any sympathy with education for women. Both twins attribute their alleged high tempers to the discordant relations that existed between them and their respective foster-mothers.

PHYSICAL AND HEALTH ENVIRONMENTS

Helen claims to have been very healthy as a child and seems to have had no serious illnesses as an adult. Gladys, on the contrary, was very delicate as a child and had several serious illnesses, including scarlet fever and a very severe attack of measles, which was almost fatal. At present she seems a very healthy, robust woman. There seem to be few marked contrasts in physical environments.

PHYSICAL RESEMBLANCES AND DIFFERENCES

At the present time, when they are thirty-five years old, Helen looks about her age or a little older, but Gladys looks about forty. This may be due to lack of polish and feminine coquetry, which her sister shows in a well-developed form. They are of about the same build, but Helen has a better figure. Helen weighs 140¾ pounds and Gladys, 139¼ pounds. Helen is 62.1 inches in stature and Gladys, 61 inches. Gladys is broader shouldered and rather more mannish in carriage and figure. The head length of Helen is 18.8 centimeters; that of Gladys, 18.6 centimeters; and the head width of Helen is 14.9 centimeters; that of Gladys, 15.4 centimeters. Thus, Gladys has the larger head.

The hair of both is dark brown, with a sprinkling of gray, Helen's being a little grayer. The hair is medium coarse and nearly straight in both. The hair whorl of Gladys is clockwise, that of Helen indefinite, or partly reversed. The color of eyes is the same in both—a dark bluish-gray. The complexion is dark and clear in both. The terminal joint of the index fingers of both hands is bent radialward in a curious fashion and is the same in both. The faces are both somewhat concave in profile, with strong prominent chin, a little less prominent in Helen. Helen's lower face is a little wider, less tapering than Gladys'. The ears are strikingly similar—long and narrow with extra-long fleshy lobes at the bottom. Gladys' left ear differs slightly from the other three ears. The teeth of both are for the most part white and regular. Each has six fillings—all in the molars or biscupids, none in the front. Both are strongly right-handed. The formulas of palm and finger patterns do not afford in themselves very positive evidence of monozygocity, but they are by no means contradictory of such diagnosis. The finger patterns show extremely close resemblance between the two left hands, closer than between the right and left hand of either individual. Eight out of ten homologous finger patterns are nearly identical. In the palm patterns the right hands are more similar than are right and left hands of either individual. The least close resemblance in dermatoglyphic items appears in the total ridge-count values of the ten fingers of the two individuals, Helen having a total value of 57 and Gladys of 44—a rather large difference of 13 points but no greater than in a few cases of identical twins reared together.

On the whole, it seems that physical differences are relatively small as compared with mental and temperamental differences. What differences are present seem to be correlated with the great difference in the lives of the two women, for they are mainly associated with differences in carriage of body and facial expression—differences obviously acquired in the course of their different social activities.

Observations of the overt behavior of these twins revealed some further important personality differences. Helen is a confident and suave person with rather marked charm of manner. She makes the most of her personal appearance, moves about gracefully, and is apparently conscious of making a favorable impression on men. She conversed smoothly without a trace of diffidence and always took the lead in all matters pertaining to arrangements for the trip and the stay in Chicago. One sees at once that she is by far the more aggressive in her overt acts, but the Downey test revealed about equally strong aggressiveness in the two women. Gladys made the impression upon us of a person ill at ease. This attitude may have been partly the result of a feeling of inferiority in view of the apparent certainty that she would make a comparatively poor showing on the tests. She seemed to us to be a rather staid and stolid person, distinctly diffident. She had no affectations to match those of her sister and had no charm of manner or grace of movement. She was not becomingly dressed nor did she make the best of her physique. She never volunteered any information and was difficult to draw into conversation. She made no effort to create a favorable personal impression. In general, the contrast in overt behavior during social contacts was rather extreme.

As an advertisement for a college education the contrast between these twins should be quite effective.

TESTS OF ABILITY

Helen is much above Gladys in every test of ability. In the Stanford-Binet the difference is three years, ten months, or twenty-four points in I.Q., which is nearly five times as great as the mean difference between identical twins reared together and three times as great as the mean difference between the nineteen pairs. Helen's score is at the twentieth percentile and Gladys' at the eighty-ninth. Thus, 69 per cent of the scores of the general population would lie between these two scores. The differences between the other tests vary in amount, but even in the International Test, which is certainly not directly influenced by formal schooling, the difference is three times the mean difference between identical twins reared apart. The difference on the Otis test is least and on the American Council Test the greatest. The large difference on the latter test may be partly due to the fact that it is harder and partly to the fact that it is largely based on operations with language. The difference in total educational attainment is five years and nine months. Even in spelling and language, which Gladys uses in her vocation of proofreading, Helen is superior by two years and six months, and one year and eight months, respectively. The differences in test intelligence are greater for this pair than for any other pair of separated twins, and, strikingly enough, this largest difference is correlated with the largest difference in educational experience.

TESTS OF PERSONALITY

On the Downey test there is a remarkable combination of likenesses and differences. The total score is vastly different, Helen having the larger total. The difference is three times the mean difference. This difference is made up entirely of large differences at both ends of the scale. Helen makes much higher scores in speed and fluidity and very much higher in the tests indicating motor control and interest in detail. On the other hand, they are almost identical in the reactions which are taken to indicate aggressiveness and persistence. There appears to be a real and rather profound difference in speed, flexibility, and control of responses. For example, when instructed to write the phrase "United States of America" as slowly as possible, Helen, in three successive trials, took 3'50", 6'06", and 12'13", while Gladys could take only 15", 14", and 16". Helen was better also at disguising her hand

TABLE 69

TEST RECORD AND ENVIRONMENTAL RATING OF PAIR NO. 11
(GLADYS AND HELEN)

Test	Gladys	Helen	Diff.	Ratio of Diff. to Mean Diff.
Stanford-Binet:				
M.A.	14–8	18–6	46 mo.	2.98
I.Q.	92	116	24	2.92
Otis S.-A.:				
Score	36	48	12	. . . .
I.Q.	94	106	12	1.50
Percentage right	65.5	69.6	4.1	.29
American Council score	5	93	88	3.25
International score	143	188	45	2.90
Stanford Achievement:				
Reading age	15–5	18–10	41 mo.	. . . .
Spelling	15–0	17–6	30	. . . .
Language	16–3	17–11	20	. . . .
Literature	9–6	19+	114	. . . .
History and civics	11–5	19+	91	. . . .
Geography	15–0	19+	48	. . . .
Physiology and hygiene	13–1	19+	71	. . . .
Arithmetic	12–2½	17–1	58½	. . . .
Total	13–1	18–10	69	4.24
Downey:				
Total	54	82	28	3.06
Pattern difference	. . . .	. . . .	2.9	1.46
Woodworth-Mathews:				
Number of neurotic traits	30	30	0	0
Pressey Emotions:				
Total crossed out	232	164	68	1.44
Deviations	39	51	12	2.45
Kent-Rosanoff:				
Number of common responses	79	71	8	.83
Average frequency	128	121	7	.18
Number of identical responses	6	6*	. . . .	. . . .
Average of all tests	. . . .	. . . .	. . . .	1.96
Environmental rating:				
Educational	. . . .	. . . .	37	2.45
Social	. . . .	. . . .	25	1.40
Physical	. . . .	. . . .	22	1.38

* Ratio to mean, .42.

and at imitating another hand. Considering the almost identical responses in other tests, such as reaction to contradiction and resistance to opposition, we are led to conclude that the differences which do exist are due to education and other experiences.

* The scores on the Woodworth-Mathews Personal Data Sheet are remarkable in two respects—their equality and their size. Thirty unfavorable responses out of 75 is a large number. While only 16 out of the 30 are common, the equality in the total number indicates that these twins are in general about equally disposed to neurotic behavior. It is a curious fact that

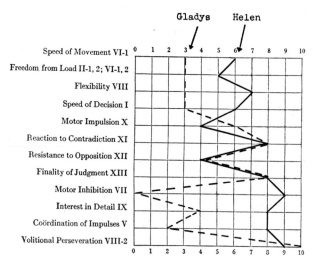

Fig. 25.—Downey Individual Will-Temperament Test profiles

each reports that there was much friction between herself and her foster-mother. Can this have been responsible for the high scores of both, or is similar native disposition responsible? We cannot say, but we incline to the former explanation.

The responses on the Pressey Test of the Emotions seem to contradict the finding of the Woodworth-Mathews test in regard to the similarity of these twins. A large difference appears both in "total affectivity" and in the number of deviations. The comparative number of words crossed out on the four parts by the sisters differs widely. Gladys crosses out many more on Test I and Test III, and Helen on Test IV. Again we are led to suspect that a test which depends on whether or not the person reacts is more ambiguous in its outcome than is one which requires a series of definite responses to be made. In this case Gladys marks more words, but she marks fewer words which differ from those commonly marked. Helen, on the other hand, makes more responses which indicate a neurotic disposition. One of our tests, then, indicates close similarity and the other diversity. The evidence is mixed.

The Kent-Rosanoff test indicates similarity in the general character of the responses—about the same number of common responses—but little identity in the particular responses given. Perhaps it is not far-fetched to

TABLE 70

TOTAL NUMBER OF WORDS CROSSED OUT AND NUMBER OF
DEVIATIONS ON THE PRESSEY X–O TEST

TEST	WORDS CROSSED OUT		DEVIATIONS	
	Gladys	Helen	Gladys	Helen
Test I: Unpleasant words................	73	27	6	12
Test II: Words associated in mind with given word........................	39	33	7	11
Test III: Things thought wrong............	92	61	10	12
Test IV: Worries........................	28	43	16	16
Total........................	232	164	39	51

say that they have the same tendency to conform to the ways of thought of their environment but that they have had widely different environments to conform to.

HANDWRITING

The styles of handwriting are decidedly different, but whether the difference is entirely due to different amounts of specific practice in handwriting, or whether it is also symptomatic of more general differences, it is rather hard to say. Helen's writing is in a decidedly mature, adult style, while Gladys' might be the writing of a fourteen- or fifteen-year-old child. However, Gladys has doubtless done a good deal of writing in her present occupation, and it is not certain that all the difference is due to the amount of practice in writing. Helen's writing is neater, more delicate, and more feminine. While the letters are not formed with pedantic accuracy and the writing has dash and fluency, there is a firmness of line, a regularity and general form, which give the writing some beauty and character. Gladys'

PLATE XXIII

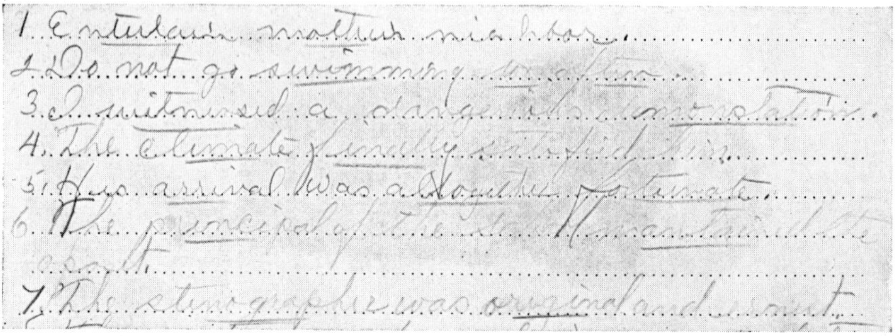

HANDWRITING OF GLADYS, CASE XI

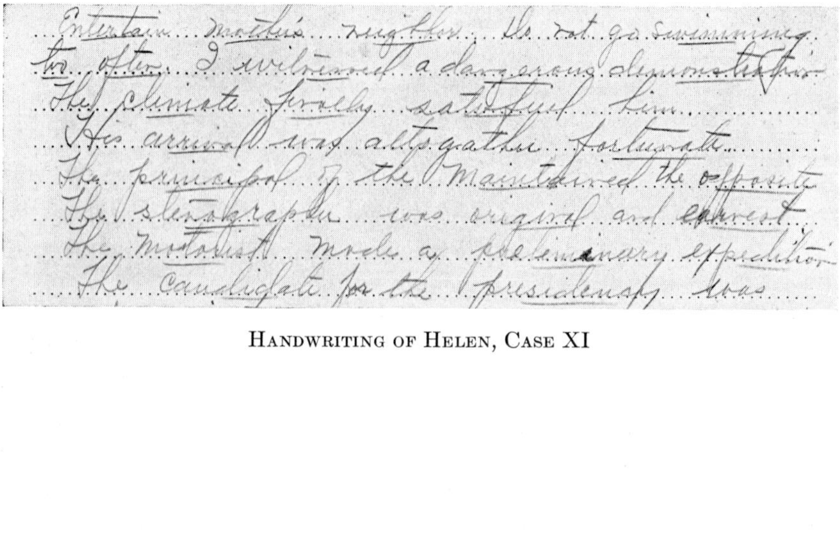

HANDWRITING OF HELEN, CASE XI

writing is largely lacking in these characteristics. On the other hand, there are some similarities. Notice, for example, the great length of the f, which extends almost from the line above to the line below. This long upward and downward reach appears in nearly all of Helen's letters which extend beyond one space and in some but not all of Gladys'. It appears as though Gladys were restrained from dashing off in the style she would like, perhaps by lack of facility, perhaps by some other cause. Another difference is that Helen's words are clearly separated by an open space between, while Gladys' tend to run together. We are inclined to think that the handwriting reveals some native similarities in behavior and that the differences are due partly to general characteristics of behavior which have been produced by the environment as well as the different amounts of specific practice.

SUMMARY

The physical differences of these twins are rather marked, Helen being better preserved and apparently physiologically younger, due probably to a much easier life.

Marked differences in ability obviously accompany the extreme difference in education. The relation is too clear to need emphasis. In personality the effects are mixed and difficult to disentangle. The Downey test shows marked and definite differences in overt behavior. The evidence on emotional balance is mixed. The handwriting reveals differences which suggest, at least, the differences in personality which appear from observation. This is a case in which differences in observable social behavior are somewhat more marked than are differences in test behavior. While the differences in personality are not so clearly and simply shown in the tests as are the differences in ability, it can scarcely be doubted that differences of both kinds do exist in rather marked degree and that they have been produced by the environment. This inference is drawn from the fact that differences between the sisters and between their environment are both very large and the further fact that the differences between the twins are in the direction we should expect them to be from the nature of the environmental differences.

CASE XII. TWINS THELMA AND ZELMA[5]

These young married women were twenty-nine years old when examined. Their mother died when they were about a year a and half old, and, since the father could not take care of them, the twins were adopted by two

---

[5] Unfortunately, the photograph of these twins, which was made at the time of the examination, was spoiled as it was being developed. We have now no publishable picture of them.

different families. Since their separation the twins have never lived together and have seen each other only at long intervals.

Thelma was reared in a family, the father of which had been a schoolteacher and later a county supervisor of education. He taught Thelma
correct English speech, which may account for her present rather cultured
mode of expression. For six or seven years she was proprietor of a beauty
shop. She married at twenty-one years of age, her husband being a farmer
and carpenter with a high-school education and decidedly intelligent,
though "he speaks terrible English," preferring German, the language
spoken in his home. Thelma has been in very ill health for some years. She
has one child four years old.

Zelma's foster-father was a railroad man and a high-school graduate, who
had taught school for some time but had to give it up in order to live an
outdoor life on account of tuberculosis. Her foster-mother had almost no
schooling but had regular lessons and recited them to her teacher-husband.
The financial circumstances of Zelma's foster-family were moderate and
rather closely comparable with those of Thelma. Zelma had to leave school
when on the point of beginning high school because she was needed at home
to help her invalid foster-mother. She was anxious to study nursing, but
this ambition was thwarted. After the death of the foster-mother Zelma
earned her own living as a clerk in stores and was for some time cashier in
a coffee shop. The confinement for long hours indoors did not agree with
her health, which seems to have been rather poor when she was in her teens.
She married when very young, seventeen years, and lived with her first
husband off and on for eight years. He is described as a restless wanderer,
who absented himself for long intervals and finally disappeared about five
years ago.

Zelma has no living children, but has had four miscarriages. Two
years ago Zelma obtained a divorce from her first husband and married
again, this time to an older man described as a "shell-shocked war veteran."
She finds life more placid and satisfactory than ever before and is now in
very good health.

EDUCATIONAL CAREERS

Thelma finished high school in a small-town school and attended normal
school for part of a year—long enough to qualify as a grade-school teacher.
She taught school, however, only one year in an Indian school in the state of
Washington. She also received rather more home instruction in English
than did her sister. Zelma was forced to forego high-school education on
account of the pressure of home circumstances, and, of course, she has never
taught school. She also has received some good home training in English

from her teacher-foster-father and now speaks like a well-educated person. There is a difference of about five years of schooling between these twins— a difference which is reflected only very slightly in the intelligence tests.

SOCIAL ENVIRONMENTS

It is difficult to envisage the differences in social environment. Possible influential factors may have inhered in Thelma's longer academic experience, in her having a child, and in her moving about much more extensively. She has lived in Illinois, Wisconsin, Montana, and Washington, while Zelma seems to have lived only in Illinois. Thelma has had some very trying experiences as inmate in tuberculosis sanitariums. The general social and financial status of the foster-families and the husbands of the twins seem to have been about the same.

PHYSICAL ENVIRONMENTS

While these twins were with us, Thelma, an appealingly courageous and cheerful little person, made such an impression upon our physical examiner that it was decided to send her to the University of Chicago Clinics for study and treatment. She weighed only 72.25 pounds and was excessively frail. The director of the Clinics became interested in the case and offered all the facilities of the hospital free of charge to the patient. She remained nearly two weeks, improved greatly, and was sent home with orders to rest and take care of herself. While in the hospital her full medical history was taken and a complete diagnosis made. This report is too long and too technical to reproduce in full, but a brief digest seems necessary.

Thelma presents a history of pulmonary tuberculosis dating back ten years. There was a positive sputum test at nineteen years. She has spent short periods in sanitariums, but never long enough decisively to influence the course of the disease. In 1928, after pregnancy, she began to have abdominal pains and a diagnosis of tubercular enteritis was made. In 1931 a laparotomy was performed, followed by a hysterectomy. Tubercular peritonitis was discovered from which severe pain was suffered. Various other tubercular complications have succeeded one another. The patient has never given herself a fair amount of rest and there would be no chance of recovery without great care and much rest.

The clinical diagnosis showed tubercular conditions in lungs (moderately advanced), of abdomen, of genital organs, and probably adrenal glands.

Zelma was examined by the same physicians, and the report on her was as follows:

Although by her own report she had pulmonary tuberculosis at seventeen years of age, there is no positive indication that she ever had this disease.

The specialist doubts that she ever had active tuberculosis. The patient is now well nourished and has a good chest with good expansion. She is in good condition and without any discoverable disease. The contrast between the two sisters is very great, Zelma weighing 97.75 pounds—which is normal for a small, delicately formed person—and Thelma weighing only 72.25 pounds, a difference of 25.5 pounds. But what a difference these 25 pounds make!

This marked difference in health is the only evidence of a large and important difference in the physical environment of which we are aware. Thelma's having borne a child might be considered as another element, for it was after the birth of this child that her tuberculosis reached a marked degree of advancement. It should also be repeated that Thelma has had to do rather heavy farm work in recent years, although she has never had the robustness of physique required for such work.

PHYSICAL RESEMBLANCES AND DIFFERENCES

These twins were extremely similar in all genetic characters in spite of the very great difference in their health. They were both 59.1 inches tall. Both have fairly long heads, the head length of Zelma being 18.4 centimeters and that of Thelma 18.1 centimeters. Zelma's head width is 13.8 centimeters, and that of Thelma 13.8 centimeters. The very great difference in weight, due to advanced tuberculosis in Thelma, affected all circumferential body measurements and also made the faces somewhat different, for Thelma had hollow cheeks and the bones of the face were prominent. In spite of the great difference in facial flesh, the features and expressions of the twins were strikingly similar. No one would doubt that they are monozygotic twins. Both have the same yellowish-brown eye color and the same soft, straight, reddish-brown hair, coming to a widow's peak at the forehead. Both have equally distinct clockwise hair whorl. The ears are all extremely similar. The teeth are large, white, regular, and nearly perfect in both, and both have a pronounced overbite of the lower incisors. Both have but one irregular tooth, the left upper canine being out of line. Zelma has no cavities, and Thelma has a spot of decay in one tooth, the lower left wisdom tooth. Mirror-imaging is shown in that Zelma has slight strabismus of the left eye and Thelma of the right eye. Zelma is fully right-handed, and Thelma partly left-handed or ambidextrous.

The twins have nearly identical voices, accents, and mannerisms, and they seem in their overt behavior to have highly similar dispositions. Both are courageous in the face of hardship and difficulties, especially Thelma, who was cheerful and co-operative in all tests in spite of her very poor health. Both have a keen sense of humor and frequently saw humor in situations in which it was not obvious to us.

There would have been no difficulty in diagnosing these twins on the basis of palm and finger patterns alone. The two left palms are identical in formulas and almost so in detail. The two right hands are a little less similar. The finger patterns of the two right hands are identical in formulas and extremely similar in details, and the two lefts are almost similar; whereas the right and left fingers of the same individual are very different. The total ridge-count values were 114 points for Thelma and 113 for Zelma—a very striking correspondence. One rarely finds such a high degree of consistent correspondence between twins in all these respects.

TESTS OF ABILITY

The abilities of these twins are not significantly different. Though Thelma is nearly 7 points higher in Binet I.Q., the scores on the other intelligence tests are about equal. Thelma also makes a higher score on the Stanford Achievement Test taken as a whole, but this superiority is due solely to higher scores in literature, geography, and arithmetic.

The results of these tests are an exception to the rule that the twin with more schooling does correspondingly better on the tests of ability. A possible explanation is that Thelma's prolonged ill health and present deficiency in physical strength and vigor may prevent her from doing better on the tests. The difference on the Downey test, which will be described later, lends some color to this hypothesis. Against it is the fact that little correlation has usually been found between physical condition and mental ability and that tuberculosis in particular does not, according to common observation, impair the intellectual powers. However, the opportunity has not previously been had of studying the effects of such profound differences under the condition in which the genetic factors are rigidly controlled. Hence, it may very well be that her poor physical condition has impaired Thelma's ability to do intellectual work.

TESTS OF PERSONALITY

The results of the Downey test bear on the foregoing conclusions. It will be remembered that the Downey test is exceptional among the tests of personality in that it yields a sizable correlation with the scores of the tests of ability. The present is a case in point. The difference in total score, however, must be somewhat discounted by the fact that Thelma uses a backhand, semiprinting style, while Zelma uses the somewhat more rapid forward-slanting cursive style. The other large differences are in reaction to contradiction and co-ordination of impulses. There was some question in the mind of the tester whether Thelma really yielded when she was contradicted or whether her memory was dim. The third test, on which there is a large difference, calls for writing the phrase "United States of America" on a $1\frac{1}{2}$-inch line without slowing down. Zelma did much better on this test.

TABLE 71

TEST RECORD AND ENVIRONMENTAL RATING OF PAIR NO. 12
(THELMA AND ZELMA)

Test	Thelma	Zelma	Diff.	Ratio of Diff. to Mean Diff.
Stanford-Binet:				
M.A.	18–7	17–6	13 mo.	.84
I.Q.	116	109	7	.85
Otis S.-A.:				
Score	58	57	1	....
I.Q.	116	115	1	.12
Percentage right	85.3	90.5	5.2	.36
American Council score	95	98	3	.11
International score	190	190	0	0
Stanford Achievement:				
Reading age	19+	19–0	0+mo.	....
Spelling	15–9	16–3	6	....
Language	19+	19+	0	....
Literature	18–10	16–7	27	....
History and civics	19+·	19+	0	....
Geography	19+	17–4	20	....
Physiology and hygiene	19+	19+	0	....
Arithmetic	16–5	15–2	15	....
Total	18–8	17–6	14	.86
Downey:				
Total	52	68	16	1.75
Pattern difference	....	....	1.9	.96
Woodworth-Mathews:				
Number of neurotic traits	26	20	6	1.20
Pressey Emotions:				
Total crossed out	201	115	86	1.82
Deviations	58	58	0	0
Kent-Rosanoff:				
Number of common responses	93	93	0	0
Average frequency	112	170	58	1.47
Number of identical responses	14	14*	....	....
Average of all tests	....	....	....	.74
Environmental rating:				
Educational			19	1.26
Social			13	.73
Physical			36	2.26

* Ratio to mean, .97.

She did it in 9 seconds, while Thelma took 19. This is a long time to take, even in Thelma's style of writing. It seems likely that she could do better. Possibly she is held back by lack of confidence. Her responses on Test I, which calls for self-ratings, suggests this interpretation. She rates herself as of inferior intelligence, inferior character, tardy, inaccurate, forgetful, and slow. The only unfavorable ratings Zelma makes of herself are tardy and slow. In intelligence and character she rates herself 50–50. It appears, then, that Thelma's ill health and physical condition have affected her feeling tone and estimate of herself and also probably, through this, her behavior. The fact that she puts on a brave front in conversation in no wise contradicts this interpretation.

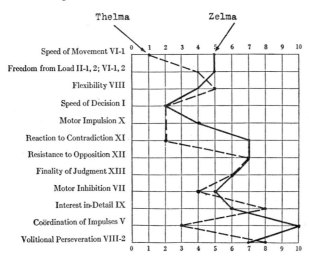

Fig. 26.—Downey Individual Will-Temperament Test profiles

The larger number of unfavorable responses made by Thelma on the Woodworth-Mathews Personal Data Sheet, while the difference is not great, is in harmony with the conclusion that her emotional life has been affected by the hardships she has endured. Both scores are a little high, which may be due to environmental or to genetic factors. Sixteen of the unfavorable responses are common, which is unusually high and suggests similarity in basic responses.

The comparatively large excess in number of words crossed out on the Pressey test agrees with the results of the other tests in suggesting that Thelma is less emotionally stable or at least more excitable. The difference is not so large on Test IV, dealing with neurotic symptoms, as in the other tests, however, suggesting that while her emotions have become more excitable as a result of her unhappy experiences, the change has not been particularly of a psychopathic nature.

The Kent-Rosanoff Free Association Test does not indicate much of significance. Zelma's responses have a somewhat higher frequency than do Thelma's, but the number of common responses is the same. The number of identical responses is about the average of our nineteen pairs.

TABLE 72

TOTAL NUMBER OF WORDS CROSSED OUT AND NUMBER OF
DEVIATIONS ON THE PRESSEY X–O TEST

TEST	WORDS CROSSED OUT		DEVIATIONS	
	Thelma	Zelma	Thelma	Zelma
Test I: Unpleasant words................	40	27	13	15

Test II:
  Words associated in mind with given
  word.........................
	43	27	12	10

Test III: Things thought wrong.............	81	31	19	16
Test IV: Worries.........................	37	30	14	17
Total.........................	201	115	58	58

HANDWRITING

The great variation in the style of writing of these sisters somewhat complicates the comparison. Whether Thelma's ambidexterity has anything to do with her backhand slant is a question, but it is doubtful. The safest conclusion is that Thelma's unusual style is due to some accidental circumstance of her educational history. For example, she may have taken up this style because it was used by some teacher or classmate she admired, or merely because the style took her fancy. It is very doubtful whether we should attribute the general difference in style to any fundamental difference in personality, either inherent or acquired.

Our task, then, is to see whether we can discern any similarities or differences in the writing in spite of the great superficial difference in style. One point of similarity, at least, is manifest. Both writings show skill and a good sense of form. They are mature styles, in spite of the fact that Thelma has adopted a style which gives somewhat less play to individuality than

PLATE XXIV

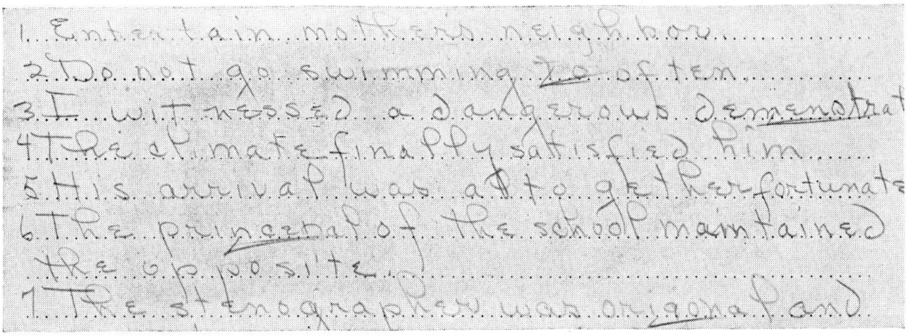

1. Entertain mother's neighbor
2. Do not go swimming too often
3. I witnessed a dangerous demonstrat
4. The climate finally satisfied him
5. His arrival was alto get her fortunate
6. The principal of the school maintained the opposite
7. The stenographer was original and

HANDWRITING OF THELMA, CASE XII

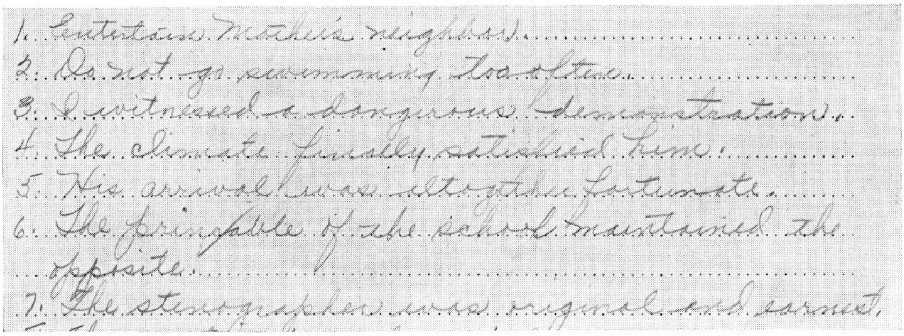

1. Entertain Mother's neighbor.
2. Do not go swimming too often.
3. I witnessed a dangerous demonstration.
4. The climate finally satisfied him.
5. His arrival was altogether fortunate.
6. The principal of the school maintained the opposite.
7. The stenographer was original and earnest.

HANDWRITING OF ZELMA, CASE XII

does Zelma's. These are fundamental and important resemblances. However, they are not specific. They merely indicate that the twins belong to the same general class in respect to sensori-motor skill. They show that nothing has occurred to change either of them so much as to produce a fundamental deterioration in performance of the type required in handwriting. Beyond this the evidence, so far as we can interpret it, does not go.

SUMMARY

These sisters are similar in the various physical characteristics which are of crucial importance in determining the existence of genetic identity. They differ greatly, however, in body weight, due to Thelma's prolonged series of illnesses culminating in tuberculosis. The economic and social environments have been similar, but Thelma has about five years more schooling.

In spite of the considerably longer schooling which Thelma has enjoyed, the abilities of these twin sisters are approximately the same. Thelma's prolonged ill health and her seriously impaired physical condition may have some effect on her performance. The tests of personality indicate close basic similarity between the sisters, but certain differences in the Downey test, the Woodworth-Mathews test, and the Pressey test suggest that Thelma's life has produced modification in her emotions and behavior which may have affected her ability to perform intellectual tasks. There is no doubt of the basic similarity, and there seems hardly less doubt of the modification of the basically similar natures in important details. The difference in ability is less than one would expect in view of the large difference in schooling and in spite of the physical difference. The difference in personality is also, perhaps, somewhat less than might be anticipated.

CASE XIII. TWINS KENNETH AND JERRY

These twin youths were nineteen years old when examined. They were born in 1914 in a large Michigan city. They were separated at three weeks because of the death of the mother and were adopted by two different families.

Kenneth was adopted by Mr. C. and his wife, who lived in a rather large Michigan city. Mr. C. was a city fireman with a very limited education. On account of domestic difficulties Kenneth's foster-parents separated when Kenneth was seven years old. He lived for some time with the foster-mother but was subsequently taken by the foster-father, with whom he lived for several years. For the last few years, however, he has lived in a very small town in Michigan with the maternal foster-grandmother, who seems to be extremely solicitous about his welfare and safety. It was difficult to persuade her to allow the boy to come to Chicago. In high school Kenneth

PLATE XXV

CASE XIII, JERRY (*right*) AND KENNETH AT THE TIME OF THEIR FIRST MEETING WHEN
THEY WERE TWELVE YEARS OLD

was much interested in athletics, playing basketball and being on the cross-country team. He has never had a remunerative job, but has gone to school steadily since an early age. Kenneth first met his twin brother when three years old, but they have not visited back and forth to any great extent except during the last few years. Their homes are now not over one hundred miles apart. Kenneth considers his home a very good one. There are no other children, and he has been treated as a real son by a devoted grandmother.

Jerry was first adopted by a married couple who lived in the city where the twins were born. For five years he lived with these people, but because the court considered the foster-parents unsuitable, for reasons we need not mention, the boy was taken away and offered again for adoption. This time he was adopted by Mr. P., who has lived in a medium-sized Michigan city, the same city where Kenneth lived until he was seven years old. Hence, for two years the boys lived in the same city, though they were unaware of the fact. Jerry's foster-father was also a city fireman with only fourth-grade education. His foster-mother had completed the eighth grade. From her he has received a good deal of instruction in manners. In high school Jerry has played baseball and basketball and, of late, has played golf to as great an extent as a caddy is permitted to play that game. For the last four summers he has been a regular caddy at a golf club and has saved some money. He has also acted as a delivery boy for a grocery store for short intervals. He seems anxious to get ahead financially. He also considers his home a good one and believes he is fortunate in his lot. He has also been the only child in the family.

EDUCATIONAL CAREERS

There is no difference in the schooling of these two boys. They both were graduated from high school on the same day in June, 1933. The schools attended have been of the same type, and there have been no great differences in the disciplines followed by the two boys.

SOCIAL ENVIRONMENTS

Although there must have been thousands of differences in the details of social relations experienced by the two boys, there seem to have been many similarities between the two social milieus. Both have had two sets of foster-parents and both foster-fathers were firemen. The two foster-homes—that is, the final ones—have been fortunate in their effect on the boys. Jerry has had a somewhat more extensive social experience through his work as a caddy, but such experience sometimes may be not too fortunate.

The health records of the boys are very similar. Kenneth remembers only chicken pox and measles, while Jerry reports having had, in addition to these, whooping cough and an operation for appendicitis. They are both in excellent health at the present time. There seem to have been no marked differences in the physical environments as to food, climate, or home care. In fact, one may rate the physical features of the environment as approximately equal.

Physically these boys are extremely similar. We never learned to differentiate them. They both have dark-brown, coarse, wavy or slightly curly hair, with clockwise hair whorl. Both have dark-greenish hazel eyes, Jerry's being a shade greener. The complexion in both is rather poor with tendency to pimples on the face; the skin is rather darkly pigmented and coarse in texture. Kenneth's face is a little wider than Jerry's. The ears are unusually small in both, lie very flat against the head, and are almost identical in form. The teeth are almost identical in size, shape, and arrangement, but Jerry's are in a little better condition (four decayed molars in Kenneth and only two in Jerry). A striking peculiarity, which is more properly temperamental than physical, is common to both: all fingernails are bitten almost entirely away, no nail being more than $\frac{1}{4}$-inch long, and some even less than that. Efforts have been made to break them of this habit, but without success. Both are right-handed in everything.

The anthropometric measurements are very similar indeed. Jerry is .3 inches taller and $1\frac{1}{2}$ pounds heavier. The head length is the same in both, but Kenneth has a head width 7 millimeters greater than Jerry, which corresponds to his wider face. Kenneth is also $1\frac{1}{2}$ centimeters broader in the shoulders, while Jerry is 4 centimeters greater in waist circumference.

On the whole, these boys are as similar physically as almost any pair of identical twins reared together that we have studied.

The finger patterns show 9 out of a possible 10 correspondences between the two individuals—a much higher correspondence than between the two hands of the same individual. The total ridge-count values are 86 for Kenneth and 83 for Jerry—a very close correspondence. The palm patterns show a mixed condition. In some respects mirror-image resemblances are stronger; in other respects same-sided correspondences are greater. On the whole, the dermatoglyphics alone would serve to diagnose the twins as monozygotic.

TABLE 73

TEST RECORD AND ENVIRONMENTAL RATING OF PAIR NO. 13
(KENNETH AND JERRY)

Test	Kenneth	Jerry	Diff.	Ratio of Diff. to Mean Diff.
Stanford-Binet:				
M.A.................	15–1	15–2	1 mo.	.06
I.Q.................	94	95	1	.12
Otis S.-A.:				
Score................	48	45	3	....
I.Q.................	106	103	3	.38
Percentage right........	64.0	72.6	8.6	.60
American Council score.........	90	32	58	2.14
International score............	151	139	12	.77
Stanford Achievement:				
Reading age............	16–6	16–8	2 mo.	....
Spelling..............	17–8	17–4	4	....
Language.............	17–0	16–0	12	....
Literature............	16–2	14–6	20	....
History and civics.......	16–6	16–0	6	....
Geography............	16–0	16–8	8	....
Physiology and hygiene.....	15–9	15–8	1	....
Arithmetic............	16–0	13–8	28	....
Total............	16–4	15–9	7	.43
Downey:				
Total..............	66	65	1	.11
Pattern difference........	....	....	1.9	.96
Woodworth-Mathews:				
Number of neurotic traits......	24	19	5	1.00
Pressey Emotions:				
Total crossed out...........	202	181	21	.45
Deviations..............	52	47	5	1.02
Kent-Rosanoff:				
Number of common responses......	90	97	7	.73
Average frequency...........	116	167	51	1.29
Number of identical responses......	14	14*	....	....
Average of all tests............	....	....	....	.72
Environmental rating:				
Educational............	....	....	11	.73
Social..............	....	....	13	.73
Physical.............	....	....	9	.57

* Ratio to mean, .97.

On three of the four intelligence tests the brothers make almost the same scores. Only on the American Council Test is there a very significant difference. On this test the difference is extreme, Kenneth excelling Jerry by twice the average difference. If we analyze the difference on this test, we find that it is confined to two subtests—the one on artificial language and the one on analogies. On analogies Kenneth makes a percentile score of 79 and Jerry of 2. An examination of the test papers suggests that Jerry, probably through carelessness, misunderstood the directions. The items are presented in this form:

1. dog—puppy::cat — (1) kitten (2) dog (3) tiger (4) horse —

The testee is to indicate by writing a number on the dash the word which is related to cat as puppy is related to dog. The number in this case obviously is "1." Jerry used only the numbers "3" or "4." The failure to grasp the directions may indicate carelessness rather than lack of ability.

The other test on which Kenneth is superior is artificial language, which requires that one translate from English into an artificial language and vice versa. Curiously enough, Kenneth is also definitely superior in the tests of language and literature of the Stanford Achievement Test. Does this show special ability in language possessed by Kenneth but not shared by Jerry? Kenneth is also superior by two and one-third years in arithmetic. No facts in our possession indicate a difference in training which would explain this superiority of Kenneth in language and arithmetic. That the difference is real can scarcely be doubted. It hardly seems likely that specialized differences like these would be inherent. It seems more likely that they are due to particular experiences in the educational careers of the boys, of which we have no record and of which they are doubtless unaware. Kenneth may have received special stimulation from skilful teachers at critical points in his development in these subjects; or Jerry may have failed to receive help or encouragement at times when he met with difficulty in them. Such marked and consistent differences in these special lines in persons who are identical genetically and so similar in their general ability makes some such explanation the most probable one.

TESTS OF PERSONALITY

The responses on the Downey test are very similar in total score and rather similar in pattern. The only difference of over three points on an individual part of the test is on "flexibility," in which Jerry makes the higher score, and "co-ordination of impulses" in which Kenneth's score is higher. The boys' overt behavior, then, is not identical, but it exhibits rather close similarity. The larger differences are probably real, but we have no clue to their explanation.

Both boys make a rather large number of unfavorable responses on the Woodworth-Mathews Personal Data Sheet, Kenneth the larger of the two. It will be remembered that both bite their fingernails, which is commonly taken as a symptom of a neurotic disposition.

Kenneth also crosses out more words on the Pressey test, the difference being confined to Tests I and IV, "things which are unpleasant" and "things you have worried about." He also deviates somewhat more from the responses commonly given.

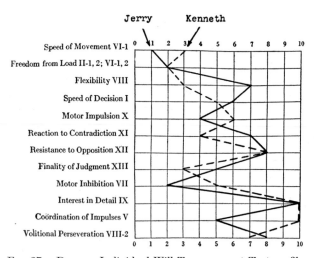

Fig. 27.—Downey Individual Will-Temperament Test profiles

On the Kent-Rosanoff test Kenneth's responses are somewhat less like those of people in general than are Jerry's. The number of identical responses is about average.

On the whole, it appears that both boys are somewhat disposed to be neurotic, Kenneth somewhat more so than Jerry. We do not have sufficient information about their life-histories to be sure whether this difference is due to differences in their experience. Both boys have changed homes since babyhood—Kenneth twice and Jerry once. One of Kenneth's changes was due to the separation of the foster-parents.

HANDWRITING

The handwriting of the brothers differs rather markedly in general appearance. Both write a consistent and fairly definite and matured style,

PLATE XXVI

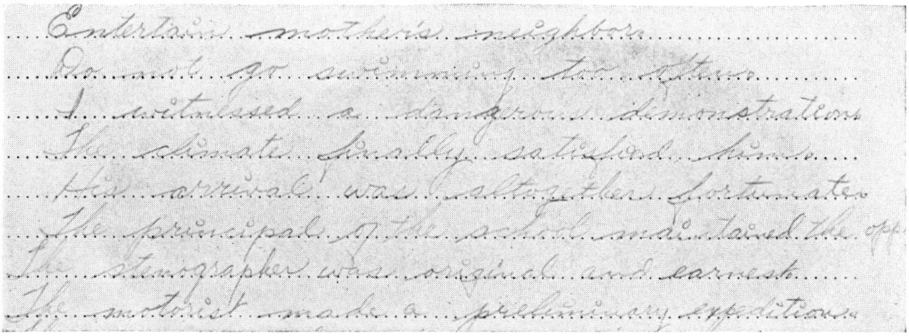

Entertain mother's neighbor.
Do not go swimming too often.
I witnessed a dangerous demonstration.
The climate finally satisfied him.
His arrival was altogether fortunate.
The principal of the school maintained the off
The stenographer was original and earnest.
The motorist made a preliminary expedition

HANDWRITING OF JERRY, CASE XIII

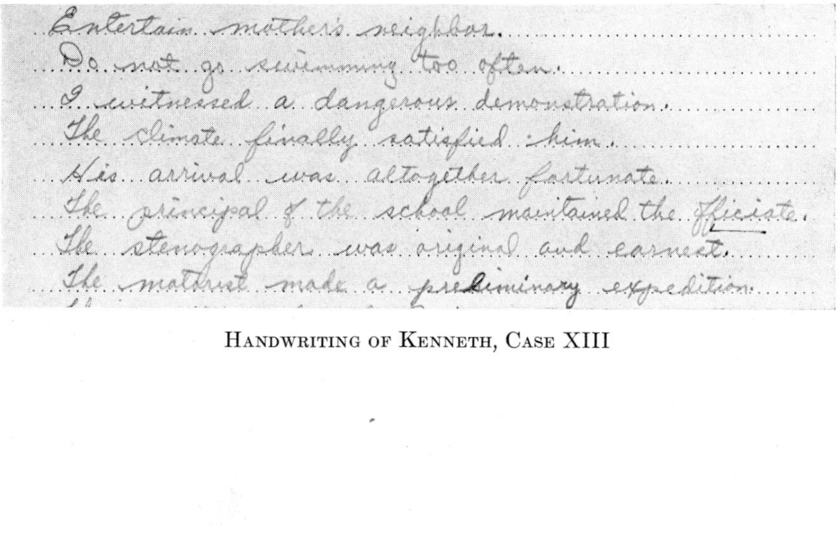

Entertain mother's neighbor.
Do not go swimming too often.
I witnessed a dangerous demonstration.
The climate finally satisfied him.
His arrival was altogether fortunate.
The principal of the school maintained the officiate.
The stenographer was original and earnest.
The motorist made a preliminary expedition.

HANDWRITING OF KENNETH, CASE XIII

which gives the differences significance. Kenneth's writing is more careful and restrained than Jerry's. The end strokes are stopped more abruptly, the loops are shorter, and the strokes are somewhat heavier. His writing is more upright and covers less space. The letters are more rounded. A peculiarity of Jerry's writing is the use of circles instead of the dots of the *i*'s and the periods. This may be a passing fad. Whether it has any significance for character, we shall not attempt to say, though graphologists attach a significance to it. The writings are similar in that both are neat and legible. The differences are marked and indicate a genuine difference in this particular form of behavior.

TABLE 74

TOTAL NUMBER OF WORDS CROSSED OUT AND NUMBER OF
DEVIATIONS ON THE PRESSEY X–O TEST

Test	Words Crossed Out		Deviations	
	Kenneth	Jerry	Kenneth	Jerry
Test I: Unpleasant words................	56	36	13	9
Test II: Words associated in mind with given word.........................	51	50	8	5
Test III: Things thought wrong.............	56	69	14	12
Test IV: Worries.........................	39	26	17	21
Total........................	202	181	52	47

SUMMARY

These twins are very similar physically. They are clearly identical. They are also very similar in ability. They are as much alike in these respects as though they had been reared together. On the other hand, they show certain rather definite differences in personality as shown by the tests. They are not extreme, and it is impossible to say whether or not they are greater than is common in identical twins reared together.

The physical, economic, and educational environments of these brothers are very similar. We should probably not expect greater difference in ability than we find on the ground of a difference in environment. The case shows that when opportunity is similar the intellectual development of identical twins is likely to be similar. The social environment is apparently alike in general features, but there are differences in details which may account for the moderate difference in personality revealed by the tests.

CASE XIV. TWINS ESTHER AND ETHEL

These women were examined when they were thirty-nine years old. They were born in a small Colorado town to very young parents. The burden of twins was too much for these young people, and it was necessary to offer the babies for adoption when they were six months old. They were adopted by two different families, Ethel being taken by friends of the family living in the same town, Esther by a family living in another town.

Ethel lived with her foster-parents only until she was six years old, at which time her foster-mother died. She was then placed in a Catholic orphanage, where she lived continuously until she was nineteen years old, when she left to obtain work. Within a year she married a drayman. One child was born of this marriage. After a few years domestic difficulties arose, and Ethel obtained a divorce. In 1924 she married again, this time a police officer, who was a widower with a small daughter. No children have been born to this second marriage. Although reared a Catholic, Ethel has been for a long time a very active member of the Methodist church. Ever since she can remember she has been very fond of outdoor life—boating, hiking in the mountains, hunting, and fishing. Her present home life seems very placid.

Esther was placed for adoption, as the result of an advertisement, in the family of a police officer who, though married for a long time, had no children. Through the irony of fate, seven months after adopting a baby they had one of their own. The two little girls were so nearly of an age that they were sometimes considered as twins, and they were reared as twins by the foster-parents, being dressed alike and treated alike in every way. A few years later two boys were born to this family. When the father died shortly before the last child was born, the mother went back to her father's farm, taking the four children with her. Esther lived on this farm until she was nineteen, when she married a young druggist in a small Colorado town near the farm. When, after several years, they had no children of their own, they adopted a baby girl. Esther also had domestic difficulties and obtained a divorce in 1928, shortly after which she married the proprietor of a dry-cleaning establishment in a large city in Missouri, and has lived happily with him up to the present. Her home is now her main interest. She has been an active member of the Baptist church since she was fifteen. The dramatic story of the first meeting of these twins after twenty-four years of complete separation is told in another place (chap. ix).

PLATE XXVII

CASE XIV, ESTHER (*left*) AND ETHEL WHEN THEY WERE ABOUT THIRTY YEARS OF AGE

They are more similar in features than the photograph indicates

EDUCATIONAL CAREERS

Ethel received her entire education in connection with the Catholic orphanage. The schooling obtained was roughly equivalent to grade-school education. Esther finished the eighth grade in a country school near the farm and afterward took a sewing and tailoring course. The difference in quality of education is difficult to estimate, but Ethel's schooling extended through a larger number of years and probably for more months in each year.

SOCIAL ENVIRONMENTS

The contrasts are mainly these: Ethel spent the formative period in a city orphanage and Esther on a farm. Both have had an outdoor life to about the same extent, though under different conditions. They both were unhappy in their first marriage, were divorced, and have been happy in their second marriage. Both have one child, but that of Esther is adopted while that of Ethel is her own. They are both active in church work though affiliated with different denominations. On the whole, the social environmental milieus have been moderately similar but with some differences.

PHYSICAL AND HEALTH ENVIRONMENTS

They both lived in Colorado during a large part of their lives, Ethel living in that state all her life, while Esther has lived for the last five years in a large city in Missouri and has not had much opportunity there for active outdoor experience. Ethel, however, has always spent much of her time in the open. From the physical standpoint, having a child of her own differentiates Ethel from Esther. Ethel has always had good health except for the usual children's diseases and an operation in 1929, the nature of which was not revealed. Esther reports the same health record as Ethel, including a serious operation in 1929, the nature of which she prefers not to state.

On the whole, the physical elements of their environments have been somewhat different, but they correspond in their main features.

PHYSICAL RESEMBLANCES AND DIFFERENCES

These twins belong to the category of somewhat unlike "identical" twins. They are, however, no more different than were a few of our least similar identical twins reared together. Ethel is a little more robust, Esther a little taller. Ethel is 63.3 inches tall; Esther, 63.75 inches. Ethel weighs 116½ pounds; Esther, 113½. Ethel's head length is 17.6 centimeters; Esther's, 18.5 centimeters; Ethel's head breadth is 14.5 centimeters; Esther's, 14.6 centimeters. Thus, Esther has the larger head. Ethel is much stronger in hand grip, registering 70 pounds with right hand and 68 pounds with left hand, while Esther registered 62 pounds with right and 40 pounds with left hand.

Both have yellow-blond hair of the same shade and texture. The hair whorl is clockwise in both. Their eye color is blue-gray with large light-brown flecks in both. The condition of the skin is markedly different, that of Esther is smooth and well cared for, while that of Ethel shows the effects of much exposure to sun and mountain air. The ears are extremely similar in all respects. Ethel's face is a little longer and chin a little more prominent, hence a little less attractive than that of Esther, whose face is more femininely smooth and rounded. The teeth are peculiar in both. They are widely spaced, especially in front. Each has two teeth of the milk dentition which have never been replaced—the upper first premolars in both cases—though Ethel's left first premolar became decayed and was extracted, no permanent tooth taking its place. Ethel is fully right-handed, while Esther is reported to be naturally left-handed though trained to use the right hand. Ethel has a short defective little finger on her right hand, and Esther the same deformity on her left hand.

The reversal in handedness is plainly reflected in the palm patterns, the right hand of each being far more like the left hand of the other than like own left hand. This mirror-imaging is not present in the finger patterns, but the two left hands are much more similar than are the two hands of either individual. The ridge-count values of finger patterns are 94 for Esther and 91 for Ethel—a close correspondence.

On the whole, these twins show moderate differences in physique, though there is an extremely close mirror-image correspondence in several genetic unit characters.

TESTS OF ABILITY

The difference on three of the four tests is negligible. Both make low scores for adults on all the tests. This is probably due in part to the fact that their schooling was equivalent only to the first eight grades. On the test in which a substantial difference appears, the Otis test, Esther, who had her schooling in the public rural school, is superior. Her superiority is due to her greater accuracy. She attempted four fewer problems and made thirteen fewer errors. It would appear that, with naturally equal ability, the education of the public school or some other influence has led Esther to attack problems with much more care than is exercised by Ethel, who was educated in the orphanage. The exact nature of this difference in habit is not revealed.

Esther also exhibits a substantial difference on the educational test, particularly on reading, language, literature, and physiology and hygiene. Apparently her education has been superior in these subjects, since it seems hardly likely that such specialized differences would be native. While, then, Ethel's education lasted longer, Esther's was apparently superior in quality.

TABLE 75
TEST RECORD AND ENVIRONMENTAL RATING OF PAIR NO. 14
(ESTHER AND ETHEL)

Test	Esther	Ethel	Diff.	Ratio of Diff. to Mean Diff.
Stanford-Binet:				
M.A.	13–8	13–5	3 mo.	.19
I.Q.	85	84	1	.12
Otis S.-A.:				
Score	38	28	10	. . . .
I.Q.	96	86	10	1.25
Percentage right	79.2	54.9	24.3	1.69
American Council score	11	4	7	.26
International score	94	103	9	.58
Stanford Achievement:				
Reading age	16–10	15–2	20 mo.	. . . .
Spelling	14–10	14–1	9	. . . .
Language	17–11	14–4	43	. . . .
Literature	12–10	11–6	16	. . . .
History and civics	11–9	11–10	1	. . . .
Geography	12–7	12–7	0	. . . .
Physiology and hygiene	16–8	15–6	14	. . . .
Arithmetic	12–10	12–3	7	. . . .
Total	14–8	13–3	17	1.05
Downey:				
Total	55	53	2	.22
Pattern difference	. . . .	. . . .	1.2	.61
Woodworth-Mathews:				
Number of neurotic traits	37	15	22	4.40
Pressey Emotions:				
Total crossed out	187	148	39	.83
Deviations	48	48	0	0
Kent-Rosanoff:				
Number of common responses	84	87	3	.31
Average frequency	47	155	108	2.74
Number of identical responses	12	12*	. . . .	. . . .
Average of all tests	. . . .	. . . .	. . . .	1.02
Environmental rating:				
Educational	. . . .	. . . .	12	.79
Social	. . . .	. . . .	15	.84
Physical	. . . .	. . . .	9	.57

* Ratio to mean, .84.

The Downey profiles are remarkably similar, indicating that, whatever differences in the environment existed, they apparently did not affect the basic reactions which are called forth by this test. Both make scores a little below average in the test of speed and fluidity, high in aggressiveness, and varying similarly in the last four tests. This close similarity suggests, at least, that such differences as may be found on other tests are of environmental origin.

We find such a difference, of large magnitude, on the Woodworth-Mathews Personal Data Sheet. Ethel's score is about average, but Esther's

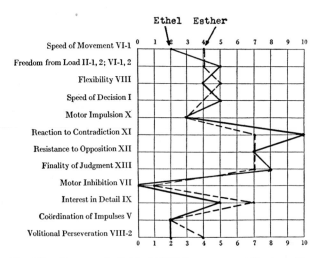

FIG. 28.—Downey Individual Will-Temperament Test profiles

is very large. Esther gives 14 of the 15 unfavorable responses given by Ethel and, in addition, 23 more. If the verdict of this test is to be relied on, Esther is decidedly neurotic, while Ethel is not. Was the deficiency of the orphanage in academic education counterbalanced by the favorable influence of its protective environment on emotional and nervous stability?

That a difference exists is confirmed by the Pressey test, on which Esther marks decidedly more items, particularly in Tests I and IV, which are most significant. On the free-association test, also, Esther gives responses of a lower mean frequency than does Ethel.

Observation of the social behavior of these sisters reveals rather large differences in personality, but whether these differences correspond to those revealed in the tests is doubtful. Ethel was more aggressive, more positive, and more vigorous. Esther was more gentle, more hesitant, more refined in manners, speech, and dress. Ethel is the breezy western woman, very matter of fact, and fond of speaking of her woodsmanship, etc. Esther was more inclined to speak of the academic interest she felt in the examination she and her sister were undergoing and of her pleasant home life. One would say, without any further data than those that a few hours conversation afford, that Esther is considerably more cultured than Ethel but that Ethel is more capable in an executive way and more masterful.

TABLE 76

TOTAL NUMBER OF WORDS CROSSED OUT AND NUMBER OF
DEVIATIONS ON THE PRESSEY X–O TEST

TEST	WORDS CROSSED OUT		DEVIATIONS	
	Esther	Ethel	Esther	Ethel
Test I: Unpleasant words..................	43	31	10	11
Test II: Words associated in mind with given word...........................	36	28	6	10
Test III: Things thought wrong.............	60	62	14	9
Test IV: Worries..........................	48	27	18	18
Total..........................	187	148	48	48

HANDWRITING

It will be remembered that Esther is reported to be naturally left-handed but trained to use her right hand. This may have had some influence on her handwriting, which varies in style more than does Ethel's. In general, Esther's writing is also somewhat larger and bolder. Some parts of it, e.g., the word "satisfied" in the fourth sentence and the word "fortunate" in the fifth sentence, seem to give evidence of a more fluent style developed by good training. In other respects the writings are rather similar. The words "mother's neighbor," for example, are a good deal alike. It appears that, on top of a basic similarity in motor reactions, some differences have been produced by the conventional style of writing each learned and that some are of a more general nature and are the expression of general modes of behavior.

PLATE XXVIII

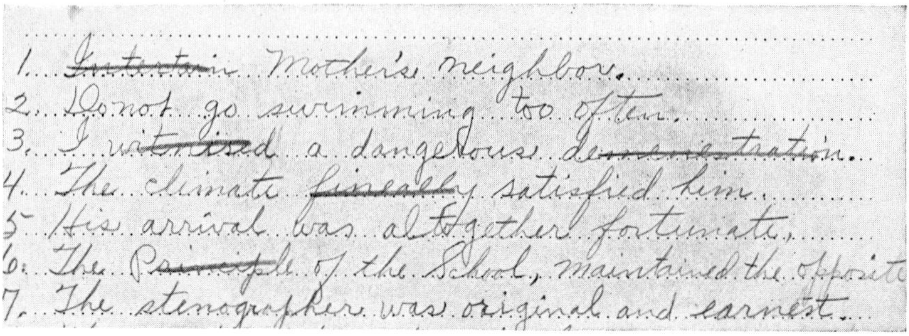

1. ~~Entertain~~ Mother's neighbor.
2. Do not go swimming too often.
3. I witnessed a dangerous dem~~onstration~~ tration.
4. The climate fin~~ally~~ satisfied him.
5. His arrival was altogether fortunate.
6. The Prin~~cip~~le of the School, maintained the opposite
7. The stenographer was original and earnest.

HANDWRITING OF ESTHER, CASE XIV

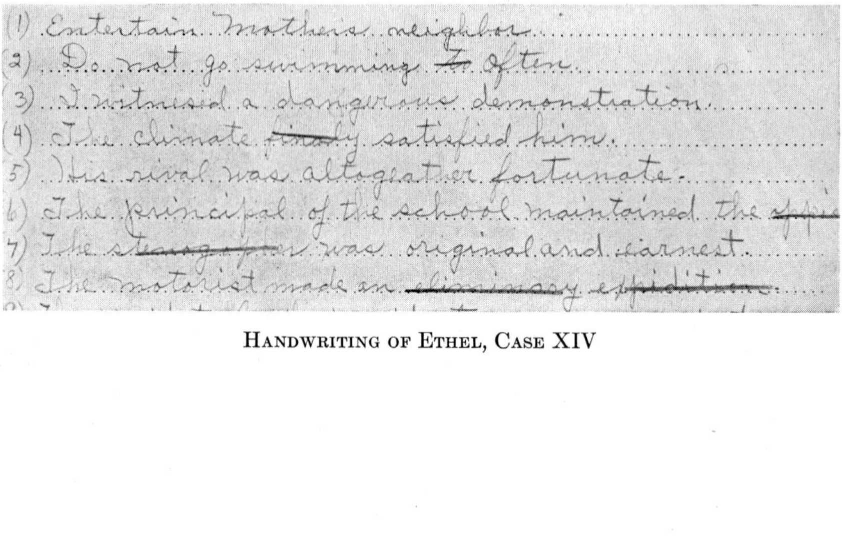

(1) Entertain mothers neighbor.
(2) Do ~~not~~ go swimming ~~to~~ often.
(3) I witnesed a dangerous demonstration.
(4) The climate fin~~ally~~ satisfied him.
(5) His rival was altogether fortunate.
(6) The principal of the school maintained the oppi
(7) The steno~~gra~~ was original and earnest.
(8) The motorist made an ~~eliminary~~ expidition.

HANDWRITING OF ETHEL, CASE XIV

SUMMARY

In physical appearance and general behavior these twins are less alike than are many identical twins. The difference in their physical environment, particularly during the last five years, may partly account for this.

There are clear indications that these sisters are similar by nature. However, differences in the environment have apparently produced certain rather marked differences in behavior and ability. The contrast in education or other environmental influences appears to have favored Esther's· intellectual performance, but the differences are relatively small. On the other hand, Esther exhibits certain indications of disorganization. These appear in the Woodworth-Mathews and Pressey tests, and perhaps, also, in the irregular character of the handwriting. It is possible that this latter feature and even, perhaps, some of the others are connected with the changing over of hand use, but we are skeptical of this suggestion.

In general, the differences in physique and ability are rather small, and the differences in personality in some respects small and in some large. These differences are not out of harmony with what we know of the environmental differences.

CASE XV. TWINS EDWIN AND FRED

This is a remarkable case of identical twins, young men of twenty-six years, who were separated in very early infancy and have lived separate lives up to the present. The story of their first meeting after learning that they were twin brothers is told in an earlier chapter.

They were adopted by two different families, both living in the same New England town. The two families were of essentially the same social and economic status. The two boys were brought up as only children. They even went to the same school for a time but never knew that they were twin brothers. They had even noticed the remarkable resemblance between them, but they were not close companions. When the twins were about eight years old, their families were permanently separated, and the boys did not meet again until they were twenty-five years old, as the result of Edwin being repeatedly mistaken by strangers for Fred.

Though separated all these years, these twins have led extremely parallel lives. Both have been electricians for telephone companies. Both married at about the same time, the wives being of similar types. Each has a four-year-old son, and they lay stress on the fact that each owns a fox terrier dog named Trixie. Other parallels in the life-stories of these twins may be found in chapter ix.

PLATE XXIX

CASE XV, EDWIN (*left*) AND FRED TAKEN AT THE TIME OF THEIR FIRST MEETING, SHORTLY BEFORE THEY CAME TO US

Reproduced by permission of *The American Weekly*

EDUCATIONAL CAREERS

Both had some high-school education, Edwin having completed one year and Fred three years. There is evidence that Edwin had more continuous and better instruction, though the actual facts are difficult to obtain. Both twins admit that they were poor in their studies.

SOCIAL ENVIRONMENTS

Resemblances far outweigh differences in social milieus. Edwin has lived most of his life in a very large city in eastern Michigan, while Fred has lived about the same length of time in a medium-sized city in western Iowa. Both have had steady employment until recently, but Fred has been unemployed for some time and has worried about the matter considerably, as is natural. Both have had a conviction that they once had a brother who died. Both have been electricians with equivalent duties. On the whole, there seem to be no marked differences in their social environments.

PHYSICAL AND HEALTH ENVIRONMENTS

These twins have had no serious illnesses and are now decidedly healthy. The climatic and food features of the environment were certainly not materially different, though they have lived nearly a thousand miles apart. There is no basis for assuming any real contrasts in physical environmental conditions.

PHYSICAL RESEMBLANCES AND DIFFERENCES

These twins are at the present time as similar physically as almost any pair of identical twins reared together. Edwin is $\frac{1}{2}$ inch taller than Fred and weighs $1\frac{1}{2}$ pounds more. The head length of Edwin is 19.4 centimeters; that of Fred, 19.2 centimeters. The head breadth of Edwin is 14.4 centimeters; that of Fred, 14.8 centimeters. The hair of both is dark brown, soft, and fine, and inclined to be wavy. Both have clockwise hair whorl. The eye color is the same in both—a dark hazel. The ears are nearly identical—large and flat—but Fred's left ear is a little larger than the others. The complexion is clear and smooth and a little swarthy in both. The facial hair has the same characteristics in both. The features are regular and extremely similar. The teeth of both are irregular in the same way and are in equally good condition. In both, the upper middle incisors are turned inward in the middle line. Each had originally a supernumerary upper canine tooth placed far too high in the gum, but Edwin has had this tooth extracted. The extra tooth was in the right side in Edwin, and that of Fred is on the left side—a case of mirror-imaging. Both are fully right-handed. The general body build and carriage is the same in both. The palm patterns of the two right hands are extremely similar, those of the two left hands rather less similar.

TABLE 77

TEST RECORD AND ENVIRONMENTAL RATING OF PAIR NO. 15
(EDWIN AND FRED)

Test	Edwin	Fred	Diff.	Ratio of Diff. to Mean Diff.
Stanford-Binet:				
M.A.	14–7	14–3	4 mo.	.26
I.Q.	91	90	1	.12
Otis S.-A.:				
Score	34	26	8	....
I.Q.	92	84	8	1.00
Percentage	73.9	66.7	7.2	.50
American Council score	28	30	2	.07
International score	123	95	28	1.80
Stanford Achievement:				
Reading age	12–6	13–3	9 mo.	....
Spelling	12–7	14–4	21	....
Language	15–2	14–6	8	....
Literature	11–4	10–11	5	....
History and civics	13–7	13–9	2	....
Geography	15–9	14–8	13	....
Physiology and hygiene	14–10	16–10	24	....
Arithmetic	13–5	12–7	10	
Total	13–3	13–5	2	.12
Downey:				
Total	70	63	7	.76
Pattern difference	....	....	2.7	1.36
Woodworth-Mathews:				
Number of neurotic traits	11	7	4	.80
Pressey Emotions:				
Total crossed out	170	112	58	1.23
Deviations	44	53	9	1.84
Kent-Rosanoff:				
Number of common responses	97	88	9	.93
Average frequency	155	127	28	.71
Number of identical responses	28	28*	....	....
Average of all tests	....	....	....	.82
Environmental rating:				
Educational	....	....	9	.60
Social	....	....	7	.39
Physical	....	....	8	.50

* Ratio to mean, 1.95.

There is much greater resemblance between right hands than between the rights and lefts of the two individuals. The same is true for the fingerprints. The ridge-count values of the two individuals are exactly the same. Both have a value of 47 for the left hand and 40 for the right hand—the only case of identity in ridge count we have ever found in twins.

TESTS OF ABILITY

The evidence on the relative abilities of this pair is conflicting. On two tests their scores are equal, but on the other two Edwin is slightly superior. From the combined evidence it appears that Edwin has slightly higher general intellectual ability.

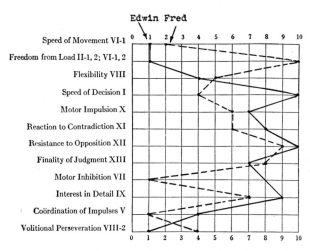

FIG. 29.—Downey Individual Will-Temperament Test profiles

In educational achievement the general average of attainment is the same, but there is considerable diversity on the various parts of the test. Each does better on four of the parts. This diversity in attainment may be due to a diversity of abilities or interests, or it may be due to a difference in educational opportunity or emphasis. The differences found are no greater than in a good many pairs of identical twins reared together and attending the same school.

TESTS OF PERSONALITY

The Downey Will-Temperament Test reveals marked general similarity but some very striking differences in details. The total scores are both fairly high (Edwin, 70; Fred, 63). Both are low in speed of movement, co-ordination of impulses, and volitional perseveration and high in motor impul-

sion, reaction to contradiction, resistance to opposition, finality of judgment, and interest in detail. But they differ widely in freedom from load,
motor inhibition, and speed of decision. The test designated "freedom
from load" evidently reveals a real difference in behavior, whether or not
it is properly described. Fred writes the phrase, "United States of America," much faster at his ordinary speed. His average is $12\frac{1}{2}$ seconds to Edwin's $20\frac{3}{4}$ seconds. When they speed up, however, Fred is able to reduce
his time to only $10\frac{3}{4}$ seconds, while Edwin reduces his to $8\frac{1}{2}$ seconds—less
than half the time for ordinary writing. That this is not done at the sacrifice

TABLE 78

TOTAL NUMBER OF WORDS CROSSED OUT AND NUMBER OF
DEVIATIONS ON THE PRESSEY X–O TEST

TEST	WORDS CROSSED OUT		DEVIATIONS	
	Edwin	Fred	Edwin	Fred
Test I: Unpleasant words...............	42	23	10	9
Test II: Words associated in mind with given word........................	37	31	6	14
Test III: Things thought wrong............	59	37	15	17
Test IV: Worries........................	32	21	13	13
Total........................	170	112	44	53

of quality is shown by the fact that his writing shows less deterioration than
does his brother's. Almost equally striking is the difference in "motor inhibition"—the ability to modify the usual speed of movement in the opposite direction, viz., by writing slowly. Edwin can prolong the writing to 8
minutes, while Fred can slow his down to only 53 seconds. In short, Edwin
can modify his accustomed movement in either direction, and Fred in
neither. Perhaps the difference in speed of decision is related to this. Edwin makes his series of ratings in 1 minute, 22 seconds, while Fred requires
3 minutes, 34 seconds. (Both, incidentally, rate themselves as modest and
of superior intelligence and superior character.) Here, then, apparently is
a fundamental difference in flexibility or control of movements, standing
out on a background of general similarity in other characteristics.

On the Woodworth-Mathews Personal Data Sheet both displayed comparatively few neurotic symptoms. Edwin gave 11 unfavorable responses and Fred only 7. In general, their emotional reactions indicate that they are very similar and normal in emotional balance.

On the Pressey X–O Test Edwin appeared to be more susceptible to emotions than Fred, at least he indicates more objects which are unpleasant, which he thinks wrong, or which he worries about. He crossed out 170 words as compared with 112 for Fred.

On the Kent-Rosanoff Free Association Test the number of identical responses was high, 28—nearly four times the expectancy, indicating a good deal of similarity in associations. The mean frequency of the responses did not differ greatly, being 155.5 for Edwin and 127.5 for Fred.

The tests seem to indicate that Edwin is somewhat more emotional than Fred, though the difference is not great. Perhaps this is associated with the greater modifiability of movements and quicker decision.

This judgment agrees in part with the impressions gained from observing their overt behavior. One could scarcely fail to notice that Edwin was considerably more vivacious than Fred. He conversed much more freely and had a livelier facial expression. He was also less diffident and more aggressive. He was in a more cheerful frame of mind. One seemed to feel that Fred was worried.

HANDWRITING

There is a good deal of similarity in handwriting. Both write the small letters in a rather small, pinched hand and make the loops and two or more space letters relatively long, though Fred extends the long strokes farther than does Edwin. Edwin's writing shows more erasures, but this is doubtless due to his poorer spelling. Even aside from this, however, Fred's writing is firmer, better formed, and better co-ordinated. Perhaps we may say that, on the basis of the tests as well as the handwriting, Fred's behavior is less flexible but more stable.

SUMMARY

In all physical characteristics these twins are very similar. Both in ability and in personality there is striking general similarity between these brothers. In ability Edwin seems to be slightly superior, but the difference is small. In behavior and personality there is close basic similarity but a few striking and consistent differences. Edwin is more flexible, emotional, and easily aroused. In social behavior this is represented in greater vivacity and responsiveness. Whether the difference is due to unknown environmental influences we cannot say. The general similarity in environment is accompanied by a general similarity in physique and ability. The brothers exhibit somewhat greater differences in personality, but the source of these differences is uncertain.

PLATE XXX

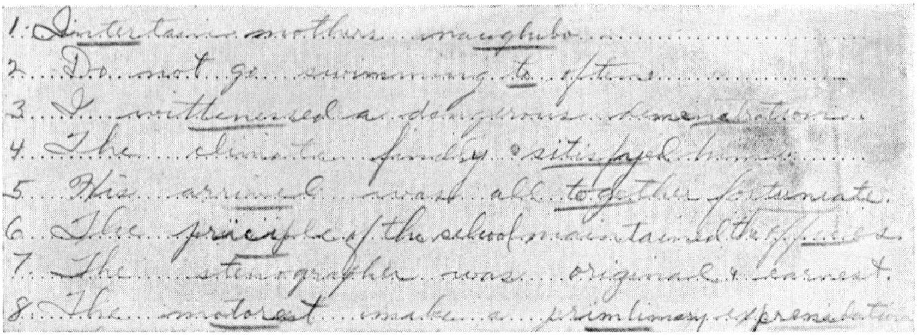

HANDWRITING OF EDWIN, CASE XV

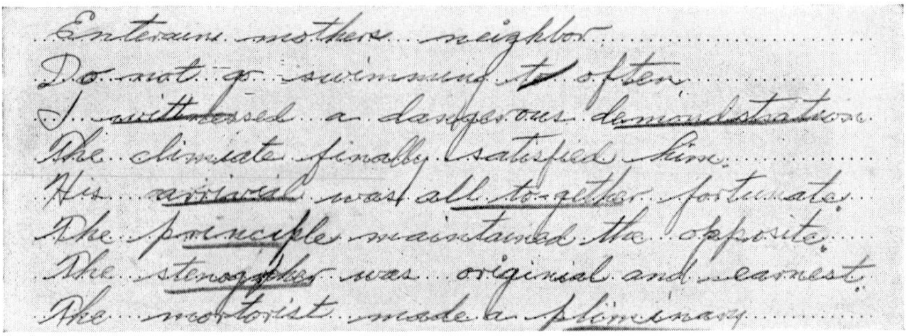

HANDWRITING OF FRED, CASE XV

CASE XVI. TWINS MAXINE AND VIRGINIA

These twin girls were eleven and one-half years old when examined. They were separated when they were about two and one-half years old, when the father died and the burden of the family of four children was too great for the mother. All four fatherless children were at first put in an orphanage in a rather large Michigan city. The mother subsequently remarried and took back her two sons from the orphanage, but the twin girls were left with the two families who had adopted them as babies.

Mrs. G., the present foster-mother of Virginia, at first took both twins for a trial adoption but found two babies too difficult and returned Maxine to the orphanage, from which the latter soon was taken by Mr. B. and his wife, who lived in the city where the twins were born. The twins have been reared almost entirely apart with only a few visits of a few hours at a time. They are not now very well acquainted, and the two foster-families show no marked cordiality toward each other.

Maxine has lived all her life in the city where she was born. Her foster-father is a middle-aged man, extremely fond and proud of his foster-daughter. He has for a long time been an ice-cream maker and has had a very modest income, though steadily employed. He is a somewhat underendowed but kindly man, who has had only part of a grade-school education and has done only rather simple manual work since he was a boy. The foster-mother has had even less education than the foster-father. Maxine has been brought up as an only child and has been a source of great comfort and satisfaction to her foster-parents.

Virginia was adopted by Mr. and Mrs. G., who have no children of their own. Mr. G. is an expert structural-steel operative, who has been in charge of some very difficult pieces of work, such as constructing the steel framework of the carillons in the University of Chicago Chapel. He has had the full grade-school education and has studied structural-engineering problems. He impresses one as a man of superior abilities. He owns his own home and car. The home is small but attractive. Mrs. G. is a woman of refinement, has had a high-school education, and impresses one as a person who would exercise a beneficial influence upon a child.

EDUCATIONAL CAREERS

When examined both girls were in the sixth grade of apparently equally good schools. Unless the more highly educated status of Virginia's parents could be regarded as playing a role in education, there seems to be no marked difference in their educational opportunities, though Virginia missed the last four months of school on account of illness.

SOCIAL ENVIRONMENTS

Virginia has always lived in Chicago, and Maxine in a rather large city in Indiana. Maxine has visited frequently in the country but not for long periods. Both girls have been reared as only children, but neither seems to have been spoiled on that account. Virginia's home environment is somewhat superior to that of Maxine, but the difference is not very great. Maxine seems to have had more friendships in school than Virginia. There appear to be only minor differences in the social milieus of the two girls.

PHYSICAL AND HEALTH ENVIRONMENTS

Maxine has had the usual children's diseases: measles, chicken pox, mumps, and whooping cough. At the age of five she apparently had incipient tuberculosis, indicated by "a spot on the lungs," but rest cure and cod-liver oil seem to have brought about complete recovery. Virginia, in addition to all the children's diseases listed for Maxine, had scarlet fever in the winter of 1933 and was very much run down. Tuberculosis was suspected but not definitely diagnosed. She was kept out of school from March 1 until the end of the school year. During this period she was required to rest a great deal of the time and was placed on a special building-up diet recommended for tubercular suspects. During the spring and summer she gained about 20 pounds in weight and 3 inches in height. Whether this treatment alone was responsible for the very marked physical change, or whether the rich food and rest promoted the beginning of sexual maturity, cannot be determined. It is a fact, however, that Virginia is now physiologically apparently a year ahead of Maxine. Further comment on this situation appears in connection with the description of differences in physical measurements.

PHYSICAL RESEMBLANCES AND DIFFERENCES

If one had had to attempt to diagnose these twins as monozygotic or dizygotic at the time they were examined, one would have had some reason for hesitation because Virginia is physically so far in advance of Maxine. A photograph (Pl. XXXI) of the twins taken several years ago is most convincing evidence of their monozygocity. Virginia was $3\frac{1}{4}$ inches taller than Maxine and weighed over 20 pounds more, which is a very great difference when it is considered that Maxine weighs only 72 pounds. The great size difference extends to all body parts, even to head size. Virginia has a head length of 17.9 centimeters; Maxine, 17.1 centimeters. Virginia has a head breadth of 14.4 centimeters; Maxine, 13.6 centimeters. Virginia was also stronger in hand grip than Maxine.

It will be interesting to determine by a later examination whether the very great physical difference is merely the temporary result of a difference

PLATE XXXI

CASE XVI, MAXINE (*left*) AND VIRGINIA AT THE TIME OF THEIR FIRST MEETING, WHEN
THEY WERE FIVE YEARS OLD

At that time they were physically nearly identical

in the timing of the growth cycle or represents a permanent physical divergence between the twins.

Both girls have medium-brown hair with a glint of red in it, Maxine's being a little redder. The hair is straight and soft in both. Both have a clockwise hair whorl. Both have the same shade of eye color—a rather dark blue-gray. The ears are nearly identical in form but somewhat larger in Virginia. There is a marked difference in their dental arches. Virginia has a relatively wide arch and Maxine a much narrower one. The result is that Virginia's teeth, which are the same in size and shape as Maxine's, are widely spaced in front, while those of Maxine are in close contact. Each of the girls has two molar teeth filled. The eyelashes are exceptionally long and dark in both, and the eyebrows long, narrow, and arched. Apart from size differences these twins are unusually similar.

The palm and finger patterns are definitely confirmatory of a monozygotic diagnosis. The two left palms are extraordinarily similar, while each left palm differs markedly from own right palm. The finger patterns of the two right hands are far more similar to each other than those of either right hand to own left hand. The total ridge-count values of finger patterns of the two individuals is 75 for Maxine and 83 for Virginia—a difference equal to the mean difference found in identical twins in general. This is another case in which the dermatoglyphics alone would have assured a monozygotic diagnosis.

TESTS OF ABILITY

These two eleven-and-a-half-year-old girls are indistinguishable in general ability. Their scores on the various intelligence tests might have been made by the same person.

Their achievement scores are equal, on the average, but they differ somewhat in detail. Maxine is decidedly poorer in language usage but makes up for it by superiority in all the other subjects except reading. These differences may be due to variations in emphasis in formal schooling or to a difference in home influence and example.

These twins are as similar in test intelligence as if they had been reared together.

TESTS OF PERSONALITY

On the Downey Will-Temperament Test the scores are strikingly similar. On eight of the twelve traits the scores are identical. On the other four they differ by 3, 2, 1, and 1 point, respectively. The total scores are 49 for Maxine and 54 for Virginia. Such marked similarity in scores could not be attributed to chance. There must be a marked temperamental similarity to account for such markedly similar behavior reactions. Such results as

TABLE 79

TEST RECORD AND ENVIRONMENT RATING OF PAIR NO. 16
(MAXINE AND VIRGINIA)

Test	Maxine	Virginia	Diff.	Ratio of Diff. to Mean Diff.
Stanford-Binet:				
M.A.	10–3	10–0	3 mo.	.19
I.Q.	90	88	2	.24
Otis S.-A.:				
Score	10	13	3	. . . .
I.Q.	87	90	3	.38
Percentage right	31.3	28.9	2.4	.17
American Council score	24	29	5	.18
International score	103	106	3	.19
Stanford Achievement:				
Reading age	11–3	11–7	4 mo.	. . . .
Spelling	11–7	11–0	7	. . . .
Language	7–5	11–1	44	. . . .
Literature	9–11	9–4	7	. . . .
History and civics	11–10	11–0	10	. . . .
Geography	11–11	11–5	6	. . . .
Physiology and hygiene	10–6	10–1	5	. . . .
Arithmetic	11–7	11–0	7	. . . .
Total	10–10	10–11	1	.06
Downey:				
Total	54	49	5	.55
Pattern difference	. . . .	. . . .	.6	.30
Woodworth-Mathews:				
Number of neurotic traits	5	2	3	.60
Pressey Emotions:				
Total crossed out	179	115	64	1.36
Deviations	68	65	3	.61
Kent-Rosanoff:				
Number of common responses	60	87	27	2.80
Average frequency	40	114	74	1.88
Number of identical responses	5	5*	. . . .	. . . .
Average of all tests	. . . .	. . . .	. . . .	.68
Environmental rating:				
Educational			8	.53
Social			12	.67
Physical			14	.88

* Ratio to mean, .35.

these tend to increase one's confidence in the reliability of the Downey test. In more detail, the tests show that both girls are relatively slow in movement but quick in decision. Both are high in finality of judgment and comparatively low in carefulness and attention to detail. They rated themselves highly similar in the twenty-two pairs of traits listed in Test I. In general, their similarity in temperament, as indicated by this test, is remarkable.

The Woodworth-Mathews Personal Data Sheet showed again very great similarity between the twins. They are both remarkably free from neurotic traits. Maxine gave 5 unfavorable responses, and Virginia gave only 2—both very low numbers.

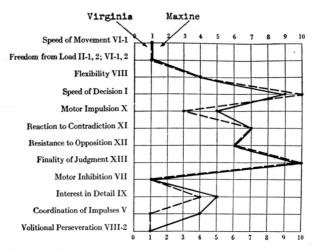

FIG. 30.—Downey Individual Will-Temperament Test profiles

On the Pressey X–O Test the difference is greater. Maxine crossed out 179 words; Virginia only 115. This would appear to indicate that Maxine is more easily aroused emotionally, unless they interpreted the instructions differently. The number of deviations from the normal was practically the same for both (68 for Maxine; 65 for Virginia). The excess in the number of words crossed out by Maxine is all in Tests I and III. While it does not indicate a neurotic disposition, then, it appears that Maxine is considerably more easily aroused. It might be suggested here that Virginia seems to be in a resting state at present, as the result of her prolonged rest cure and heavy diet, and is somewhat indolent.

On the Kent-Rosanoff Free Association Test it is doubtful whether the similarities found are greater than would be found in the responses of two children picked at random. The number of identical responses was only 5. Maxine gave 39 individual responses; Virginia only 8. The mean frequency of Maxine's responses was 40 as compared with 114.5 for Virginia. This test seems to indicate that the girls differ markedly in their ideational associations.

Observations of the overt behavior of these girls agree with, and help to elucidate the differences in test scores. Maxine is at present rather small and a little underweight. She is very lively and active and apparently is considered too nervous, for the foster-father made repeated efforts to calm her down. Virginia is just the opposite in behavior. She seemed to us to

TABLE 80

TOTAL NUMBER OF WORDS CROSSED OUT AND NUMBER OF
DEVIATIONS ON THE PRESSEY X–O TEST

Test	Words Crossed Out		Deviations	
	Maxine	Virginia	Maxine	Virginia
Test I: Unpleasant words...............	77	25	20	19
Test II: Words associated in mind with given word........................	17	29	6	10
Test III: Things thought wrong............	58	36	22	17
Test IV: Worries........................	27	25	20	19
Total........................	179	115	68	65

be rather sluggish, somewhat indolent, and difficult to arouse. She seems to be dormant emotionally. She was much less interested in the whole experience of testing than Maxine. The trip was rather a lark for Maxine and more of a duty to be performed for Virginia. This difference in behavior may be an accompaniment of the very marked difference in physiological state. Another test taken after their physiological condition has become equalized, if it ever does, would be valuable.

HANDWRITING

While the handwriting of these girls is still rather juvenile in character, it appears to be sufficiently developed at least to suggest considerable differences. Virginia's writing is more vertical, more rounded, and considerably

PLATE XXXII

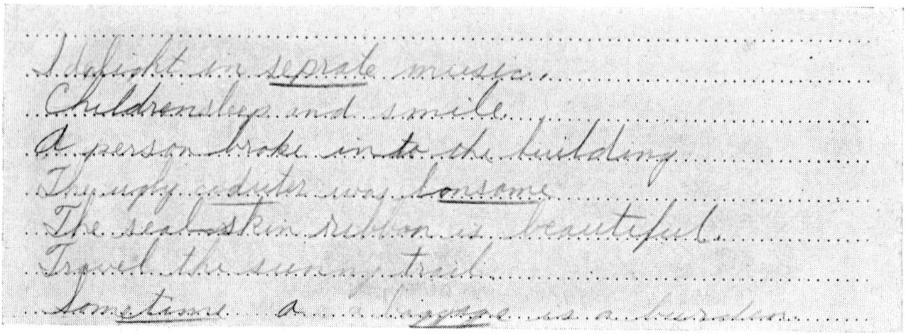

HANDWRITING OF MAXINE, CASE XVI

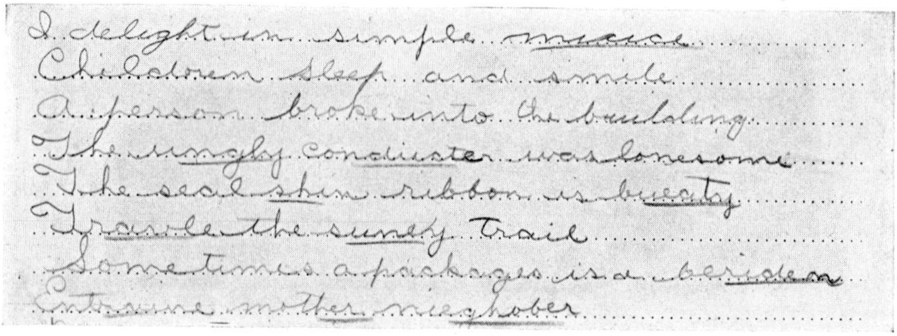

HANDWRITING OF VIRGINIA, CASE XVI

more spread out than Maxine's. Maxine's tall letters are much longer than Virginia's. In fact, the two specimens seem hardly more similar than those of two unrelated children of the same age and schooling. If anything, Virginia's writing seems the less mature, in spite of the fact that she is more mature physiologically.

SUMMARY

The environment of these twins is very similar, with one exception. Virginia has been given special feeding and rest on account of an incipient attack of tuberculosis. Perhaps as a result of this treatment she is taller, larger, heavier, and a year or more advanced in physiological development. In the distinctive marks of genetic similarity, genetic identity is indicated.

We have here a case of striking similarity in ability and some forms of overt behavior, as represented by the Downey test, and a close similarity in emotional balance, together with rather marked differences in excitability, in particular association of ideas, and in the form of behavior represented in the style of handwriting. The difference in excitability may, perhaps, be ascribed to the difference in physical condition and stage of development, though this is not certain, and this in turn may be due to the rest and forced feeding. The other differences suggest more permanent variations in behavior and thought, which may be either innate or environmental in origin. To sum up, these twins are very similar in mental ability and will-temperament but rather markedly different in physique, emotional excitability, and social behavior.

CASE XVII. TWINS GENE AND JAMES

These twin boys, fourteen years old when examined, are able to give no information about their real parents. The foster-parents are also uninformed on this point. The twins at a very early age were placed in an orphanage in a large Kentucky city, where they stayed for a little over two years before they were adopted. Mr. B. and his wife adopted James and intended to take Gene also if they found James satisfactory. When they came back for the latter, however, Gene had been adopted by Mrs. E. Since separation the boys have seen very little of each other, and correspondence has been very desultory, for both "hate to write letters."

James has always lived in somewhat rural surroundings, never having dwelt in a town of over two thousand population, and, for the most part, in towns and villages of smaller size. Mr. B. has been a section foreman on a railroad and has been shifted about from place to place. This has meant a great deal of change of scene for James. Mr. B., now a man in the middle fifties, is extremely fond of James and has always had his best interests at

PLATE XXXIII

CASE XVII, GENE (*right*) AND JAMES WHEN THEY WERE ABOUT EIGHT YEARS OLD

heart. Mr. B. has had only a parochial-school education and no cultural experience to speak of. The first Mrs. B., who died four years ago, was in very poor health and for some years before her death was mentally unsound. She did not show any affection for James, but the new foster-mother has come to be very fond of the boy and proud of his modest accomplishments. There have been no other children in the family.

Gene has lived all his life, except the first two years after adoption, in a large city of some three hundred thousand population. For the first two years after adoption he lived in the country. During the early years of his life, Gene's foster-parents were in fairly good circumstances, Mr. E. being a skilled special operative in a piano factory. He was a man of scarcely any education. Mrs. E., however, is a high-school graduate and has studied music rather extensively. For over ten years, since separation from her husband, she has lived a life of sacrifice in order to give Gene various advantages. She has been a devoted mother to him, and there is a very strong mutual affection between them. Our visit to the home, humble though it was, left a very favorable impression.

EDUCATIONAL CAREERS

James was in ninth grade at the time of the examination. He has attended five or six different schools, but they have been rather small schools whose curriculums lacked the "frills and fads" that have characterized Gene's schools. James has always had a good record in school but seems to place less stress on such matters than does Gene. James has had no particular home stimulus toward scholastic or cultural pursuits. He seems more interested in mechanical matters and has a well-equipped shop at home, where he spends a good deal of time designing models of airplanes. He has traveled about much more than Gene, for the family has a pass on the railroad. James is fond of drawing and designing and has tried his hand at oil-painting but has had no instruction along these lines. Also, he has had no training in music. He is fond of athletics and has been successful in baseball and basketball.

Gene was also in ninth grade when examined. He had attended seven different schools during his life—two in the country and five in the city. During the last five years, he has attended very good schools and has enjoyed his work. In his present school there are good courses in music, drawing, and painting, and Gene has been an outstanding pupil along those lines. He plays the violin in the school orchestra. His mother has taught him to play the piano. Like his brother James, he is also mechanically inclined and designs miniature airplanes. Gene has also shown considerable ability in athletics but has had very little time for such activities because of his devotion to art and music. Mrs. E. has exercised a very stimulating influence on Gene, helping him with his music and being very enthusiastic about everything he does. Having heard him play, we can justly say he shows rather unusual talent. Our personal contacts with Gene and his foster-mother gave us the impression that Gene was somewhat overstimulated. On the whole, Gene has had a slight advantage over James educationally.

SOCIAL ENVIRONMENTS

James's environment has been largely rural; Gene's urban. James has had slightly more physical and economic advantages; Gene more cultural advantages. Both boys have been reared as only children, with much affection lavished upon them. This is somewhat more marked for Gene than for James. Gene has had more social contacts than James. On the whole, it appears that the social environments of the two boys have been only slightly different, the advantages of one being counterbalanced by those of the other.

PHYSICAL ENVIRONMENTS

James has lived more in the open and has been under less pressure at home than has Gene. The health records are not greatly different. James was healthier as a young child than Gene. James had the usual children's diseases, and in addition had a serious attack of pneumonia several years ago and is subject to bronchial attacks in the winter. Otherwise, he seems robust and healthy. His food habits are very peculiar, for he dislikes all meat, except breakfast bacon, and will eat almost no fresh vegetables. It seems strange that, in spite of his restricted diet, he is at present better nourished than Gene, who "eats everything."

Gene as a child was in very poor health. He was early suspected of having tuberculosis, but examination showed no positive symptoms of that disease. He is also very subject to bronchial attacks. When six years of age, he fell and injured his spine and still feels some local soreness at the point of injury.

Apart from the striking difference in food habits, there seems to be no other marked difference in their physical and health environments.

PHYSICAL RESEMBLANCES AND DIFFERENCES

These twins are as similar physically as the average of those reared together. Gene is $\frac{2}{3}$ inch taller, but James is $3\frac{1}{2}$ pounds heavier, due largely to noticeably greater muscular development. The head length of Gene is 18.2 centimeters; that of James, 18.5 centimeters. The head width of Gene is 13.50 centimeters; that of James, 13.15 centimeters. The total sizes of the two heads are about the same.

The hair of both is dark brown, medium coarse, and nearly straight. The eye color is dark-greenish gray in both. The complexion is rather poor in both, being somewhat sallow and inclined to pimples. The shape and set of the eyes are peculiar. Both of them keep the eyes about half-closed, and in both the lids are slightly oblique. The ears of the two are extremely similar in form and set, but James is able to wiggle his ears freely, an accomplishment not possessed by Gene. Both have had a great deal of trouble with ingrowing toenails. Both have a large brown birthmark on the back of the left thigh, though the location of the mark is higher and more toward the inside in James than in Gene. The teeth are highly similar, the upper incisors being unusually small and widely separated in both. James's teeth are all sound, but Gene has two fillings in molars. In both boys the upper canines are very small, sharp, and in shape like those of a cat. They show asymmetry reversal in three features: Gene is right-handed, while James is partially left-handed; Gene has clockwise hair whorl, while James has a partial reversal of the whorl; Gene's right eye is the master-eye, while James's left eye is the master-eye.

The fingerprints also show complete mirror-imaging, the right of each being like the left of the other. There is only 1 point difference in the ridge-count total of the fingers; but Gene has a count of 26 on the left hand and 18 on the right, while James has 26 on the right hand and 17 on the left—again a reversal of asymmetry. The palm patterns fail to show mirror-imaging; but the two left hands have identical formulas, while the left hand of each is entirely different from his right.

TESTS OF ABILITY

Gene is superior in three intelligence tests and equal in one. The burden of evidence is that his general ability is somewhat above that of his brother. The difference between them is not great; but it is probably significant that Gene, who has had somewhat better education and slightly more cultural advantages and more home stimulus, is somewhat superior in three of the tests. The totals in the achievement test are equal, and each is superior in four tests. The differences in months on the individual tests do not necessarily average the same as the total score because in the latter the two tests for reading and arithmetic are taken separately. The differences here must be classed as slight—no greater than those found in a considerable number of cases of identical twins reared together, though somewhat greater than the average of the latter.

TESTS OF PERSONALITY.

In the Downey Will-Temperament Test the profiles show a fair amount of similarity (Fig. 31). Both are low in speed and fluidity, motor impulsion,

TABLE 81

TEST RECORD AND ENVIRONMENTAL RATING OF PAIR NO. 17
(GENE AND JAMES)

Test	Gene	James	Diff.	Ratio of Diff. to Mean Diff.
Stanford-Binet:				
M.A.	16–0	14–7	17 mo.	1.10
I.Q.	115	105	10	1.22
Otis S.-A.:				
Score	40	40	0	....
I.Q.	119	119	0	....
Percentage right	80.0	80.0	0	....
American Council score	33	22	11	.41
International score	153	135	18	1.16
Stanford Achievement:				
Reading age	15–7	15–11½	4½ mo.	....
Spelling	13–3	12–6	9	....
Language	15–9	15–6	3	....
Literature	15–9	13–11	22	....
History and civics	12–2	13–5	15	....
Geography	15–4	15–11	7	....
Physiology and hygiene	14–1	12–10	15	....
Arithmetic	14–5	15–2	9	....
Total	14–8	14–8	0	0
Downey:				
Total	53	62	9	.98
Pattern difference	....	....	1.6	.81
Woodworth-Mathews:				
Number of neurotic traits	15	26	11	2.20
Pressey Emotions:				
Total crossed out	188	145	43	.91
Deviations	45	50	5	1.02
Kent-Rosanoff:				
Number of common responses	85	83	2	.21
Average frequency	70	103	33	.84
Number of identical responses	14	14*	....	....
Average of all tests	....	....	....	.78
Environmental rating:				
Educational			15	.99
Social			15	.84
Physical			15	.94

* Ratio to mean, .97.

and volitional perseveration, and both are high in finality of judgment, motor inhibition, and interest in detail. The greatest difference is in coordination of impulses, where James is higher by 6 points. James got the entire phrase on the line, while Gene got only "United States of" on it. The total of Gene was 53; that of James, 62—the difference being largely due to the contrast in one item.

On the Woodworth-Mathews Personal Data Sheet, James showed decidedly more unfavorable responses than Gene (26 *vs.* 15). Gene made a score that is about average, while that of James is high. There is, thus, some indication of a marked difference in nervous stability.

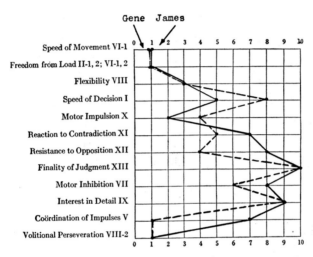

Fig. 31.—Downey Individual Will-Temperament Test profiles

On the Pressey X–O Test, Gene crossed out more words in the first part, indicating, apparently, that he is more sensitive. He also thinks that more things are wrong. On the other hand, James marks more words in the fourth test, indicating more worries, thus responding as in the Woodworth-Mathews test. On the whole test, Gene marked the larger number of words, 188, as compared with 145 for James. The deviations from the normal, however, are about the same for both.

On the Kent-Rosanoff Free Association Test the number of common reactions is the same for the two boys, but the mean frequency of James's responses is higher than Gene's (103 *vs.* 70.5). This is, however, not a large difference. Both gave many responses not very commonly given by people in general. The number of identical responses is 14—a fairly high number, considering the comparatively low frequency of their responses.

Observations of the overt behavior of these boys revealed greater contrasts than did the tests, but in the same direction. Gene was far more confident and affable toward us than James. He talked freely and seemed eager to display his talents. James was very silent and glum during the whole period of tests and did not seem happy. We are under the impression that he was somewhat envious of his brother's musical attainments and felt that he was at a disadvantage. The foster-parents claim, however, that the differences we noticed in their behavior were characteristic, not merely temporary.

TABLE 82

TOTAL NUMBER OF WORDS CROSSED OUT AND NUMBER OF
DEVIATIONS ON THE PRESSEY X–O TEST

| | WORDS CROSSED OUT | | DEVIATIONS | |
| TEST | | | | |
	Gene	James	Gene	James
Test I: Unpleasant words................	61	31	8	13
Test II: Words associated in mind with given word.........................	37	40	10	6
Test III: Things thought wrong.............	79	36	10	12
Test IV: Worries.........................	11	38	17	19
Total.........................	188	145	45	50

We judge that there is a moderately large difference at present in the temperament of these boys, which may be partly the result of the fact that Gene has been accustomed to showing off his accomplishments, while James has for some time kept more to himself.

HANDWRITING

The handwriting shows marked differences. James's is crowded; Gene's well spaced. James's is very irregular and confused; Gene's clear and legible for a boy of his age. James uses excessive pressure and ends his strokes abruptly, indicating much tension. Gene uses a moderate pressure and swings his strokes easily to a gradually diminishing pressure at the finish of the strokes, indicating easier and more relaxed co-ordination. Gene's writing is rounded; James's angular, which indicates, with the other marks,

PLATE XXXIV

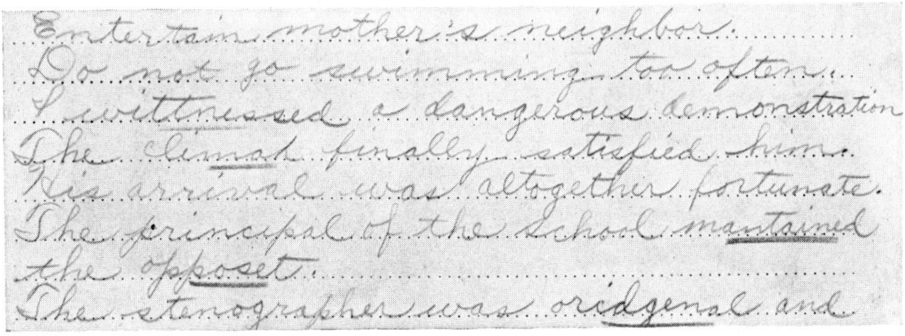

Entertain mother's neighbor.
Do not go swimming too often.
I wittnessed a dangerous demonstration
The climax finally satisfied him.
His arrival was altogether fortunate.
The principal of the school maintained
the opposet.
The stenographer was oridgenal and

HANDWRITING OF GENE, CASE XVII

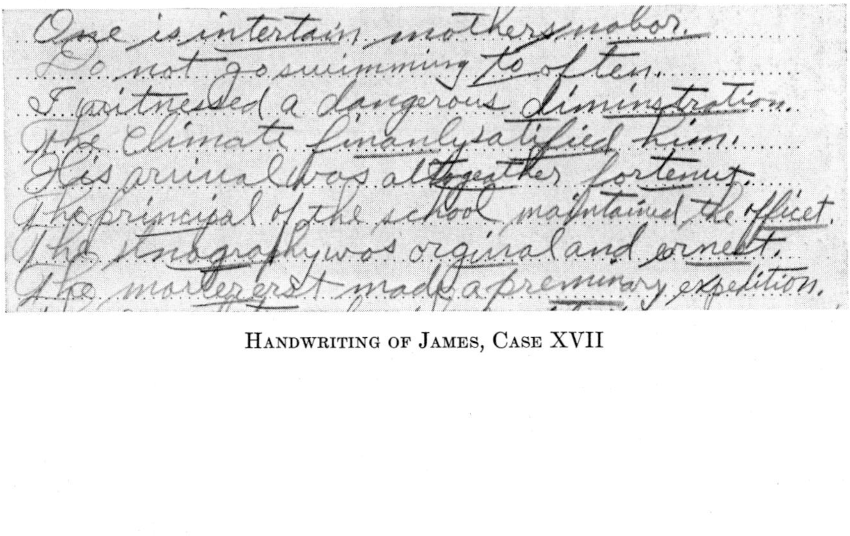

One is intertain mothers nabor.
Do not go swimming to often.
I witnessed a dangerous diminstration.
The climate finanly satified him.
His privval was altogether fortenut.
The principal of the school maintaind the officet.
The stnography wos orgiral and erneet.
The marterest made a premunary expedition.

HANDWRITING OF JAMES, CASE XVII

the same thing. James's writing gives, in general, the picture of high nervous tension and lack of control. This agrees with the observation of the boys and confirms the indications of the tests, but in more decided fashion.

SUMMARY

In general physique and in detailed bodily characters these boys are very similar indeed. No marked contrast was found in their physical environment. The formal education of the boys is very similar and their educational attainment equal. Gene has had somewhat more opportunity and encouragement in supplementary activities of an educational and cultural nature. His general ability seems to be slightly higher than James's. There are definite indications in social behavior, the tests, and the handwriting that Gene is better balanced emotionally, though the reactions on the Downey test indicate basically similar reactions. We do not know the origin of these differences but are confident that they are real.

In general summary, we may say that these twins are only slightly different physically and intellectually and moderately different temperamentally. In physique and ability they are no more different than the average pair of identical twins reared together, but in temperament they probably are more different.

CASE XVIII. TWINS JAMES AND REECE

These twins, twenty-seven years old, were born in a mountain village in southeastern Tennessee. The mother died in childbirth. The father, a coal miner, managed to keep the twins for a time, but, when he remarried less than a year after his first wife died, the twins' grandparents took the infants, James going to the maternal and Reece to the paternal grandparents. Because of strained relations between the two foster-families, the twins have never associated. In fact, their visit to Chicago was the first time they had spent more than a few hours together.

James's grandparents are people of steady and industrious character. His grandfather and his maternal uncle have lived in a small town and have operated a sawmill and a sand-and-gravel business. James has been for nearly ten years employed as engineer in this business. The grandfather had never received much education but was very "good at figures." The uncle seems to be a man of superior ability and character and seems to have had a very steadying influence on James. This family is considered as rather well to do in the small community. James seems to be very greatly interested in machinery, especially in boat engines and dredging machinery, and is considered more or less of an expert along those lines. He has been steadily employed ever since he was graduated from high school. He was married in 1930 and has had two children, one of whom died in infancy. His wife has had one year of high-school training but is disinclined to do any kind of reading that might "improve her mind." James himself is fond of reading "improving literature." He is fond of hunting and fishing but has no other recreations. He has done no traveling of any consequence. It was difficult to persuade him to come to Chicago. James may be characterized as a steady, reliable person, but he is rather indifferent and apparently not much interested in anything going on about him.

Reece was reared by his paternal grandparents. His own sister, two years his senior, was also reared in this home. This family is one of a type common in the mountains of Tennessee. They are regular mountaineers of the more primitive sort. The grandfather had never worked steadily but had tried his hand at coal-mining, blacksmithing, and work on the railroad. He was a Confederate veteran, and his pension was almost enough to live on, so steady work was not essential. He lived to be ninety years old. Both grandparents could read and write, but that was the extent of their intellectual attainments. Reece has followed the custom of the family in avoiding regular work. He has had very few jobs. For a short time he worked in an automobile factory, but this was "too much like slavery" to him, so he returned to the mountains. It would not be fair to recount in this place any of his less creditable occupations and experiences. Suffice it to say that his whole life has had a totally different tenor from that of James. Reece was married at nineteen to a mountain girl, but they have no children.

EDUCATIONAL CAREERS

James completed grade school and high school in a town of about two thousand inhabitants. He was moderately interested in his studies, enjoying science and mathematics but disliking English. He was a member of the high-school football team but did not care for the milder sports. Since boyhood he has shown great interest in machinery of all sorts and has done some reading along those lines. He also reads history and historical novels.

Reece attended a mountain school when he felt so inclined, but never for more than five months in the year, usually much less. He continued, however, through the eighth grade. He liked arithmetic and history but disliked English. He has no pleasant memories of school. It is obvious that Reece has had educational advantages far inferior to those of James.

SOCIAL ENVIRONMENTS

In this case we must leave it to the ingenious reader to infer the facts, for we shall not give them directly. It must suffice for present purposes to say that the contrast is very great.

PLATE XXXV

CASE XVIII, JAMES (*left*) AND REECE AT TWENTY-SIX YEARS OF AGE

Under this head there is very little to add to what has been given in the life-stories. Except for the usual children's diseases, James has never been seriously ill. He had a bad automobile accident in 1929, in which three ribs were broken and a lung punctured, but his recovery has been complete. Reece knows of no serious illnesses or accidents in his life. Steady work, largely in the open, on the part of James, and the free life in the mountains, except when he was not so free, on the part of Reece, seem to offer no great contrasts from the purely physical standpoint.

PHYSICAL RESEMBLANCES AND DIFFERENCES

In appearance these twins are as similar as the average pair of identical twins reared together. The photograph (Pl. XXXV) shows that their faces are extremely similar.

James is .1 inch taller and weighs nearly 14 pounds more than Reece. The other physical measurements are all about what would be expected in view of the weight difference. The head length of James is 19.2 centimeters; that of Reece, 19.3 centimeters. The head breadth of James is 15.5; that of Reece, 15.2 centimeters. Thus, James has a very slightly larger head. Reece's left arm is 2 inches shorter than his right and is slightly deformed, yet he is fully left-handed; while James is definitely right-handed.

Both have nearly black hair, rather coarse and wavy and slightly gray at the temples. James has definitely clockwise hair whorl, but Reece has a partially reversed hair whorl. Both have the same peculiar iris pattern—a very dark outside ring surrounding a greenish-brown center. Both left eyes are slightly strabismic and have no image-forming power, merely reacting to light and darkness. The ears are nearly identical—medium sized and shapely. The teeth are extremely similar in shape and arrangement. In James the first and second right lower molars have been extracted; in Reece only the second lower left molar has been lost. The fingernails of both have been bitten down to an extreme extent.

TESTS OF ABILITY

The difference in intelligence is marked, amounting to about 20 points in I.Q. It is fully as great on the International Test as on the others. The smaller difference on the American Council Test is due to the fact that the test was too difficult, and both made low scores. This is the second largest difference we have found among the separated twins.

The difference in educational attainment is equally large, being about three years. It is pronounced in favor of James in each part of the test, but especially in reading, geography, physiology and hygiene, and arithmetic.

TABLE 83

TEST RECORD AND ENVIRONMENTAL RATING OF PAIR NO. 18
(JAMES AND REECE)

Test	James	Reece	Diff.	Ratio of Diff. to Mean Diff.
Stanford-Binet:				
M.A..............................	15–4	12–4	36 mo.	2.33
I.Q..............................	96	77	19	2.31
Otis S.-A.:				
Score............................	46	26	20	....
I.Q..............................	104	84	20	2.50
Percentage right.................	79.3	48.1	31.2	2.17
American Council score.............	53	35	18	.67
International score.................	124	89	35	2.25
Stanford Achievement:				
Reading age......................	15–6	13–1	29 mo.	....
Spelling.........................	14–1	12–6	19	....
Language.........................	14–1	12–11	14	....
Literature.......................	13–5	11–10	19	....
History and civics................	16–10	15–6	16	....
Geography........................	19–2+	14–10	52+	....
Physiology and hygiene............	17–4	12–10	54	....
Arithmetic.......................	16–9	12–9	48	....
Total......................	16–0	13–1	35	2.15
Downey:				
Total.........................	58	57	1	.11
Pattern difference.................	....	....	1.3	.66
Woodworth-Mathews:				
Number of neurotic traits..........	5	11	6	1.20
Pressey Emotions:				
Total crossed out.................	117	161	44	.93
Deviations......................	53	53	0	0
Kent-Rosanoff:				
Number of common responses......	85	88	3	.31
Average frequency................	145	117	28	.71
Number of identical responses......	13	13*	....	....
Average of all tests............	....	....	....	1.31
Environmental rating:				
Educational.......................	....	....	28	1.85
Social...........................	....	....	31	1.73
Physical.........................	....	....	11	.69

* Ratio to mean, .90.

This consistent and very large difference in test scores is about what one might expect in view of the large difference in educational experience. James's educational experience has been at least twice as extensive as Reece's.

On the Downey Will-Temperament Test the profiles are very similar in pattern. The totals are almost the same—James, 58; Reece, 57. Both are relatively slow and low in motor impulsion. Both are high in resistance to opposition and in finality of judgment and comparatively low in co-ordination of impulses and volitional perseverance. The resemblance is particularly striking because of the peculiar character of the profiles.

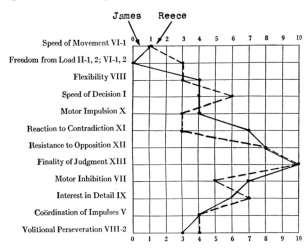

Fig. 32.—Downey Individual Will-Temperament Test profiles

The similarity of these profiles, in spite of the sharp contrast in the experiences and social behavior of these brothers, is striking. Two persons may be alike in basic temperament or modes of behavior but very different in their actions, as judged from the point of view of their aim or social significance. For example, both may be hasty or deliberate in making decisions, but the one, due to the standards of behavior which exist in his community or to other social influences, may habitually make very different kinds of decisions from the other. Or, both may resist opposition vigorously, but one may express this resistance by primitive modes of action, while the other restrains his primitive impulses in favor of actions which are acceptable in a higher level of civilized life. We must, therefore, not infer that, because the environment has not modified the basic modes of reaction, it has not modified behavior. It may have done so to a large degree.

We do not imply by this interpretation that even the basic modes of reaction, the will-temperament, may not be modified by the environment. We have indicated that they have been so modified in the case of other pairs. What we now say is that, even though the will-temperament has remained the same, due to its original likeness and its imperviousness to the environment in this case, other significant modifications have been made which are of great social importance.

On the Woodworth-Mathews Personal Data Sheet both made very few unfavorable responses, but Reece made a few more than James (11 *vs.* 5).

TABLE 84

TOTAL NUMBER OF WORDS CROSSED OUT AND NUMBER OF
DEVIATIONS ON THE PRESSEY X–O TEST

TEST	WORDS CROSSED OUT		DEVIATIONS	
	James	Reece	James	Reece
Test I: Unpleasant words................	20	45	9	10
Test II: Words associated in mind with given word........................	19	25	8	16
Test III: Things thought wrong.............	52	67	19	12
Test IV: Worries.........................	26	24	17	15
Total.........................	117	161	53	53

The test indicates that James is slightly the more emotionally stable of the two, but neither is neurotic.

On the Pressey X–O Test, Reece marked 161 words; James, 117 words. Most of the difference is in the first part, involving words that are unpleasant. There is no difference in number of worries. The test suggests that Reece is somewhat more emotional than James, but both cross out a small number of words.

On the Kent-Rosanoff Free Association Test the number of identical responses was 13, which is about average. The mean frequency of both is fairly low, but James's is higher than Reece's (145 *vs.* 117). The test indicates stronger similarities than differences, but again James is a little more like people in general than is Reece.

In general, these tests fail to reveal any fundamental differences in basic temperament between these men. They are very similar in personality traits in spite of the rather marked differences in mental ability and life-experiences.

Observations of their overt behavior support the findings of the tests. They are both tall, rather formidable-looking men, typical of their part of the country. They were very quiet, undemonstrative, co-operative to a high degree in the tests, and courteous. Neither showed any noticeable surprise at the size or activity of the great city. Both were extremely matter of fact about the whole experience. The only behavioral difference detected was that Reece seemed a little less inclined to relate his experiences and was less inclined to look one in the eye.

HANDWRITING

One might expect the handwriting to differ markedly on account of the different amounts of education the brothers have received. Such a difference, however, does not appear in the handwriting itself. Both men have a mature and individual style. The differences which do exist are probably not due to the different amounts of schooling.

Striking differences are obvious on a moment's inspection. Reece's writing is much heavier, is more sloping, and is more consistent in slope. The letters, while not conforming meticulously to the conventional form, are made with greater firmness of outline and sureness of form. An idiosyncrasy of Reece's writing is the exaggeration of the small *a*, made in rather peculiar style. Another is the broad loops, extending even to the *d*. James exhibits none of these, except occasionally the broad loops. Reece's writing suggests a more original character, set and uncompromising, whereas James's suggests greater flexibility and adaptability. We make this only as a very tentative suggestion.

An unusual feature that is present in the pen writing of both, but does not appear in the pencil writing, is a rather marked tremor. See Plate XXXVII. This doubtless has a physiological basis, but we are unable to say what it is.

SUMMARY

The twins are very similar physically and are clearly monozygotic. In intellectual ability and in educational achievement they differ to an extreme degree. Two-thirds of the population lie within the range of scores which separate them. Of course, James, who has the better education, makes the higher scores. The facts regarding personality are not so simple. In some basic elements of temperament these brothers, brought up under such diverse conditions, are remarkably similar. This is brought out most

PLATE XXXVI

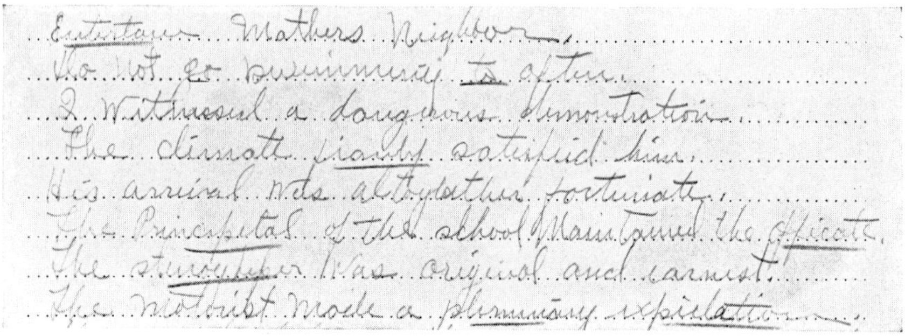
Entertain Mathers Nieghbor.
Do not go swimming to often.
I Witnessed a dangerous demonstration.
The climate fianly satisfied him.
His arrival was altogather fortuniate.
The Principetal of the school Maintained the officate.
The strungtiper was original and earnest.
The mothiht made a plemmany expislation.

Handwriting of James, Case XVIII

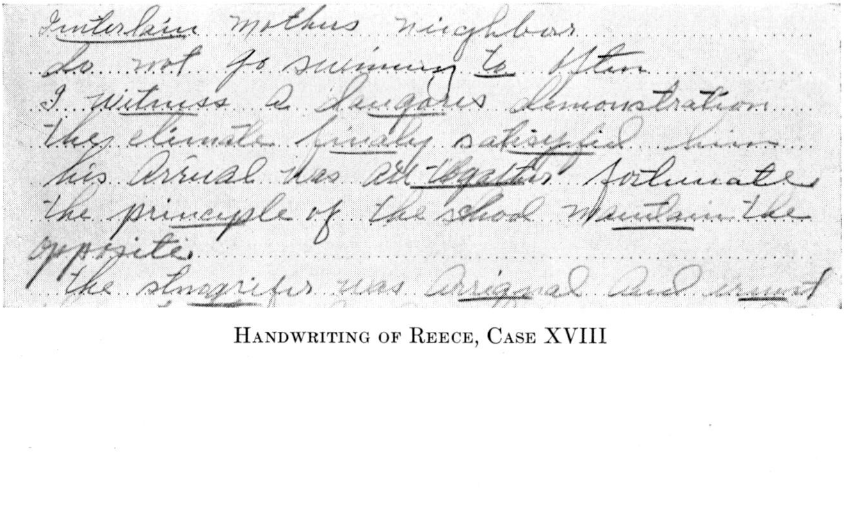
Interlain mothers nieghbor
do not go swiming to often
I witness a daugarus demonstration
they climate finaly satisyfied him
his Arrival was all-togather fortunate
the principle of the school maintain the opposite.
the stmagrifer was arrignal and ernest

Handwriting of Reece, Case XVIII

PLATE XXXVII

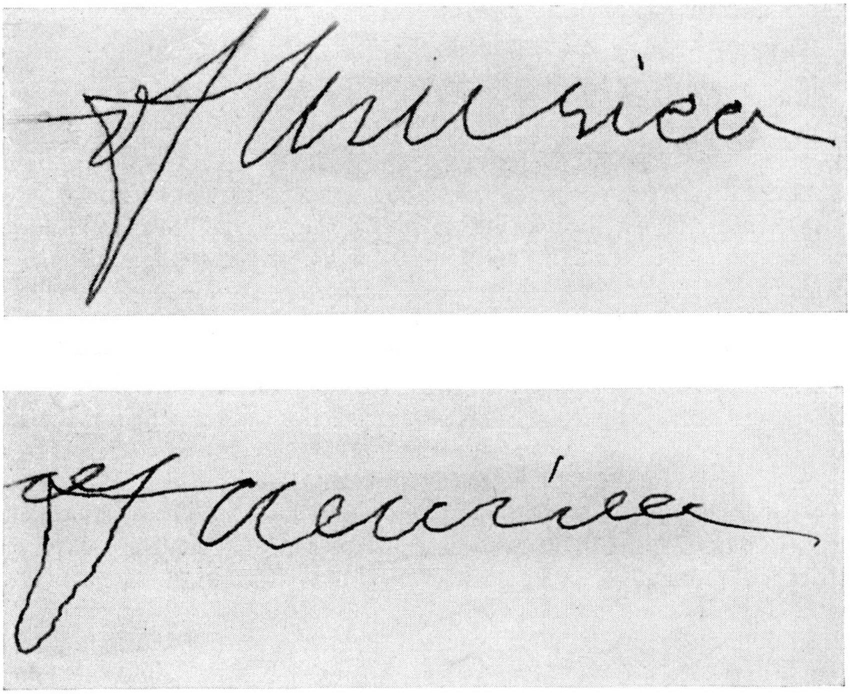

SPECIMENS OF PEN WRITING OF JAMES (*upper*) AND REECE (*lower*) TO SHOW TREMOR

strikingly in the Downey test. In the tests of neurotic disposition and of emotions, also, they are rather similar. In behavior, judged from the point of view of its social productiveness and acceptability, however, the contrast is sharp. There is also a marked contrast in handwriting. While, then, a certain basic similarity in mode of reaction exists by nature and persists in spite of differences in the environment, some rather fundamental modification has apparently been made, and marked effects in the aim, direction, and content of behavior are obvious.

CASE XIX. TWINS AUGUSTA AND HELEN

These twins, both married women, were forty-one years old when examined. They were born in New York City. When they were very young, their parents brought them to a medium-sized city in Kansas, where they lived until the death of the mother. The twins were six years old when the mother died. The father, unable to take care of the entire family of six youngsters, placed the twins and two of the younger children in a Catholic orphanage, from which they were soon adopted by two different families. Helen was the first to be adopted. She remained only a short time with the family which adopted her, for the authorities considered this home unsuitable. Before she was ten years old, Helen was recalled to the orphanage, where she remained until she was seventeen. Augusta was adopted from the orphanage about a year after Helen was first taken away. Her foster-parents were an elderly childless couple who lived in a small Kansas town. She lived with this family until she was seventeen, when she decided to join her twin sister in studying nursing. Augusta's foster-mother was very strict with her and demanded a great deal of waiting on, for she was not well. There was very little opportunity for companionship with other children. During the period of separation there was scarcely any communication between the sisters. This period of separation began considerably later than was the case in any of our other pairs of separated twins, but we have decided to include this case because the environmental differences reported to us were rather greater than in some of the other cases.

EDUCATIONAL CAREERS

Augusta finished her grade-school education in her home town and was urged to go on into high school. This she preferred not to do on account of the demands upon her time at home. Helen attended the parochial school connected with the orphanage where she was reared. She also finished only the eighth grade. When she was seventeen, Helen decided to enter upon a three-year course in nursing in a hospital in Kansas City. Augusta, hearing of this plan, decided to join her sister and study nursing with her. Thus, they were again together after eleven years of separation. They remained together, however, for only six months, for Augusta was in poor physical condition. Tuberculosis was suspected, and she was advised to go farther south. This she did. Her course in nursing was resumed in a city in southern Texas, and she completed the three-year course there, becoming a graduate nurse. Both women have practiced their profession of nursing ever since, Augusta having had the more extensive experience. As to educational experience, it should be said that Helen has five daughters and has always helped them with their school work, while Augusta has no children and has missed this additional training. On this account we were prepared to find Helen making better scores on the intelligence tests. Evidently, Augusta expected this result also, for she said to us: "I hope you don't expect me to be as bright as my sister." As a matter of fact, the tests showed Augusta to be a little brighter.

SOCIAL ENVIRONMENTS

The social environments of these women were, of course, the same until they were six years old but have been rather markedly different since then. Augusta was brought up by an elderly couple and without having any close companions of her own age. Helen was reared among children in the orphanage. The children were rather repressed and inhibited in their activities but were well treated in most respects. Helen was not happy during her childhood. Another large contrast has to do with the home lives of the two women. At twenty-four Helen married an ambitious young taxi driver who has worked up in the business until he is now part owner of a taxicab business in a small Missouri town. Helen's marriage has been a happy one, and she has five daughters, aged fifteen, thirteen, twelve, ten, and five. She has always been exceptionally fond of children, having grown up with so many around her.

Augusta married a Texan at twenty-three years of age and has lived in Texas ever since. Her husband is a man much older than she. She is his second wife. He has a number of children and grandchildren. One child was born to this marriage, but it died in infancy. Thus, neither in her foster-home nor in her own present home has Augusta had anything to do with children. Now she does not care much for children, does not understand them. Her husband is a building contractor, but lack of work on his part has caused Augusta to be more active than usual in her own profession of nursing. The fact that both women are professional nurses contributes an important common factor in their social environments.

PHYSICAL ENVIRONMENTS

Ever since they were very young, Helen has been heavier than Augusta but not markedly so until recent years. Helen has grown heavier with each pregnancy and now is decidedly stout. Augusta has always remained slender. She has lived most of her life in a considerably warmer climate than that of Helen. As a girl of seventeen years Augusta was in very poor health, as was stated earlier. She was decidedly anemic and was threatened with tuberculosis. Since she recovered from this attack, she has been in quite good health. Helen, while she was with us, became seriously ill with a kidney infection and spent a week in the hospital here. At present her general health is not so good as that of Augusta.

PHYSICAL RESEMBLANCES AND DIFFERENCES

When these twins were first seen by the various examiners, some skepticism was expressed as to their being monozygotic twins. Their great difference in weight (Helen, 169.1; Augusta, 130 pounds) makes a great difference in their appearance and carriage. When, however, the photograph of the twins at twenty years (Pl. XXXVIII) was shown, all skepticism vanished. A rigid test for monozygocity was made, and the result was positive.

Augusta is $\frac{1}{2}$ inch taller, but this difference would be eliminated if Helen, who is round-shouldered, could stand straight. All the circumferential measurements are, of course, much greater in Helen and merely reflect the great difference in weight. The head length of Augusta is 18.8 centimeters; that of Helen, 18.6 centimeters. The head breadth of Augusta is 14.0 centimeters; that of Helen, 13.8 centimeters. Helen is fully right-handed; Augusta was originally left-handed but has learned to use her right hand for most monomanual operations. The hair of both was originally dark brown but is now very gray in both, Augusta's being a little grayer. The hair is soft and straight in both. Helen has a distinct clockwise hair whorl, while Augusta's is incompletely counterclockwise. The eyes of both are large, prominent, and dark brown. The noses are small, pointed, and with a Roman arch. Both have a prominent chin, but that of Augusta seems more prominent, possibly because her face is much thinner. The teeth of both were very poor and have been largely extracted. Helen now has a complete artificial denture, while Augusta has only the upper plate. The ears are extremely similar. The complexion is brunette, smooth, and somewhat sallow in both. They have both been myopic since childhood and they have nearly the same correction in their glasses. Both had a hooflike nail on the second toe—Augusta on both feet and Helen only on the right foot. Operations were necessary to remove this abnormality in both cases. The voices are indistinguishable in quality. These twins do not at all resemble their three sisters, nor are they at all like their brother.

The palm-print and fingerprint tests would in themselves have resulted in a positive diagnosis of monozygocity. The right palm of Helen is identical

PLATE XXXVIII

CASE XIX, AUGUSTA (*left*) AND HELEN WHEN THEY WERE TWENTY YEARS OF AGE

TABLE 85

TEST RECORD AND ENVIRONMENTAL RATING OF PAIR NO. 19
(AUGUSTA AND HELEN)

Test	Augusta	Helen	Diff.	Ratio of Diff. to Mean Diff.
Stanford-Binet:				
M.A....................	14–0	12–7	17 mo.	1.10
I.Q.....................	88	79	9	1.10
Otis S.-A.:				
Score...................	31	32	1	....
I.Q.....................	89	90	1	.12
Percentage right.........	72.1	68.1	4	.28
American Council score........	40	38	2	.07
International score............	95	94	1	.06
Stanford Achievement:				
Reading age................	15–8	14–10	10 mo.	....
Spelling...................	15–9	15–9	0	....
Language..................	17–2	16–3	11	....
Literature.................	12–3	12–11	8	....
History and civics..........	13–1	13–1	0	....
Geography.................	13–5	12–10	7	....
Physiology and hygiene......	17–0	16–8	4	....
Arithmetic.................	13–3	12–8	7	
Total..................	14–9	14–4	5	.31
Downey:				
Total..................	65	55	10	1.09
Pattern difference.........	....	....	1.3	.66
Woodworth-Mathews:				
Number of neurotic traits..........	13	15	2	.40
Pressey Emotions:				
Total crossed out................	165	231	66	1.40
Deviations.....................	44	45	1	.20
Kent-Rosanoff:				
Number of common responses......	98	98	0	0
Average frequency...............	117	161	44	1.12
Number of identical responses.....	22	22*	....	....
Average of all tests...........	....	....	....	.57
Environmental rating:				
Educational......................		....	9	.60
Social...........................	....	....	14	.78
Physical.........................	....	....	22	1.38

* Ratio to mean, 1.46.

in formula with the left palm of Augusta, and the detailed correspondence between these two hands is much closer than those of the two hands of either individual. The finger patterns do not show mirror-imaging, but the two left hands are much more similar than either left is to own right hand. The total ridge-count values are Helen, 76; Augusta, 72—a small difference quite in accord with a monozygotic diagnosis.

TESTS OF ABILITY

Augusta has slightly more ability than Helen as shown in three of the four intelligence tests, but the difference is too slight to be statistically significant except on the Binet test. She excels her sister in five of the eight parts

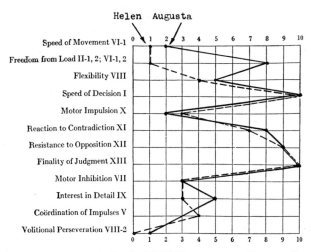

Fig. 33.—Downey Individual Will-Temperament Test profiles

of the achievement test and by five months on the average. Her superiority in attainment is probably slightly greater than her superiority in ability. The differences are certainly not great, but they are in the opposite direction from that anticipated, for we had been told that Helen had kept up a close contact with school work in connection with her daughters, while Augusta had had no such opportunities. In justice to Helen it should be said that she was not in good health when she took the tests. This makes it impossible to say whether the tests give an accurate measure of ability. In any case, it may be said that these twins show no greater differences in I.Q. than do many pairs of identical twins reared together.

TESTS OF PERSONALITY

On the Downey Will-Temperament Test the profiles were very similar. Helen made a lower score because, while she is able to write as rapidly as her sister under pressure, her natural tendency is to write more slowly. We cannot be sure that this difference extends to other forms of behavior. In other words, she does not habitually move up to her maximum speed. This is responsible for the greater part of the difference of 10 points in the total scores (Augusta, 65; Helen, 55). Apart from this difference the profiles are remarkably similar. Both are low in speed of movement and motor impulsion as well as in carefulness and attention to detail. Both are high in speed of decision and traits of aggressiveness. The similarity indicates the desirability of re-examining this much-maligned test.

TABLE 86

TOTAL NUMBER OF WORDS CROSSED OUT AND NUMBER OF
DEVIATIONS ON THE PRESSEY X–O TEST

TEST	WORDS CROSSED OUT		DEVIATIONS	
	Augusta	Helen	Augusta	Helen
Test I: Unpleasant words................	36	57	6	6

Test II:
  Words associated in mind with given
  word........................
	36	56	10	9

Test III: Things thought wrong............	55	79	12	15
Test IV: Worries........................	38	39	16	15
Total........................	165	231	44	45

On the Woodworth-Mathews Personal Data Sheet the number of unfavorable responses is much the same (Augusta, 13; Helen, 15). The two women are apparently very similar in nervous balance, and their reactions are about average.

On the Pressey X–O Test, Helen crossed out decidedly more words than Augusta except in the last part, "worries," in which there was no difference. The totals were Helen, 231; Augusta, 165. It appears either that Helen is more emotional or that she is inclined to express herself more fully about her emotions. The equality on Test IV agrees with the Woodworth-Mathews test.

On the Kent-Rosanoff Free Association Test the number of common responses is the same, and the mean frequency of responses not very different, Helen's being 161.5 and Augusta's being 117.5. The number of identical responses is rather high, being 22 out of 100 words. Most of the 22

PLATE XXXIX

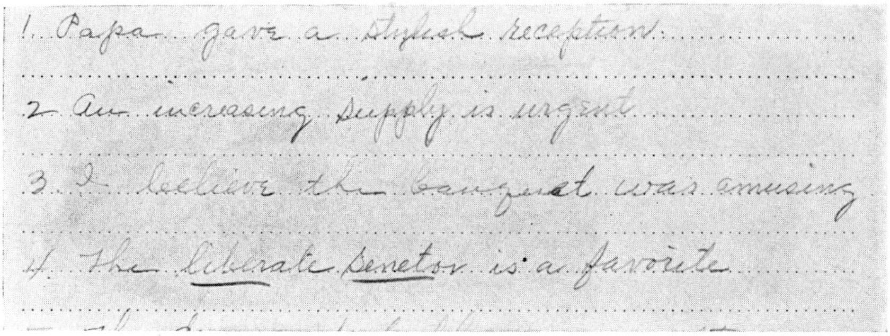

1. Papa gave a stylish reception.

2. An increasing supply is urgent.

3. I believe the banquet was amusing.

4. The liberate Senator is a favorite.

HANDWRITING OF AUGUSTA, CASE XIX

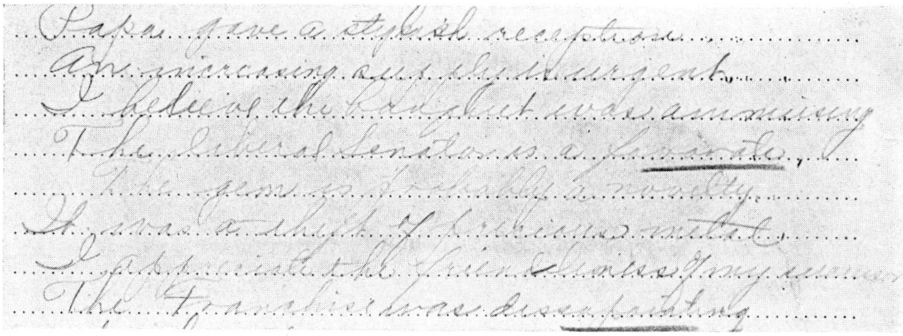

HANDWRITING OF HELEN, CASE XIX

identical responses are high-frequency responses, the lowest being "spider—bug" (frequency, 58), "Bible—church" (50), and "memory—brain" (46).

Observations of the overt behavior of these women indicate that at present they have somewhat different temperaments. Helen seems more emotional and Augusta more matter of fact. Helen seems somewhat lethargic, perhaps as the result of her excess weight and rather poor physical condition.

Whether there is any fundamental difference in temperament, it is difficult to say; but, both on tests and in overt behavior, Helen expresses her emotions more freely. The differences are, however, overshadowed by the rather close resemblances.

HANDWRITING

The two handwritings have some resemblances and some differences. Helen's is a fluent style commonly produced by so-called "arm-movement" systems. It is quite conventional and has few marks of originality. Augusta's writing is produced by a somewhat different movement. There are more modifications of the conventional letter forms, as in the g, a slight slurring-over of details of letter form, and an occasional break between the letters of a word. There is more space between words, less irregularity in size and spacing, and less slant. On the other hand, both sisters write fluently, legibly, neatly, with rather long loops. Both would probably be classed as feminine, Helen somewhat more so. The differences are marked enough to give the writings a clearly different appearance, but it is not clear how much of the difference is due to different methods of instruction.

SUMMARY

In the physical characters which indicate genetic identity these twins are closely similar. The only marked difference is in body weight, which may fairly be attributed to Helen having had five children and Augusta only one child that died in infancy. The outstanding fact, apart from this one difference, is their great similarity in mental ability, achievement, temperament, and association processes. This is rather unexpected in view of the fact that a decision was made to include this pair of twins in our collection, in spite of the fact that their separation occurred rather too late for our purposes, because we were aware of rather large differences in social environments. Either the differences were not qualitatively so great as we supposed or the native dispositions of these sisters have largely resisted being modified by them. It should be noted that the sisters lived together during the most impressionable part of their lives, that they have had the same amount of schooling, and that they have pursued the same occupation. Their similarity in ability is therefore not surprising, and their differences in temperament about as much as might be expected.

CHAPTER XI

SUMMARY OF THE FINDINGS IN THE CASE STUDIES

THE findings of the case studies may be classified into those relating to differences in ability and differences in personality, respectively. The differences in ability have already been tabulated, and certain statistical comparisons will be made in chapter xii. The average differences on some of the tests will be compared with those of identical twins reared together and with those of fraternal twins. The differences on the ability tests will also be correlated with differences in the environment. These statistical comparisons will now be supplemented by a brief analysis of the individual pairs.

DIFFERENCES IN ABILITY

This analysis is doubtless somewhat weighted in favor of the environmental interpretation. This weighting is due to the fact that the case studies represent an attempt to find indications of a correlation between environmental differences and differences between the twins. Some of the correspondences found may be coincidences. It is hard to tell whether or not they represent the influence of the environment unless the differences are large and the correspondences are present in a statistically significant group of cases. The summary of case studies may well be read with this reservation in mind. An attempt to weigh the issue in the light of all the evidence, the statistics as well as the case studies, will be made in the final chapter of interpretation.

Case I. Alice and Olive.—The differences in ability are consistent, marked, and in the same direction as the differences in educational environment. The difference in intelligence is greater than in educational achievement, which, perhaps, indicates a developmental difference in the same direction as and superimposed on educational difference.

Case II. Eleanore and Georgiana.—The difference in ability is consistent, marked, and in the same direction as the educational difference. The difference in educational achievement is somewhat greater than in intelligence and about the same as the difference in educational environment.

Case III. Paul C. and Paul O.—The tests are not entirely consistent. Paul C. is higher on four tests by about the average difference, but the brothers are practically equal on the fifth, the Stanford-Binet. The preponderance of evidence gives Paul C. a superiority about equal to the estimated superiority of his educational experience.

Case IV. Mabel and Mary.—The tests are consistent and about equally in favor of Mary, except the International Test, in which the difference is smaller. The differences are in the same direction as the difference in education but, in four out of five cases, more pronounced. This may be due to developmental differences or to other environmental influences besides education.

Case V. Edith and Fay.—The differences in ability are comparatively small but consistently in favor of Fay, whose education was also somewhat superior. No problems in interpretation are presented.

Case VI. Ada and Ida.—The differences on the tests are small and not consistent. Ada is superior in two and Ida in two. The lack of a preponderant difference in ability corresponds with a lack of noticeable difference in education.

Case VII. Raymond and Richard.—The differences on the tests are small and not consistent. On two they are negligible. On one of the others Raymond is superior, and on two Richard is superior. The similarity in ability corresponds to the similarity in education.

Case VIII. Mildred and Ruth.—Mildred is consistently superior in the five tests, by large amounts in the intelligence tests and a fair amount in the achievement test. The formal schooling is about the same, but Mildred has had much better informal educational advantages, which may account for her greater superiority in general intelligence.

Case IX. Harold and Holden.—Harold is consistently better on all the tests of ability by a moderate amount. His education is probably somewhat better since he attended a graded village school, while Holden attended a country school. The two differences agree.

Case X. Betty and Ruth.—In four tests Ruth is superior, while in the fifth they are equal. The difference is greater in educational achievement than in intelligence, which fits in well with the fact that Ruth has had one year more schooling. Ability and education agree.

Case XI. Gladys and Helen.—Four tests show a difference about three times the mean or more. The fifth shows a difference of one and one-half the mean. This corresponds to the very large difference in education.

Case XII. Thelma and Zelma.—A difference of five years in schooling is not reflected in the test scores, there being a zero or negligible difference in three tests and a small difference in favor of Thelma, who had the longer schooling, in the other two. This is a negative case. Whether Thelma's very poor physical condition, accompanied by 25 pounds less weight than her sister, who herself weighed only 98 pounds, is responsible for her failure to make markedly higher scores on the tests may be a question.

Case XIII. Kenneth and Jerry.—No ascertainable difference in education is accompanied by no significant difference in the tests of ability, except the American Council Test. Kenneth's superiority on this test is confined to two of the subtests, both of which involve language. With this exception the tests are consistent with the educational record.

Case XIV. Esther and Ethel.—On three tests the difference is negligible. On the other two Ethel is moderately superior. Both girls had a grade-school education—Ethel in a country school and Esther in a Catholic orphanage. Education and ability agree on the whole.

Case XV. Edwin and Fred.—There is a slight discrepancy between amount of education and ability. Fred has had two years more schooling than Edwin. Differences are negligible on three tests; Edwin is moderately superior in two.

Case XVI. Maxine and Virginia.—Same amount and kind of education; practically identical ability; education and tests agreeing closely.

Case XVII. Gene and James.—Have had same amount of formal schooling, Gene in somewhat better schools. Gene also had somewhat better informal advantages. In two tests Gene is somewhat superior, in three there is no significant difference. Education and tests agree fairly well, the differences, such as they are, being in the same direction.

Case XVIII. James and Reece.—A difference of over five years of schooling in favor of James is accompanied by a very large superiority in four of the tests and a moderate superiority in the fifth, a test that does not differentiate well because it is too difficult for both. The agreement is almost complete.

Case XIX. Augusta and Helen.—Same amount of schooling—grammar school plus nurse's training course. No significant difference in four tests, Augusta slightly superior in one, the Binet. The agreement is close.

SUMMARY OF DIFFERENCES IN ABILITY

The cases may be classified with respect to the relation between differences in education and in ability as follows:

a) Difference in both education and ability large or fairly large and in the same direction; five pairs, Cases I, II, IV, XI, and XVIII.

b) Difference in formal schooling large but not accompanied by marked difference in ability (possibly due to very marked physical difference); one pair, Case XII.

c) Difference in formal schooling negligible, difference in informal advantages marked, accompanied by corresponding difference in ability; one pair, Case VIII.

d) Difference in education small, difference in ability also small and preponderately in the same direction; five pairs, Cases III, V, IX, X, and XVII.

e) Difference in both education and ability negligible; three pairs, Cases VI, VII, and XVI.

f) Difference in education negligible, difference in ability negligible with one or two exceptions; four pairs, Cases XIII, XIV, XV, and XIX.

Classes *a*, *d*, and *e*, and probably *c*, including fourteen pairs, represent very close agreement between education and ability. Classes *b* and *f*, including five pairs, represent moderate discrepancy, but in no case is there a significant difference in ability in the opposite direction to a significant difference in education. In the only case in which a large difference in education is not accompanied by a large difference in ability, a large difference in physical condition may have neutralized the educational superiority. In no case is there a large and consistent difference in ability without a marked difference in the environment. On the whole, the analysis of the case studies adds convincing evidence to the statistical analysis of the marked effect of education on ability.

DIFFERENCES IN PERSONALITY

Differences in personality are not susceptible of interpretation by comparison with some common feature of the environment with which they might be supposed to vary directly. The comparison between these differences and differences in the environment are therefore not so simple as in the case of differences in ability. It is therefore necessary to seek for such relations as may seem to be plausible without following a predetermined pattern of comparison.

The data to be examined are the reports of personal observation, the scores on the Downey Will-Temperament Test, the Woodworth-Mathews Personal Data Sheet, the Pressey Test of the Emotions, and the Kent-Rosanoff Free Association Test, and the handwriting. The individual cases will be summarized as in the case of differences in ability.

Case I. Alice and Olive.—Rather marked differences in personality seem to be indicated by manner in social intercourse, the Downey test, and handwriting. Not much difference, except in detail, is shown by the other tests. The difference, in general, is consonant with the differences in environment, producing in Alice somewhat more restraint and inhibition.

Case II. Eleanore and Georgiana.—The differences on the personality tests and in handwriting are rather large. These suggest a considerable difference in personality in spite of strikingly similar physical characteristics. The chief correspondence with the environment is in the size of the difference. Specific relations have not been traced.

Case III. Paul C. and Paul O.—This pair presents a contrast between sharp differences and close similarities. The differences appear in general manner and behavior, the Pressey test, and handwriting. The other tests yield rather similar scores, and the pattern on the Downey test in particular seems to indicate much similarity in basic nervous constitution.

Case IV. Mabel and Mary.—Corresponding to the marked contrast in environment and in physical appearance and characteristics, some rather large differences are revealed by the tests and by the handwriting, though a basic similarity in pattern seems discernible. It is as though some traits had been emphasized or exaggerated in one and suppressed in the other. For example, there are sharp contrasts in the scores on the parts of Mary's Downey test, and her handwriting is like Mabel's handwriting embellished. Mary's sedentary town life has made her more excitable, and Mabel's active country life has rendered her more phlegmatic.

Case V. Edith and Fay.—These sisters were in rather similar environment up to twenty years of age and widely different since then. They differ a good deal in physical makeup and in manner but not widely on the tests. There is, however, rather wide difference on four parts of the Downey test and in handwriting. No very specific relations can be traced between differences in the environment and in personality, as revealed by the tests.

Case VI. Ada and Ida.—Similar early environment, education, and general social environment are accompanied by generally similar personality. No marked differences appear. The likeness in the Downey pattern is particularly striking.

Case VII. Raymond and Richard.—In its superficial aspect, at least, the social environment of these boys is widely different. Their personality, however, is on the whole very similar. About two-thirds of the Downey pattern is similar, and the specimens of handwriting are strikingly alike.

Case VIII. Mildred and Ruth.—In contrast with the similarity in physique rather marked differences in personality are revealed in manner, performance on the tests, and handwriting, accompanying the large difference in social situation. Some of the differences in personality and environment seem rather specifically correlated.

Case IX. Harold and Holden.—These brothers, brought up under similar circumstances, are very similar in physique, manner, and behavior in the tests. The similarity in the Downey pattern is rather close. Such similarity suggests that differences, when they occur, are not random but due to specific factors.

Case X. Betty and Ruth.—Having been reared in homes and communities differing in some important ways, these girls show a mixture of similar and different characteristics. The differences, as on the Downey, Woodworth-

Mathews, and Pressey tests, and in handwriting, seem rather plausibly attributable to known differences in environment.

Case XI. Gladys and Helen.—Large differences in environment, especially schooling, are accompanied by some marked differences in personality coupled with some similarities. The combination of similarity and difference is illustrated in the Downey profiles, which show the sisters to be alike in "aggressive" behavior, but Helen, the twin with superior education, to be much higher in "speed and fluidity" and in "carefulness and attention to detail." Helen's handwriting, moreover, is more mature, neater, more delicate and feminine in style. Her general manner differs in somewhat the same way. These differences may without much hesitancy be ascribed to the environment.

Case XII. Thelma and Zelma.—Certain basic elements of similarity in the personality of these sisters are discernible, along with important modifications. For example, the Downey profiles are similar in general form, but Thelma, who has suffered protracted illness which greatly reduced her vitality, is lower in speed of movement, reaction to contradiction, and coordination of impulses. Thelma is also much more emotionally responsive and somewhat more neurotic, as indicated by the Pressey and Woodworth-Mathews tests. In handwriting there is a very marked difference in style but similarity in general control and mastery of form.

Case XIII. Kenneth and Jerry.—Both boys are somewhat neurotic, as indicated by the tests and the fact that they bite their fingernails. Kenneth is somewhat more so. This may have some connection with the fact that both have changed homes—Kenneth twice, one of the times due to the separation of his foster-parents. The handwriting has some marked differences, along with some points of basic similarity, Kenneth's being, apparently, more restrained. The patterns on the Downey test are rather closely similar.

Case XIV. Esther and Ethel.—These sisters exhibit some close similarities and some very large differences. The Downey patterns are strikingly alike. On the other hand, Esther is very much more neurotic according to both the Woodworth-Mathews and the Pressey tests. The handwriting is rather similar. The life-histories contain some similarities and some differences. Both have been divorced and are now happily married again. Both have had serious operations. But Ethel has a child of her own and was brought up in a Catholic orphanage, whereas Esther has an adopted child and was brought up on a farm. Esther, moreover, is naturally left-handed and has been taught to write with her right hand. Do these differences account for the differences in personality? We cannot say.

Case XV. Edwin and Fred.—The similarities outweigh the differences, but some of the differences are large. This is true in the case of three of the twelve parts of the Downey test, the other nine being similar. Fred appears to be somewhat more stable and less flexible, as indicated by the Downey test and the tests of neurotic disposition. The handwriting is similar in general character. The environment seems to have been similar, corresponding to the prevailing similarity in personality.

Case XVI. Maxine and Virginia.—The Downey patterns of these eleven-and-one-half-year-old girls are almost identical—an astonishing amount of similarity in two persons' reactions—indicating basic similarity in responses. However, Virginia seems on the Woodworth-Mathews and Pressey tests to be less emotionally responsive, possibly due to her rapid growth and development following special treatment consisting of rest and feeding. The handwriting, unlike responses on the Downey test, is not closely similar.

Case XVII. Gene and James.—Some close similarities and some definite differences appear. The Downey profiles are alike in general outline with only one important exception, "co-ordination of impulses," and two minor exceptions, "speed of decision" and "resistance to opposition." The greatest difference appears in the tests of neurotic disposition, which make out James to be more neurotic, and in handwriting, in which James gives a picture of high motor tension and lack of control. During the test James was silent and glum and seemed unhappy. This seems to agree with the tests.

Case XVIII. James and Reece.—This pair also shows some close similarities and some clearly marked differences. The Downey profiles are very similar, with only one difference as great as four points out of ten and with eight parts within one point of one another. The other tests also yield only small differences. The handwriting exhibits one mark of similarity, but, in general, exhibits the only sharp contrast of our records. The similarity consists in a very noticeable tremor in the pen writing. The difference is in the pressure and form of the writing. Reece uses much greater pressure and forms the letters with greater firmness of outline and sureness of form. He also exhibits certain idiosyncrasies. His writing seems more original, set, and uncompromising. This pair suggests the existence of levels of behavior and the possibility of close similarity at one level and large difference at another. This suggestion will be elaborated in the summary.

Case XIX. Augusta and Helen.—The similarities preponderate, but some differences are evident. The Downey profiles are almost identical except for one point. Helen writes habitually at a slower speed but can write as rapidly as Augusta under pressure. This recalls the difference in the styles of handwriting which is probably to be ascribed to the conventional difference in the systems the sisters were taught. Slight differences appear in the other tests, but Helen seems slightly more emotional, or at least freer in the expression of her feelings.

It is not possible to classify the cases with respect to the relation between personality differences and environmental differences as was done in the case of ability differences. This is partly because environmental differences cannot be distinguished in terms of some common or general feature which can be measured or estimated and which varies continuously from one extreme to the other. Environmental differences, so far as they affect personality, are complex and made up of elements which may vary independently of one another and affect specific features of the personality in divergent ways. This makes it difficult to subject the relations between environment and personality to statistical analysis, or even to summarize them. However, certain general observations and suggestions may be made concerning our data, which may perhaps be the starting-point for further studies of the problem.

"Personality" is a term which designates a great variety of forms of behavior. The union of these different forms under the same term is doubtless a matter of practical convenience rather than strict psychological nature. General observation suggests that some of these forms are more fundamental and more permanent and stable than others. A sharp controversy rages as to whether personality is innate or acquired. Perhaps the opponents in the debate would not be so far apart if a distinction were drawn between features of personality, some of which are more and others less modifiable.

An example may be drawn from the reactions of our twins. If we go through the records and count the number of pairs who resemble each other in their behavior in the Downey test and in their handwriting, we find a sharp contrast. In spite of its detailed character and the many opportunities for variation, the number of pairs who yield similar profiles on the Downey test is surprisingly large. Five pairs are almost identical, with a single exception in one (Cases VI, XIV, XVI, XVIII, and XIX); ten are similar in a considerable part (Cases I, III, VII, VIII, IX, X, XII, XIII, XV, and XVII); and only four are widely different (Cases II, IV, V, and XI). By contrast, only two pairs of handwriting specimens are noted as very closely similar (Cases VII and XIV), whereas twelve are widely different (Cases I, II, III, IV, V, VIII, X, XI, XII, XVI, XVII, and XVIII). The contrast in the form and even in pressure of the specimens written by one pair (Case XVIII) is put into sharp relief by the fact that the writing of both James and Reece has a common and peculiar (for young men) characteristic, namely, a pronounced tremor. Here we find a contrast between a fundamental and a derived characteristic in the same activity.

The hypothesis which is suggested to explain the contrast is that there exist several levels of behavior. The first, and most fundamental level, is represented by the muscular tremor exhibited by James and Reece. This is probably due to the genetic or, at least, to the inborn character of the organism. A second level, represented by the reactions on the Downey test, is composed of modes of behavior which are somewhat less primitive, stable, innate, and somewhat more affected by the effects of experience. They are not incapable of modification, as is shown by the few cases in which the Downey profiles differ radically. It may be that activities of this level are not usually greatly modified by experience because they do not represent an organization into units which corresponds to definite situations of the environment according to which specific complexes of behavior are set up. This is, perhaps, why investigators have regularly failed to get a correlation between scores on the Downey test and ratings of personality. The parts of the test represent real units of behavior but not units which correspond to common social situations. From the point of view of the organization of behavior as it takes place in the individual's adjustment to his environment, they are abstract.

Handwriting, on the contrary, is the concrete representation of a form of the organization which takes place in the course of such adjustment. It expresses the individual's personality, if we mean not a fixed and unalterable innate personality but the personality which has been formed by the interaction between the given organism and its environment. (This is not an indorsement of the special interpretations of handwriting represented in systems of graphology.) This is the reason for the fact, first discovered by Galton and confirmed in our study, that style of handwriting (as distinguished from speed or general merit) is a characteristic in which identical twins are not alike.

Much the same can be said of such responses as are made in the tests of emotions and of neurotic disposition as can be said of handwriting. They represent that level of behavior which is organized in the course of the individual's adjustment to his environment and are therefore influenced in large measure by the character of that environment.

It is one thing to show the existence of differences and quite another to find the links between these differences and specific environmental differences. We have been able to make only a few hints of such links, as in the case of Mildred and Ruth (Case VIII), of Kenneth and Jerry (Case XIII), or of Esther and Ethel (Case XIV). Such links could much better be investigated by contemporary rather than by ex post facto examination.

Our conclusion is that forms of behavior exist which are determined largely by the original character of the organism. None of these forms of behavior is impervious to influence, but some of them may actually not be greatly modified because they have not, as a matter of fact, been incorporated into an organized system of learned behavior. The forms of behavior which constitute the adjustment of the individual to his environment, on the other hand, are on a higher level of performance, which is the product of both the organism and the environment interacting. This product is affected both by the original nature of the individual and by his environment and is not the sole product of either.

CHAPTER XII

STATISTICAL ANALYSES OF SEPARATED TWINS

DESCRIPTIVE ACCOUNT OF THE DIFFERENCES BETWEEN IDENTICAL TWINS REARED APART

IN THIS section are presented for inspection the data which will be subjected to statistical analysis in later sections. This inspection will give an understanding of the general nature of the data and indicate something of the size and range of the differences which were found.

The chief scores on the tests and the absolute differences between the scores for each of the nineteen pairs are given in Table 87.

A cursory inspection shows that there are large differences between some pairs on each of the tests. On the other hand, some of the pairs yield scores which are very nearly or exactly the same. Some pairs differ much, and some differ little, in each of the traits measured. This is true also of siblings, fraternal twins, and identical twins reared together. We must then look to some other fact to determine whether the likenesses and differences are due to heredity, to environment, or to some combination of both.

One such fact is the relation between the various differences found in the separated twins and the amount of difference in the environment. This will be set forth in the section entitled "Correlations of Twin Differences with Environmental Ratings."

Another significant fact is the amount of the differences between identical twins reared apart as compared with the differences between identical twins reared together. This comparison can be made for certain physical measures and for measures of intelligence. It will be set forth in the section entitled "Mean Differences between Twins Reared Together and Twins Reared Apart."

A question of some interest is whether the separated twins are equally different in all the traits examined or whether there are some traits in which the differences are greater than in others. This comparison will not show conclusively whether some traits are more subject to environmental influence than others because we do not know whether the differences in the various traits are the same genetically. However, if the differences are of about the same order, it may be presumed, lacking evidence to the contrary, that the various traits are influenced by differences in the environment in similar degree.

The differences in the various traits cannot, of course, be compared in terms of the scores themselves because the units of measurement differ so greatly. We may, however, compare them in terms of the standard deviation of the scores of the entire group of individuals by finding the ratio between the average difference between the twins and the standard deviation. The standard deviations, mean differences, and ratios are given in Table 88.

TABLE 88

THE RATIO OF THE MEAN DIFFERENCES TO THE STANDARD
DEVIATIONS OF THE SCORES

Trait	S.D. Score	Mean Diff.	Ratio
Stanford-Binet I.Q.	13.00	8.21	.63
Otis I.Q.	13.58	8.00	.59
Otis percentage right	27.93	14.36	.51
Stanford Achievement	23.47	16.26	.69
Thurstone Psychological	36.74	27.06	.74
International	34.71	15.53	.45
Woodworth-Mathews	7.65	5.00	.65
Kent-Rosanoff: Number common Average frequency	12.14 40.85	9.63 39.42	.79 .96
Pressey Emotions: Total crossed out Number of deviations	35.44 6.91	47.16 4.89	1.33 .71
Downey Will-Temperament total score	8.88	9.16	1.03

There is some variation in these ratios, but they are of the same general order. In particular, the differences in personality are only slightly greater than the differences in intelligence or ability. Consequently, we may say that, in so far as they are due to environment, the differences in personality are produced by the environment to the same degree as are those in ability. This reasoning is admittedly not at all rigorous but is only presumptive. Unfortunately, we cannot, as in the case of the intelligence and achievement tests, compare separated twins with those reared together. We can, however, correlate the differences in scores with estimated differences in environment.

ENVIRONMENTAL RATINGS FROM CASE HISTORIES

Ratings of educational, social, and physical environmental differences were made from the case histories. The difference in environment for each pair of twins was judged on a scale of 1–10 for each of the three types of environment. Five judges participated in the rating, and, with the exception of raters D and E, no evidence except that of the case history was used. Raters D and E were familiar with some of the twins or had participated in some of the measurements.

Twenty pairs of twins were rated, but in the distribution of ratings presented in Table 89 only nineteen pairs have been considered because some

TABLE 89

COMPOSITE ENVIRONMENTAL RATINGS FOR TWIN
DIFFERENCES BY FIVE JUDGES
(SCALE OF 5–50)

RATING	ENVIRONMENTAL TYPE		
	Educa-tional	Social	Physical Health
34.5–39.5	1	....	1
29.5–34.5	1	2	....
24.5–29.5	1	4	....
19.5–24.5	1	....	5
14.5–19.5	3	5	3
9.5–14.5	6	7	5
4.5– 9.5	6	1	5
Median rating....	12.4	16.0	14.0

of the measurements common to these were not made for the twentieth pair (Muller's case).

From the frequency distributions in Table 89 it will be noted that the majority of the ratings were relatively low. For only a few cases were the environmental differences of the twin pairs judged to be large. These distributions have a very important bearing upon the comparisons which follow because the effect of each type of environment on the whole group of twins will not be so pronounced as if each pair had marked differences in environment. In so far as the ratings are valid, the net effect of environmental differences upon twin characters will be largely determined by one-third to one-half of the cases.

The reliability of the ratings is highly satisfactory. Correlation coefficients were computed between raters' judgments for each of the three types of environment. Correlations were also obtained between the rating of each judge with the pooled ratings of the other four judges.

From Table 90 it is apparent that the correlations between judges are generally high. By use of the Spearman-Brown formula the reliability of the pooled ratings of five judges for each of the environmental types was computed. These values (bottom row of table) indicate that the reliability

TABLE 90

RELIABILITY COEFFICIENTS FOR RATINGS OF ENVIRON-
MENTAL DIFFERENCES (JUDGES A, B, C, D, AND E)

JUDGE	EDUCATION				SOCIAL				PHYSICAL HEALTH			
	B	C	D	E	B	C	D	E	B	C	D	E
A.....................	.845	.808	.761	.742	.587	.877	.538	.627	.727	.807	.690	.705
B.....................	....	.814	.885	.843	....	.704	.673	.591	....	.816	.365	.505
C.....................	....	....	.863	.818	....	....	.680	.686	....	....	.653	.658
D.....................	....	....	....	.946	....	....	....	.643	....	....	....	.843
Reliability of five judges...........	.961				.907				.913			

TABLE 91

CORRELATIONS OF EACH JUDGE WITH THE
POOL OF THE OTHER FOUR

Judge	Education	Social	Physical Health	Total of Three Types
A.........	.834	.760	.857	.869
B.........	.909	.734	.677	.795
C.........	.882	.876	.859	.865
D.........	.932	.727	.723	.842
E.........	.897	.732	.779	.818

of the pooled ratings exceeds .90 in every case. Such a reliability is gen-erally considered very satisfactory with tests and more so with ratings.

The correlation of each judge's rating with those of the other four is of some interest in showing agreement in rating (Table 91). These last corre-lations indicate that differences with pooled ratings are generally not great. Raters A and C, who were totally unfamiliar with any of the cases or the measurements, showed the greatest consistency with the pool of the rest.

The foregoing ratings are, of course, limited to the extent that they were all based on a single descriptive account (made by rater E). In these descriptive accounts, however, there was seldom any direct appraisal of the environment, so that the judgments of the raters generally represent a fairly independent pooling of descriptive evidence.

The next question of interest is with regard to the independence of the three types of environmental rating. Any correlation between these types may be due in part to a true relationship or to the "halo effect" of judging a large social and educational difference, for example, for the same pair of twins because of a general impression.

From the correlations in Table 92 it is apparent that there was no significant correlation between the social and physical ratings. The total correlation of .167 between educational and physical ratings suggests some relationship, but it is not statistically significant. The total correlation .260 between educational and social ratings is possibly significant, although low.

TABLE 92

CORRELATIONS BETWEEN ENVIRONMENTAL TYPES

Judge	Educational and Social	Educational and Physical	Social and Physical
A.............	.310	.160	−.054
B.............	.479	−.066	−.167
C.............	.118	.263	−.024
D.............	.170	.108	.008
E.............	.406	.198	.294
Total......	.260	.167	−.023

In general, we may say that these three types of environment were rated as nearly independent, with a slight relationship probable between educational and social ratings. If a part of this correlation be due to halo effect, the remainder can hardly be significant. Separation of the ratings into the three foregoing types seems well justified in view of these correlations.

CORRELATIONS OF TWIN DIFFERENCES WITH
ENVIRONMENTAL RATINGS

Differences between the separated twin pairs were correlated with the five judges' ratings of differences in educational, social, and physical environment. The correlations with five physical traits were based on twenty pairs of twins (including Muller's case), while the correlations with eight mental traits were worked out on nineteen pairs (omitting Muller's case). For the sake of completeness and as a check on the expected correlation, all the possible fifty-one coefficients were worked out, although no relationship would be expected between such traits as height with educational environment. A complete list of these correlations is given in Table 93. Using Fisher's Table V A, with $P = .05$ as a standard, we may regard all correlations less than .45 as insignificant; if $P = .10$ be used as standard, correlations less than .38 are insignificant. Correlations printed in heavier type are regarded as significant, while those between .38 and .45 may be viewed as having possible significance.

TABLE 93

CORRELATIONS OF TWIN DIFFERENCES ON CERTAIN TRAITS WITH ESTIMATED DIFFERENCES IN THREE ENVIRONMENTAL RATINGS

TRAIT	ENVIRONMENTAL DIFFERENCE RATING		
	Educational	Social	Physical and Health
Height..........................	−.015	−.005	−.175
Weight..........................	−.095	.226	**.599**
Head length.....................	−.139	−.256	−.102
Head width......................	−.024	.150	−.352
Cephalic index..................	.105	.154	−.375
Binet I.Q.......................	**.791**	**.507**	.304
Otis I.Q........................	**.547**	**.533**	−.225
International Test...............	**.462**	**.534**	−.026
American Council Test...........	**.570**	.321	.082
Stanford Educational Age.........	**.908**	.349	.139
Woodworth-Mathews:			
Number of neurotic traits........	.044	−.075	−.291
Kent-Rosanoff:			
Number of common reactions.....	−.218	.102	−.342
Average frequency of responses....	−.272	.014	−.128
Pressey Emotions:			
Total number crossed out........	.249	−.418	.124
Number of deviations...........	.221	.349	−.183
Downey Will-Temperament:			
Total score....................	.411	.271	**.465**
Pattern difference..............	.435	.021	.142

Significant correlations of physical difference with environmental difference are found between weight and physical health. This relationship is expected since differences in physical and health conditions should produce differences in weight. The remaining correlations with physical traits are also in line with expectation because educational and social changes would probably not be expected to affect such characters. The negative correlations of head measurements with physical ratings are probably insignificant, but they suggest a little negative association from unknown causes. It is possible that obstetrical deformations of head form might be involved. The first-born twin would be more affected in this case.

In the case of the intelligence tests, consistent and significant positive correlations with educational ratings are found. The largest of these is .791 between Binet I.Q. differences and educational differences. The correlations for Otis, International, and American Council tests are somewhat lower but indicate definite correlation between intelligence and educational differences.

Turning next to the correlations of trait differences with social rating differences, we find that the Binet, Otis, and International tests each yields a significant relationship. There thus appears an undeniable tendency for wide social differences to be associated with differences in intelligence, whether measured by verbal or nonverbal tests.

The large correlation of .908 between differences in educational background and differences on the Stanford Achievement Test is surprisingly high. We should expect considerable correlation here, however. The advantages of several years of schooling of one twin over the other produce marked differences in the broad educational test. It is interesting to note that this correlation is in the neighborhood of the reliability of the test itself. This suggests that the pooled rating of the five judges was about as reliable and valid a measure of educational status as the test.

Three of the four personality tests fail to yield significant positive correlations. Either a difference in the environment does not produce a difference in the characteristics measured by these tests, or the factors in the environment which do produce such differences in personality are not those of formal education, social position, or gross physical advantages. It may very well be true that these are not the effective factors in determining personality. They may rather consist in subtle human relations which are revealed only by individual analysis.

Taken as a whole, these correlations indicate that differences in educational and social environment produce undeniable differences in intelligence and scholastic achievement as measured by our tests. It has already been noted that most of this relationship was produced by a relatively few cases with extreme difference in rating. If we eliminate the four pairs of twins whose mean difference in educational rating is 30, the correlations between Binet I.Q., Otis I.Q., International score, and Stanford Achievement, each with educational difference ratings, are, respectively, .406, .248, .342, and .450. For fifteen cases none of these would be regarded as statistically significant by the standard used above, but they are all consistent and positive. The large drop in correlation when the four extreme cases are omitted is evidence of their contribution to the original correlation values. This contribution will next be illustrated in another way by use of coefficients of determination using the Binet differences.

For the correlations based on nineteen cases, the necessary coefficients are .791 (Binet and educational), .507 (Binet and social), and .304 (Binet and physical). We also need .260 (educational and social). The remaining correlations between environmental ratings are taken as negligible. From these values we find the following contributions to variance in Binet I.Q. differences:

Per Cent

    50 attributable to educational differences

    10 attributable to social differences

    12 attributable to joint educational and social differences

     9 attributable to physical differences

    19 attributable to unknown causes

    ——

    100 of variance in I.Q. differences

Next, using the same form of analysis with the four extreme cases omitted, the necessary coefficients are .406 (Binet and educational), .441 (Binet and social), .400 (Binet and physical), .300 (educational and social), and .480 (educational and physical). From these coefficients we find the following contributions to I.Q. variances:

Per Cent

     1 attributable to educational differences

    16 attributable to social differences

     3 attributable to joint educational and social differences

    12 attributable to physical differences

     4 attributable to joint educational and physical differences

    64 attributable to unknown causes

    ——

    100 of variance in I.Q. differences

Some of the correlations used in the foregoing analysis are insignificant, and some of the resulting percentages of variance are also doubtful. Certain broad conclusions, however, may be drawn from the foregoing analyses. When all nineteen cases are used, the separate and joint influences of educational and social differences account for 72 per cent of the variance in I.Q. difference; when the four extreme cases are omitted, educational and social differences account for only 20 per cent of the I.Q. variance. This drop is much more striking than that suggested by the correlations alone. It is also noteworthy that for the nineteen cases only 19 per cent of the I.Q. variance is unaccounted for, while for the fifteen cases 64 per cent is unknown and the remaining 36 per cent cannot be assigned to different environmental influences with satisfactory reliability.

This difference in the proportion of the variance attributed to environment in the two groups confirms the statement made in chapter vii that effect of differences in the environment is a function of the magnitude of these differences. The importance of differences in the environment in relation to the importance of differences in genetic character can be estimated, therefore, only with reference to particular amounts of these differences.

MEAN DIFFERENCES BETWEEN TWINS REARED TOGETHER AND TWINS REARED APART

For the twenty pairs of identical twins reared apart and for the fifty pairs of identical twins reared together, it was possible to work out twin differences for four physical characters common to both groups. Similar differences for four common mental characters were also found for nineteen of the separated pairs (omitting Muller's case) and the fifty pairs. The mean of these differences for the separated and unseparated twins should furnish valuable evidence as to the effect of varied environment upon such characters.

It must be borne in mind that the educational, social, and physical environment of the twins reared together was by no means the same for each twin of a pair. It is also probable that the effective environmental differences for some of the separated cases were not much greater than for those reared together. Evidence for this is found in the ratings of the three types of environmental difference described in the preceding section. Thus, the mean difference for the six pairs of twins reared apart and showing greatest likeness in educational training was only 8 points on a 50-point scale.

We may symbolize the factors affecting twin differences as A (genetic factor), V (postnatal environment), and N (prenatal environment, asymmetry, and other factors not A or V). In the previous discussion of the relative effect of nature and nurture, V plus N was designated as the nurture factor B. We shall assume that all these factors are uncorrelated. Inasmuch as the fraternal-twin group will also be brought into some of the subsequent comparisons, we may list the differences for all three groups in the following symbolism:

Separated identicals.................. $_sD = {_sV} + {_sN}$
Unseparated identicals............... $_iD = {_iV} + {_iN}$
Fraternals......................... $_fD = {_fV} + {_fN} + A$

It is thus assumed that a difference between fraternal twins is a function of genetic and of the two types of environmental factors. Differences between identical twins, however, are a function of V and N alone.

If we assume now that factors $_sN$ and $_iN$ are, on the average, the same for the two identical groups, the difference of the means $_s\overline{D}$ and $_i\overline{D}$ is equal to the difference between $_s\overline{V}$ and $_i\overline{V}$, or $_s\overline{D} - _i\overline{D} = _s\overline{V} - _i\overline{V}$. Under the above assumption, such a difference is a measure of the effect of postnatal environmental factors in producing trait differences. This formula shows the extent to which differences in the external environments of separated and unseparated cases affect trait differences.

The foregoing setup of factors may be illustrated in the case of weight. The mean difference in weight for the twenty separated cases is $_s\overline{D} = 9.9$ pounds, while the corresponding value for fifty pairs of unseparated identical

TABLE 94

MEAN DIFFERENCES FOR TWO GROUPS OF IDENTICAL-TWIN PAIRS

Trait	Twins Reared Apart ($_s\overline{D}$) (19–20 Cases)	Twins Reared Together ($_i\overline{D}$) (50 Cases)	$_s\overline{V} - _i\overline{V}$ Difference between Means	PE_D*	$\dfrac{Diff.}{PE_D}$
Height (cm.)............	1.80	1.61 ± 0.15	0.19	0.31	0.6
Weight (lb.)............	9.90	4.03 ± 0.36	5.87	1.22	4.8
Head length (mm.)......	2.20	2.59 ± 0.21	−0.39	0.42	0.9
Head width (mm.)......	2.85	2.25 ± 0.17	0.60	0.40	1.5
Binet I.Q..............	8.21	5.35 ± 0.41	2.86	0.95	3.0
Otis I.Q..............	8.00	4.54 ± 0.37	3.67	0.89	4.1
Stanford Achievement (mo.)................	16.26	6.38 ± 0.57	9.88	1.91	5.2
Woodworth-Mathews...	5.00	5.48 ± 0.47	−0.48	0.93	0.5

* These values were computed from the sums of squares for both groups with $(20 - 1) + (50 - 1) = 68$ degrees of freedom.

twins is $_i\overline{D} = 4$ pounds. Each of these means is *assumed* to be a function of postnatal environment V, and of prenatal and other factors N. The difference, $_s\overline{D} - _i\overline{D} = _s\overline{V} - _i\overline{V} = 5.9$ pounds, is not a function of N under our assumptions and represents the differential effect of that part of the postnatal environment of separated twins in excess of that for unseparated twins.

In Table 94 of mean differences and differences between means for groups it is apparent that $_s\overline{V} - _i\overline{V}$ is significant only for weight, I.Q., and Stanford Achievement. These are the same traits which showed the effect of environment by the method of correlating twin differences with estimated differences in various types of environment. In the present comparisons no attempt is made to distinguish types of environment, the mean difference representing the pooled effect of all such influences.

From these values we conclude that, owing to the excess of the postnatal environmental factor in separated as compared with unseparated twins, significant mean twin differences occur in the case of weight, intelligence, and scholastic achievement. For traits such as height and head measurement no such difference occurs. These latter findings are as important as the former in that they indicate traits unmodifiable by the type of environmental change here studied. All these inferences are, of course, limited by the small number of separated cases and the small environmental difference by twin pairs for a considerable proportion of these.

We shall next make a parallel analysis by the method of variance, which permits a study of the factor contribution by additive combination.

ANALYSIS OF TWIN DIFFERENCES IN TERMS OF VARIANCE FOR SEPARATED AND UNSEPARATED TWINS

The advantage of the method of variance is that we can compare the effect of various factors contributing to a total variance as additive portions provided the factors are uncorrelated. Using the factor setup of the preceding section, we may write

$$\begin{aligned}
{}_s\sigma_D^2 &= {}_s\sigma_V^2 + {}_s\sigma_N^2 & \text{(separated identical twins)} \\
{}_i\sigma_D^2 &= {}_i\sigma_V^2 + {}_i\sigma_N^2 & \text{(identical twins reared together)} \\
{}_f\sigma_D^2 &= {}_f\sigma_V^2 + {}_f\sigma_N^2 + {}_f\sigma_A^2 & \text{(fraternal twins)}
\end{aligned}$$

where σ_D represents the standard deviation of a twin difference, ${}_s\sigma_V$ the standard deviation of V differences for the separated twins, etc.

In the subsequent analysis we shall assume that ${}_s\sigma_N^2 = {}_i\sigma_N^2$ (just as we assumed ${}_s\overline{N} = {}_i\overline{N}$). We shall also assume that ${}_i\sigma_V^2 + {}_i\sigma_N^2 = {}_f\sigma_V^2 + {}_f\sigma_N^2$ (as was done in the section on the "Relative Effect of Nature and Nurture" in chap. vi).

The difference ${}_s\sigma_D^2 - {}_i\sigma_D^2 = {}_s\sigma_V^2 - {}_i\sigma_V^2$ then represents the part of the variance attributable to the difference in postnatal environment of separated and unseparated cases, and the quotient $({}_s\sigma_D^2 - {}_i\sigma_D^2) / {}_s\sigma_D^2$ represents the portion of the total variance attributable to such causes. Likewise the ratio ${}_i\sigma_D^2 / {}_f\sigma_D^2$ indicates the proportion of fraternal-twin variance attributable to V and N. This last quantity corresponds to $1 - h^2$ of the section on the "Relative Effect of Nature and Nurture," where h^2 is the proportion of the fraternal-twin variance attributable to A. All these quantities are next presented in Table 95.

From the quotients $({}_s\sigma_D^2 - {}_i\sigma_D^2) / {}_s\sigma_D^2$ it is apparent that the major portion of the twin difference variance is attributable to the difference in postnatal environment between separated and unseparated cases for such characters as weight, Binet I.Q., Otis I.Q., and Stanford Achievement score.

For head width the value of this quotient is .58, which is relatively high. It is possible that a part of this variance is due to the same nutrition factors which produce large variance in weight differences. Obstetrical deformations may also play an important part in these variations. On the whole, the foregoing findings substantiate those of the preceding section. The advantage of the present analysis, however, lies in the fact that we can now obtain a quantitative measure of the proportionate effect of $_sV - _iV$ upon separated-twin variance. Such a comparison cannot be made so precisely using mean differences because the algebraic signs of the various factors in our setup may lead to wrong interpretations of mean differences.

For comparative purposes we have added $_i\sigma_D^2 / _f\sigma_D^2$, which expresses the proportion of fraternal-twin variance attributable to V and N, and h^2, which

TABLE 95

VARIANCE OF TWIN DIFFERENCES AND CERTAIN DERIVED VALUES

Trait	$_s\sigma_D^2$	$_i\sigma_D^2$	$_f\sigma_D^2$	$\dfrac{_s\sigma_D^2 - _i\sigma_D^2}{_s\sigma_D^2}$	$\dfrac{_i\sigma_D^2}{_f\sigma_D^2}$	h^2
Height.................	3.44	2.61	14.79	.24	.18	.82
Weight.................	115.18	14.51	69.09	.87	.21	.79
Head length............	6.06	4.93	20.60	.19	.24	.76
Head width............	7.93	3.35	10.32	.58	.32	.68
Binet I.Q..............	44.27	18.04	58.97	.59	.31	.69
Otis I.Q...............	41.85	14.97	94.89	.64	.16	.84
Stanford Achievement....	277.35	35.64	99.92	.87	.36	.64
Woodworth-Mathews.....	23.79	24.29	28.50	....	.85	.15

gives the proportion of this variance attributable to A. Thus, for the case of weight, the two factors V and N do not have so great an effect upon the variance for fraternal twins reared together (only 21 per cent) as does the factor difference $_sV - _iV$ for separated twins (here 87 per cent). For the two mental-test measures the effect of $V + N$ as compared with $_sV - _iV$ varies from about one-half (31/59) to one-fourth (16/64). In the case of Stanford Achievement, the proportion of variance for fraternals due to $V + N$ is only .36 as compared with .87 for the factor difference $_sV - _iV$.

In the last column of Table 95, the values of h^2 give the proportion of fraternal-twin difference variance attributable to A. It is interesting to note that for weight, I.Q., and Stanford Achievement these proportions are similar to the proportions of separated-twin variance attributable to $_sV - _iV$. These comparisons suggest that for the foregoing four characters, which are modifiable by environment, the extra environmental factors represented by $_sV - _iV$ have had a net effect of the order of the factors A

for fraternal twins. It may also be noted that, since the environmental difference $_sV - {_i}V$ was not great for the majority of the separated cases, its relative effect could have been much greater for twins all reared under widely different conditions.

It would have been desirable to have obtained the trait differences for a group of fraternal twins separated under conditions similar to those of the identical cases. If this were possible, the relative effect of the genetic factor could be obtained in relation to the factors V and N for varied environments by pairs. The foregoing analysis suggests that the value of h^2, instead of being about .75 as for twins reared together, might be of the order .50 or even smaller under very different environmental conditions. The relative role of heredity and environment is thus a function of the type of environment.

TABLE 96

CORRELATIONS FOR THREE GROUPS OF TWINS

Trait	Identical	Fraternal	Separated
Standing height................	.981	.934	.969
Sitting height.................	.965	.901	.960
Weight.......................	.973	.900	.886
Head length..................	.910	.691	.917
Head width...................	.908	.654	.880
Binet mental age..............	.922	.831	.637
Binet I.Q.....................	.910	.640	.670
Otis I.Q......................	.922	.621	.727
Stanford Achievement..........	.955	.883	.507
Woodworth-Mathews...........	.562	.371	.583

TRAIT CORRELATIONS

The trait correlations for the fifty pairs of identical and fraternal twins have been presented in Table 25 of chapter vi. Owing to lack of complete data on the nineteen separated cases, not all of the corresponding correlations for this group could be worked out. It was possible, however, to determine the correlations for the separated cases for ten basic traits. These correlations are shown in Table 96, where they are brought into comparison with the corresponding values for the two groups of unseparated twins.

It will be observed that the correlations for standing and sitting height and for head measurements are practically the same for separated and unseparated identical twins. The correlation for weight is .886 for separated identical twins, which is very close to the value .900 obtained for unseparated fraternals.

In the case of the three measures of intelligence, the correlations for the separated cases are again fairly close to the values for fraternal twins and much lower than the corresponding values for unseparated identical twins.

For the Stanford Achievement Test there are striking differences among the three groups, the correlation for separated cases being significantly lower than for both the unseparated groups. The Woodworth-Mathews test appears to show no very definite trend in the correlations, possibly because of the nature of the trait and also because of the unreliability of the measure.

Height and head dimensions are not affected even by great changes in environment, while weight is appreciably modified. The change in this latter character for separated cases is of the order of the change produced in fraternal twins for whom both hereditary and slight environmental factors have been operative.

For the Binet and Otis tests we may also conclude that variations in the intelligence of the separated twins are of the same order as for unseparated fraternals.

The correlations for the Stanford Achievement Test indicate that the differences in environment of the separated twins, which, on the average, were not extreme in amount, produce differences in scholastic achievement greater than those for fraternal twins, the coefficients being .507 and .883, respectively.

The foregoing correlations, then, indicate that the environmental differences for the separated cases are accompanied by little changes for some traits, such as height, and very great changes for other traits, as in the case of school achievement. It is also apparent that for weight and intelligence the effect of extreme variation in environment alone is of the order of that produced by both nature and nurture within a family. Finally, the effect of environmental differences on school achievement is greater than that produced by both positive hereditary and slight environmental differences of fraternal twins living together.

In agreement with the findings of the preceding section of this chapter, we then find that the environmental factor, operating alone in the case of separated identical twins, can produce differences as great as or greater than those produced when both hereditary and environmental factors operate within twin families, as in the case of fraternal twins.

SUMMARY

The general conclusions which may be drawn from the comparisons of the present chapter may be indicated as follows:

1. Considerable variation in the amount of difference in educational, social, and physical environments was found for the pairs of separated cases. Fifteen of the pairs had only a moderate variation in environment,

whereas four pairs were reared in extremely different surroundings. If the contrast in environment had been greater for all cases, the influence of this factor would have been much larger.

2. Correlation between the three types of environments rated indicates that they were, in general, fairly distinct and worthy of separate consideration in judging effect upon twin characters.

3. By correlating the difference in environmental rating with trait differences in twins, measures of various environmental effects were obtained. It appears that educational and social changes in environment are effective in producing variations in such traits as intelligence and school achievement. Some slight change is also suggested in the case of temperament. Variations in physical environment are responsible for changes in weight and again to some extent in temperament.

4. By the use of mean differences for separated and unseparated groups of twins, a measure was formed expressing the effect of external environmental factors in producing twin differences. The effect of the difference in postnatal environment for the separated cases and unseparated cases was such as to produce significant changes over the unseparated twins for weight, intelligence, and school achievement.

5. A supplementary method of analysis in terms of variance showed the portions of the twin variance attributable to the difference in the environments of the separated and unseparated cases. It was found that in the case of weight, Binet I.Q., and Stanford Achievement Test the major portion of this twin difference variance is attributable to the difference in the environment of the two classes of twins. The analysis indicates that the role of heredity and environment in producing twin differences is a function of the type of environment. Thus, for twins reared together, most of the difference between members of a pair may be due to the nature factor; whereas for twins reared under strikingly different environments, the nurture factors will have a relatively greater influence.

6. It is apparent from several of the comparisons made that the relative effect of hereditary and environmental differences is also a function of the type of trait. Any fixed ratio of these two factors for all traits and conditions is thus impossible. We must consider their relation always in connection with the kind of trait and grade of environmental difference.

From the viewpoint of the educator it is important to note that extreme differences in educational and social environments are accompanied by significant changes in intelligence and educational achievement as measured by our tests.

CHAPTER XIII

GENERAL SUMMARY AND INTERPRETATION

THE general purpose of this study is to secure evidence on the extent to which the characteristics of human beings, especially their ability and behavior, are determined by their genetic constitution and the extent to which these characteristics are influenced by the conditions of the environment. The authors have at no time conceived their problem to be to discover whether heredity or environment determines the development of the individual, nor even to derive a ratio to express, in any universal or final sense, the relative potency of the two sets of factors. The first statement of the problem is meaningless since development is always a function both of genetic constitution and of environmental conditions. The second is indeterminate since such a ratio depends upon the type of trait and the amount of variation which exists in both the genetic and the environmental factors which are compared.

It may be possible to estimate roughly how much variation in ability or behavior may be expected to accompany such a range of difference in genetic constitution as occurs in a given community of people, assuming a uniform environment, or, on the other hand, to estimate the variation accompanying the range of difference in environment which is to be found in a given community, assuming a uniform genetic constitution. The evidence we have gathered enables us to take a step in the direction of such an estimate but hardly gives the basis for making it definite. We shall undertake to formulate as general a statement as we can after reviewing our procedure and results.

The two parts of our study represent the two possible general approaches to the problem. Each approach seeks to trace the variations in individuals which accompany variations in one of the two sets of factors when the other is held constant. Thus, we may compare individuals who are brought up under the same environment (so far as possible) but differ by specified degrees in genetic constitution. This was the procedure of the first part of our study, in which we compared the resemblances (or differences) between identical twins and fraternal twins when both types were reared together. On the other hand, we may compare individuals who are genetically the same but are subjected to different environments. This was done in the second part of the study, in which we compared the resemblances (or differences) of identical twins reared in environments differing in varying amounts with those reared together. In both cases the comparisons are complicated, and the inferences which may be drawn from them are subject to qualification and open to some difference of opinion.

In the study of the unseparated twins, which constitutes the first part of the investigation, the first step was to secure an adequate sample of twins divided into the two classes of identical and fraternal. This had never been done before the beginning of our study. We obtained fifty pairs of each type, confining the fraternal twins to those of the same sex to avoid the complication of sex differences occurring in one group and not in the other. The diagnosis was based solely on physical characteristics, chiefly palm prints and fingerprints, general appearance, eye, hair, and skin color, and shape of teeth. From the consistency of the multiple evidence furnished by these criteria we believe the separation of the two classes of twins to be highly accurate.

A number of physical measurements and of mental and educational tests were applied to these 100 pairs of twins. The list of these measurements and tests is given in chapter ii. The results were used in the comparisons of the first part of the study, and they were also employed for comparison with the separated cases in the second part of the study.

A detailed analysis of the distribution of the differences between twins of the two types shows that they are of two different orders. A composite of the measured physical differences indicates that the great majority of twins previously classified[1] as monozygotic showed the smallest differences, while a similar majority of the dizygotic twins exhibited the largest composite physical differences. There is some overlap between the two groups, so that the composite index of physical measures alone is not sufficient to differentiate between the two classes of twins. This fact does not cast doubt on the theory that two classes of twins exist since this theory rests on other biological grounds than merely that of similarity in dimensions. For the same reason the approximate separation of the two groups in physical measurements is not taken as a proof of the existence of two types, though it is, in a measure, confirmatory since it fits the theory. Again, the fact that there is some overlap and that the composite of the physical measures is not a safe basis of diagnosis in the middle range of difference is no argument against the theory of two types. That theory is compatible with the existence of some identical pairs who differ moderately in physical dimensions and of some fraternal pairs who resemble each other closely. This produces the overlap.

When other differences, such as appearance of features, eye color, hair color, shape of ears and palm prints are considered, the overlapping of the

[1] This classification was made without a knowledge of the physical measures.

two groups is almost entirely eliminated. The diagnosis based on observation at the time of examination was practically identical with the final elaborate analysis, based on quantitative differences on the entire set of physical measures. In only three out of one hundred pairs was there a reversal of diagnosis.

It is significant as an essential condition of some of the statistical calculations, and interesting as a general fact about twins, that both groups of twins were found to be normal in intelligence and in educational achievement. This is shown both in the average scores of the two groups and in their standard deviations. The only marked differences in the averages of the two groups occur in the case of number of finger ridges, and possibly intelligence, the identical twins in both cases yielding the higher average. On the whole, the two groups are remarkably alike both in average score and in spread of scores. Twins, according to our findings, are neither superior nor inferior to people in general.

Assuming that identical and fraternal twins differ in origin and that the one type has exactly the same heredity, whereas the other shares the same heredity to the extent of 50 per cent on the average, we have compared the degrees of likeness of these two classes of twins. It will be recalled that both sets of twins have been reared together and that a difference in environment is doubtless not a major cause of difference in traits, though it may be a minor cause, as we shall see.

The likeness between the two types of twins is expressed in the form both of correlations and of differences. They amount to the same thing, and the correlations will be used in this summary. We may first make simple comparisons of the correlations and consider their significance.

In most of the traits measured the identical twins are much more alike than the fraternal twins, as indicated by higher correlations. This is true of physical dimensions, of intelligence, and of educational achievement. The only group of traits in which identical twins are not much more alike consists of those commonly classed under the head of personality. For the rest it is obvious that the twins who have the same inheritance are the more alike. By and large, this indicates, since the environment is similar for both groups, that genetic constitution is a large factor in physical dimensions (as well as appearance and qualitative differences), mental ability, and educational achievement. This conclusion seems clearly warranted.

The difference in resemblance of the two classes of twins, however, is not the same in the different groups of traits. In general, the contrast is greater in physical traits, next in tests of general ability (intelligence), less in achievement tests, and least in tests of personality or temperament. In certain instances, viz., arithmetic, nature study, history and literature, tapping, will-temperament, and neurotic disposition, the correlations of identical twins are but little higher than those of fraternal twins. This seems to indicate that inheritance is a greater factor relatively in producing likeness or difference in some traits than in others.

Because earlier investigators have compared the resemblance of younger and older twins but have not distinguished adequately between identical and fraternal twins, we made this comparison. We are in some doubt concerning the bearing of this comparison on the general problem, but we present the results for what they are worth. Our chief contribution lies in a difference which appears between the two types of twins. The identical twins become neither more nor less alike as they grow older. This is true of both physical and mental traits. The fraternal twins behave differently, but only in the mental traits. In physical traits they remain as much alike as they grow older. In mental traits, however, they grow less alike. This would seem to be due to the fact that fraternal twins pursue somewhat different paths as they grow older and that the diverging environment affects their abilities and behavior. If the divergence were due to genetic factors, it would seem that it would affect the physical as well as the mental traits and the identical as well as the fraternal twins. It is reasonable to suppose that fraternal twins fall under the influence of more widely different environments than identical twins and that it is this influence which increases the difference between them.

Thus far no attempt has been made to estimate quantitatively the relative influence of the two factors. This attempt is made under certain assumptions, and with certain limitations and qualifications, by the use of formulas which yield the indices called t^2 and h^2. These designate, respectively, the ratio of the genetic to the environmental factors and the proportion of the total variance due to the genetic factors in the determination of traits of fraternal twins reared together. A value of .75 for h^2, for example, means that, with the assumptions and under the circumstances, the genetic factors are responsible for three-quarters of the variance in the trait in question.

There is one feature of the results which is not affected seriously by either the uncertainty of the assumptions or the limitation of the circumstances under which the correlations are found. This is the relative share of the genetic and the environmental factors in the different classes of traits. By this more rigid method, as by the simple comparison of differences between the correlations for the two types of twins, it appears that the physical characteristics are least affected by the environment, that intelligence is affected more; educational achievement still more; and personality or temperament, if our tests can be relied upon, the most. This finding is significant, regardless of the absolute amount of the environmental influence.

Our index shows that about 25 or 30 per cent of the variance in intelligence in fraternal twins reared together may be attributed to environmental influence. To what extent is this estimate sound, and, if sound, to what extent may it be generalized?

The soundness of the estimate rests on the correctness of the assumptions. One assumption in question is that a part of the differences between identical twins may be attributed to the effect of environment. (For the way this assumption is used in deriving the formulas, the reader is referred to chapter vi.) If the environment includes all nongenetic factors, this assumption is merely another expression of the theory that identical twins are derived from a single zygote, all parts of which, of course, have the same heredity. If, however, by environment is meant *postnatal* environment, then the question is raised whether a large share of the variance may not be due to *prenatal* environment, which is not subject to human control.

The biologist, in general, is inclined to attribute a larger share to prenatal factors than is the psychologist, who emphasizes the possibilities of postnatal differences, even in the case of identical twins reared together. The two main hypothetical classes of prenatal factors are differences in the blood supply due to unequal blood exchange between twin fetuses and differences due to the asymmetry mechanism. We have not been able to apply any statistical check to the magnitude of the former factor. The latter we have attempted to estimate by assuming that differences due to asymmetry should be greater in pairs showing many asymmetry reversals than in those showing few. The differences, however, were found to be no greater in the one class than in the other.[2] This seems to indicate that, although the asymmetry mechanism produces reversals in position or in pattern in one member of an identical-twin pair, it does not, so far as our measures indicate, produce an appreciable difference in traits characteristic of the organism as a whole.

General biological facts suggest that, in spite of this negative finding, prenatal conditions produce differences of significant magnitude in the physical characteristics of identical twins and possibly, therefore, in the

[2] The original data of this comparison have not been reported. The comparison includes five physical and three mental traits. In height, weight, and finger ridges the group showing reversals is more alike than the group not showing reversals. In head width, mental age, and educational age the reversal group shows greater average differences. In head length and motor dexterity the two groups are approximately equal. It is conceivable that pairs exhibiting slight or partial reversal would be more different, but we have no evidence on this point.

organic substrate of mental abilities and personality. For example, identical-twin embryos differ more in size than do fraternal-twin embryos, and identical twins differ as much as fraternal twins at birth. The prenatal mortality rate of identical twins is several times as high as that of fraternal twins, and very frequently one member of an identical-twin pair dies before birth, showing symptoms of injury from lack of nutrition. There is an exchange of blood supply between identical-twin fetuses which frequently produces an imbalance of blood exchange to the disadvantage of one twin. Conjoined twins (Siamese twins) show marked differences in height, weight, features, and intelligence. The differences between completely separated identical twins may have the same origin as these differences. These considerations predispose the biologist to attribute to prenatal factors the predominant share in the causation of differences between identical twins reared together.

How far the postnatal environment of identical twins may differ and how far this difference may affect them is, at present, a speculative question. Doubtless their environment is more alike than is that of fraternal twins or siblings. Our finding that identical twins retain their likeness in mental traits whereas fraternal twins grow less alike in mental traits bears this out. Still, it may differ sufficiently to affect behavior. For example, we have noticed that one twin usually takes the lead in social intercourse, while the other accepts the follower's position. A slight initial difference may produce a habitual difference in attitude and behavior which grows out of the very circumstances that might be expected to produce similarity, namely, the twins' intimate association with each other. The situation may be stated generally by saying that each twin is a part of the environment of the other, and a part which, while it does not differ much in original nature, comes to differ more because of the differentiation in attitude and behavior growing out of their mutual association. This argument is admittedly hypothetical and perhaps fine spun, but it seems to contain a possibility.

We shall not attempt to answer categorically the questions we have raised. Whether the factor of environment represented in the indices h^2 and t^2 should be interpreted as made up more largely of prenatal or of postnatal influences, we shall leave the reader to decide, in the light of the considerations we have presented and such others as may occur to him.

A comparison of the handwriting of the two classes of twins yields curious and, on the surface, discordant results. They are, however, in harmony with those of previous studies. In quality of handwriting, as measured by a handwriting scale, and in speed, identical twins are more alike than fraternal twins. When the formula to determine the relative share of genetic and environmental influence is applied it yields a ratio of .75, about the same as for intelligence. In general style or appearance, however, the handwriting of identical twins is no more alike than is that of fraternals. Galton made a similar observation. This suggests a distinction between different levels or types of behavior—a distinction which is referred to again in the review of the case studies of the separated cases. It may be that the coarser outlines of behavior, including perhaps those which are most susceptible to quantitative measurement, are relatively more determined by genetic constitution; whereas the finer details, which may be observed but are difficult to measure, are more subject to modification by the environment, or even by chance. Another possible distinction is between the vigor or energy of behavior and the degree of its control and its direction. Quality or merit of handwriting might fall under the first head and style under the second. We shall recur to this problem in discussing the case studies.

This brings us to the separated cases, in which we have attempted to trace the effects of differences in the environment upon pairs of twins who are genetically identical. One obvious way to treat the data is to compare the average differences for the group as a whole with the average differences in the case of the identical twins reared together. If the differences for the separated group are significantly greater than those for the unseparated group, we may conclude that the greater difference in traits has been produced by the greater difference in the environment (allowing for the fact that the separated group may very likely be a somewhat biased sampling). In one of the physical traits, weight, and in intelligence and school achievement the differences are significantly greater, demonstrating the effect of environment on these traits. In height, head measures, and the score on the Woodworth-Mathews test, on the other hand, no significantly greater difference is found. This is important since it indicates, as does the comparison of identical and fraternal twins, that some characteristics are more susceptible to environmental influences than are others.

Whether the amount of this excess difference can be taken as a direct measure of the amount of postnatal environmental effect is a different question. One of the authors is inclined to treat the unseparated identical twins as a control group, assuming, since they have been brought up together, that their differences are due almost solely to prenatal factors and little if at all to postnatal environmental factors. This would mean that only the excess differences of the separated twins could be attributed to increased differences in postnatal environments. The other authors, while recognizing the impossibility of disproving this position, regard it as more probable, as was argued previously, that a considerable part of the differences of identical twins reared together is due to postnatal environmental factors and that this must therefore be added to the excess difference in order to obtain a measure of the total influence of the postnatal environment.

A further argument pointing to the limitation of the effect of environment is that the differences between a majority of the separated twins, namely, those who have been brought up in similar environments, are no larger than are to be found among the unseparated pairs. In fact, if we eliminate some half-dozen pairs from the separated cases, the average differences of the remainder are about the same as those of the unseparated group. The differences in the environment between these separated pairs, so the argument runs, must be greater on the whole than are those of twins reared together; hence, small differences in the environment have no effect. This argument may be sound, so far as gross measures like general intelligence and school achievement are concerned, but it should be noted that the differences in environment between this group of separated pairs are small enough so that they cannot be detected or measured by a fairly careful study of the life-histories of the twins. Again, the argument has not quite the same significance if we regard the environment of twins reared together as differing by significant amounts as it would have if we regarded differences as zero in amount. It therefore seems safe to say that the measurable difference attributable to environment is at least equal to the excess difference found in the separated cases, plus an undetermined amount corresponding to that portion of the difference in unseparated cases attributable to the environment.

Besides comparing the separated and unseparated identical twins, we may compare the separated twins with fraternal twins. This may conveniently be done in terms of the correlations between pairs. In some of the physical characteristics, particularly height and head measurements, separated twins are more alike than fraternal twins and approximately as much alike as are unseparated identical twins. In weight, intelligence, and educational achievement, however, separated identical twins are, on the whole, as different as are fraternals. It is fair to say that, for these latter traits, if we average together the various amounts of environmental differences found in the separated identical twins, they just about balance in their effect the amount of hereditary difference which exists between fraternal twins.

The next comparison is not clouded by speculative difficulties but is clear and obvious in its implication. When the amount of difference between the separated twins is compared with the estimated amount of difference between their environments, highly significant correlations are found. They are closest between schooling and educational achievement (.91); somewhat less close between schooling and intelligence (.46 to .79) and social environment and intelligence (.32 to .53); and about the same between physical environment and weight (.60) and Downey Will-Temperament (.47). No further comment seems necessary since only one interpretation is possible. The concomitance between the amount of difference in the environment and the amount of difference between the twins can only indicate that the environment has affected the characteristics in which the correspondence occurs. Differences produced by other factors, such as prenatal conditions, could have only a fortuitous relation to the environmental differences and could therefore not bring about a correlation with them. Moreover, there is no reason to suppose that these factors have operated any differently in twins reared apart from those reared together.

At the beginning of this chapter we said that any estimate of the relative influence of genetic and environmental factors must be made with certain qualifications and limitations in mind. These can best be discussed in the light of the findings of both parts of the study, and it has therefore been deferred until this point.

In presenting the statistical estimates of the genetic and environmental factors in the differences between the fifty pairs of fraternal twins, we pointed out the fact that the variations which we studied are only such as occur within a family. This applies to both the genetic and the environmental factors. Specifically, the variation in the genetic factor is limited to that which occurs between siblings of the same sex, that is, brothers or sisters. This is much less than the variation occurring between pairs of persons picked at random, who in the vast majority of cases would not be related in any known way. (Of course, in a small stable community with much intermarriage the pairs of relatives would be more numerous.) This limits the effect of genetic differences since these differences would be greater if the pairs compared were less closely related.

The environmental differences are also severely limited in the comparison in question. It is obvious that the environmental differences of pairs of children picked from the same family are small as compared with those of pairs picked at random from the community. Again, the amount of such differences depends on the size and diversity of the community from which the pairs are chosen. A small, homogeneous New England town would yield relatively small differences, a large metropolitan city much greater differences, a whole nation still greater, and the whole world still greater. Can we say that, when our genetic and our environmental differences are such as exist within a family, the one or the other factor is more severely limited? This is a hard question.

Perhaps some light is thrown on the question by comparing the ratios which are found in the analysis of the separated cases with those obtained from the twins reared together. This comparison is made in Table 95. One set of ratios is derived by comparing the differences between the identical twins reared together and those reared apart. The other is derived by comparing the identical twins reared apart and fraternal twins reared together. Perhaps it would not be far wrong to say that the one comparison gives greater scope to the range of environmental differences and the other to genetic differences.

In any case, the difference obtained by the two modes of comparison is striking. By the comparison of identical twins reared together with identical twins reared apart, the share of environment in determining weight is .87; by the comparison of identical with fraternal twins, it is only .21. Similarly, for Binet I.Q. the two methods give .59 and .31; for Otis I.Q., .64 and .16; and for Stanford Achievement, .87 and .36; respectively. In brief, if the environment differs greatly as compared with heredity, the share of environment in determining traits which are susceptible to environmental influence is large. If, on the other hand, there is large genetic difference and small environmental difference, the share of heredity is relatively large. This is what makes the solution of the question as to the relative share of the two sets of factors indeterminate. We would have to specify what degree of genetic difference is to be compared with what degree of environmental difference. We may, however, add this statement that differences in the environment which actually sometimes occur, as exemplified in our separated pairs, are sufficient to produce differences in weight, ability, and behavior large enough to overshadow the genetic differences which occur between siblings.

The discussion thus far has dealt with the results of the study which could be formulated statistically. It remains to comment briefly on the type of evidence that has been brought out in the case studies and to speculate on the nature of the influence of the environment in relation to genetic determination.

So far as such characteristics as height, weight, mental ability, and educational achievement are concerned, the case studies do not add much to the evidence already presented in statistical form. The detailed inspection of the individual pairs does give an impression of the high degree of consistency of the relation between environmental differences and differences in ability that one might not gain from the statistical coefficients alone. The magnitude of some of the differences in ability also comes out more definitely in the examination of the figures for particular pairs than in any other way. Still, the case studies yield no additional kind of evidence concerning the determinants of ability to that presented in the tabulations of correlations and mean differences and their statistical manipulation. They may offer some suggestions as to how the environment influences ability, but that is another story.

The case is otherwise with those types of behavior which are commonly classed under the head of personality. Here it seems possible that the case studies may not merely give individual examples of relationships which are represented more generally in the statistical indices but may also yield an additional type of evidence. It may be that the correlations and mean differences in some or all of the measures of personality do not have quite the same significance as do those of the measures of ability.

The ground for this surmise lies in the fact that the correlations of measures of personality are of a different order from the correlations of measures of ability. This is shown in several ways. The correlations between identical twins in these measures are much lower than in the physical measures or the measures of ability. This seems hardly attributable mainly to a lower reliability of these measures since they have been shown in numerous studies to have fair reliability and since the correlations in the case of fraternal twins are not correspondingly lower. This general fact suggests that the forms of behavior measured may, in general, not be expressions of the genetic character of the organism to the same extent as abilities.

Again, the differences in the personality measures of separated twins have negligible correlation with differences in the environment, so far as they could be ascertained and estimated along a general scale. This suggests that such relations as exist between personality and environment are of a different sort than those between environment and ability.

Before suggesting any explanation of these differences in the results for personality and ability, let us remind ourselves of the evidence of the case studies that some type of relation appears to exist between the environment and personality. There are a number of instances in which a rather large difference exists between the personalities of twins as shown by the tests or by observation, or by both, in which a large difference also exists between their environments, and in which it seems plausible to infer a relation between the two sets of differences. The following may serve as examples:

Case I.—Alice exhibits a constrained manner in comparison with her sister, has a more cramped style of writing, and differs in the Downey test. Correspondingly, she was brought up in a narrower, more restricted, and conventional type of environment.

Case IV.—Mary has lived a sedentary town life in contrast to Mabel's active farm life. Correspondingly, Mary is more feminine in manner, more excitable, and shows large differences in handwriting and on the tests.

Case VIII.—Mildred has had a free, stimulating social environment, and Ruth a restricted, impoverished one. Correspondingly, Mildred is spontaneous and vivacious in manner, is poised and self-confident, is stable as revealed by the tests, and writes a flourishing hand, whereas Ruth manifests the opposite characteristics.

Case X.—Betty's home influence seems to have made her slightly more neurotic.

Case XI.—Helen's very superior education has brought with it an easier manner of life, and this may be responsible for her higher scores on the "speed and fluidity" and greater "care and attention to detail" on the Downey test, more mature, more delicate, neater, and more feminine handwriting, and more feminine manner.

Case XIV.—Esther was an adopted child brought up on a farm, has an adopted child, and is naturally left-handed but has been taught to write with her right hand. Ethel was brought up in a Catholic orphanage, has a child of her own, and is naturally right-handed. Esther is much more neurotic according to the Woodworth-Mathews and Pressey tests. There may be a connection.

Case XVII.—James appears to be more neurotic and appeared to be glum and unhappy in the interview. His foster-home seems to have been somewhat less happy than that of Gene.

Case XVIII.—These brothers, though brought up in widely different circumstances, are similar in manner and the measurable features of behavior. However, their conduct, from the point of view of its direction and social significance, differs very widely. We might expect them to act with equal vigor, decision or persistance, but one to a socially constructive and the other to a socially destructive end.

In the discussion of similarities and differences in personality at the end of the summary of the case studies of the separated cases two suggestions were made which may now be somewhat further elaborated. These suggestions were that there are different levels of behavior, some of which are more and others less modifiable by the environment. The other was that a given activity may be expected to reflect specifically the influence of the environment to the extent that it has been organized in response to the demand of a particular environmental situation. We should expect to find a correlation between levels of activity and degree of organization in response to particular situations, but not necessarily a complete correspondence.

Whether we should expect the forms of behavior which are subject to environmental influence to be closely correlated with definable and measurable aspects of the environment is not so certain. There is a difference between abilities and personality which alters the case. In the case of an ability we have an activity which is directed toward a clearly defined end and which is represented by a set of defined tasks to be performed or problems to be solved. The individual's performance may be measured by the number or difficulty of the tasks he performs successfully, and success is measured by commonly recognized criteria. Moreover, and this is the crucial point, systems of training have been set up in the environment to promote the ability to perform such tasks. Under these circumstances the effectiveness of the training may be measured by the correspondence between amount of training and degree of ability. The method of correlation is appropriate.

No such condition obtains in connection with the traits of personality. Influences of environment and degrees of performance do not follow parallel lines toward a common goal. A "good" environment in the economic sense or the sense of social status should not necessarily lead us to expect, in general, for example, correspondingly fewer or more neurotic symptoms, or a larger or smaller total score on the Downey test, or more or less emotional responsiveness. There may be some correlation, but it would not grow out of any such natural and direct relation as exists in the case of ability. The lack of correlation between differences in the traits we have attempted to measure and the gross features of the environment we have attempted to estimate does not, then, indicate that traits of personality are not affected by the environment. We should not expect to discover such influence by this kind of comparison. Of the techniques which we have employed, the method of individual analysis as made in the case studies is a more suitable method of detecting such influence.

CONCLUSION

If, at the inception of this research project over ten years ago, the authors entertained any hope of reaching a definitive solution of the general nature-nurture problem or even of any large section of the subordinate problems involved, in terms of a simple formula, they were destined to be rather disillusioned. The farther one penetrates into the intricacies of the complex of genetic and environmental factors that together determine the development of individuals, the more one is compelled to admit that there is not one problem but a multiplicity of minor problems—that there is no general solution of the major problems nor even of any one of the minor problems. For any particular genetic and environmental set-up it is possible by the methods presented in this book to determine what fraction of the variance is due to genetic or to environmental differences. In another setup this fraction will undoubtedly vary. We feel in sympathy with Professor H. S. Jennings' dictum that what heredity can do environment can also do.

While, then, we have not provided a comprehensive or final solution of the problems within our field of study, we have presented a body of evidence which we believe is more crucial than any previously available, and we have undertaken to analyze it as thoroughly as possible from the combined points of view of the biologist, the psychologist, and the statistician. The data themselves have been presented in sufficient detail to enable other workers in the field to evaluate our own interpretation and to seek for more inclusive interpretations of their own. We shall be satisfied if we have succeeded in tracing a few of the threads in the tangled web which constitutes the organism we call man.

INDEX

⟦ PRINTED IN U·S·A· ⟧